FATIGUE AND IMPAIRMENT IN MAN

Fatigue and Impairment in Man

by S. HOWARD BARTLEY, *Ph.D.*

Professor of Research in the Visual Sciences
Dartmouth Eye Institute, Dartmouth Medical School

and ELOISE CHUTE, *M.A.*

Research Associate in the Visual Sciences
Dartmouth Eye Institute, Dartmouth Medical School

Foreword by A. C. Ivy, *Ph.D., M.D.*
Vice-president, Chicago Professional Colleges
University of Illinois

FIRST EDITION

McGRAW-HILL BOOK COMPANY, INC.

NEW YORK AND LONDON · 1947

Reprinted with the permission of Eloise Chute and S. Howard Bartley

JOHNSON REPRINT CORPORATION
111 Fifth Avenue, New York, N.Y. 10003

JOHNSON REPRINT COMPANY LTD.
Berkeley Square House, London, W. 1

FATIGUE AND IMPAIRMENT IN MAN

47-2430

10-71

First reprinting, 1969, Johnson Reprint Corporation
Printed in the United States of America

FOREWORD

The authors of this book have elected a very timely and worth-while, though very difficult, task in seeking to organize the scattered and contradictory items in the broad field of fatigue and impairment. The task is timely because in the last quarter of a century a large amount of experimentation has been devoted to the subject. The task is worth while because any serious attempt to integrate the findings from so great a mass of research is to be gladly welcomed. The task of fruitful exposition is difficult in this case, owing to the extreme diversity of the phenomena that are generally subsumed under the heading of fatigue and the consequent diversity of the scientific disciplines represented.

In every branch of biology in which the experiential as well as the somatic aspects of behavior must be considered, difficulties in terminology have been a source of constant misunderstanding and have therefore greatly hampered progress. Contrary to the easy tendency of allowing confusion to exist where it may, the interaction of these two aspects of behavior, as well as the dissociation that may occur between them, demands precise formulation. I heartily agree with the authors that, when dealing with such subjects as "fatigue," "the taboo in 'armchairing' has been responsible for considerable general paralysis in thinking and for much irrelevant experimentation."

A book such as the present one is needed to bring to light the inadequacies as well as the achievements in our knowledge, to suggest the uneven developments and gaps, and to point out the need for particular kinds of research on the subject.

The authors have rendered a valuable service by clearly and exhaustively delineating the distinctions and relationships between fatigue and impairment. Their treatment of this problem may serve as a model for the analysis of somewhat similar problems, such as those involved in the study of emotions, hunger, and appetite, and their somatic components.

A. C. Ivy, Ph.D., M.D.

Chicago, Ill.,
April, 1946.

v

63099

PREFACE

The present book grew out of a recognition of the need for a consistent and comprehensive view of fatigue. The concept of fatigue that we have developed arose from a broad, theoretical view of the organism, which might be termed "over-all" or "holistic." The course of our thinking necessarily led us to formulations that still await experimental corroboration. It is our hope that the systematic presentation we have made will both inspire and direct empirical investigation. It is our belief that further knowledge about fatigue, which is so clearly required in every field of endeavor, calls for research that stems from a point of view such as we have attempted to formulate, rather than from any of those that place the fatigue experience in a vague and undecided category.

The viewpoint on fatigue that we have attempted to express will be more clearly appreciated if a brief account of one of the origins of interest in the fatigue problem in recent years is given. In 1938 the Committee on Scientific Aids to Learning of the National Research Council became interested in fatigue through the desire for determining whether reading microfilm induces under visual fatigue. The committee appointed an Advisory Committee on Visual Fatigue whose duty it was to recommend the kinds of experimental investigation necessary to answer the question. At the time Adelbert Ames, Jr., the chairman of both the original and expanded advisory committee, noted that the act of seeing involves the use of clues to answer the questions of *what* and *where* visual objects are localized, the individual utilizing these clues in carrying out his purpose. If the purpose is frustrated, the experience of fatigue tends to result.

It became evident from the advisory committee's deliberations that information on visual fatigue was scant. The committee accordingly circulated a questionnaire among the various investigators throughout the country who it felt would be in a position to know something about visual fatigue and the means for its further study. The committee allocated funds to individuals submitting problems for which assistance was requested.

One of these individuals was the senior author of the present volume, who developed a conflict idea of fatigue from the work on the pupillary reflex that he did under the committee grant. The fatigue concept as now presented, involving as it does so many considerations, has naturally undergone considerable evolution since the first attempt to set it forth in writing.

We wish to express our appreciation for the parts played by others in making the present book possible. The Dartmouth Eye Institute sponsored the book as a part of its scientific program. Baker Library of Dartmouth College, with its wealth of relevant literature, was of unique help in providing us with adequate reference material and with comfortable quarters for writing. Mrs. Robinson, librarian of the medical section, was particularly helpful in her generous assistance in locating references.

We wish especially to express our appreciation to Alice W. Weymouth of the institute's secretarial staff, who not only typed the manuscript through its several drafts but also performed numerous other tasks that made the book possible. Her work in the reference room and elsewhere was indispensable. Also, we wish to thank Leola Bartley for her generous and helpful assistance in proofreading and in the preparation of the indexes.

S. HOWARD BARTLEY
ELOISE CHUTE

HANOVER, N. H.,
April, 1946.

CONTENTS

Chapter I

INTRODUCTION

FATIGUE as an unpleasant experience has entered into the life of everyone. For the one who is tired, the feelings experienced are the fatigue. In spite of this, the experience is taken as merely incidental when attempts are made to analyze and understand what is called "fatigue." The very individual who experiences fatigue and regulates his life in accordance with it changes his whole outlook when he steps into the laboratory, supposedly to study fatigue. He forgets what he knows about fatigue from personal experience and attempts to measure human activity solely as the product of a physiochemic machine. The origins of fatigue are also commonly misinterpreted outside its formal study.

Fatigue has entered into daily experience in so many ways that ideas about it are highly diverse. Perhaps the commonest notion is that fatigue is closely related to exertion. It is then simply attributed to too much exertion or to lack of rest or sleep. Fatigue is also taken as a warning against supposed physiological damage in the event of further energy expenditure.

The importance of fatigue in everyday life has led to numerous attempts to study the phenomena that cluster under the fatigue label. Simple conditions have been chosen, and controlled variations have been employed in order to reduce relationships to precise formulation. Eagerness for precision and for finding phenomena susceptible to quantitative measurement has led to ignoring various aspects of the fatigue picture, until many important features have been totally lost sight of.

The main feature of lay thinking that has been retained by most scientists has been a confused type of causality and, in this, the idea that fatigue and energy expenditure are directly related. Attempts to study fatigue in the laboratory have had little clear material to start with and have accomplished little in the direction of clarification. Much investigation has actually been centered on impairment and, thus, has not of

1

itself promoted an understanding of the experience of fatigue. Work output is the standard reference in experimentation, subjects being rarely consulted as to whether or not they feel tired.

Although it is known that individuals seldom come near reaching their energistic limits under any conditions, it has not been systematically recognized that the explanation of behavior must therefore lie in other than energistic terms. Apparently it has not been taken into account in theoretical formulations that human activity is both initiated and limited in accordance with the demands the person puts upon himself. Thus in the consideration of fatigue there has been a failure to see that the individual's activity depends upon his organization.

The history of the consideration of fatigue has progressed from the identification of the experience to the many kinds of present-day laboratory studies. With the beginning of laboratory investigation, the label *fatigue* was retained, although investigators proceeded to assume that the *experience* of fatigue was not its essential feature. The experience was discarded, but investigators retained the idea that fatigue was something that happened to the body which unfitted it for activity. They also retained the idea that unfitness for work (fatigue) depends upon work already performed. In this, it was erroneously supposed that the ability to work lies solely in metabolic processes as such. Studies that might include the subject's feelings of fatigue were left to the psychologist, who chose rather to imitate his fellows, the physiologists and the biochemists, tending also to abandon feelings, sensations, and other matters of over-all personal alignment in accounting for activity.

In the history of *experimental* study of fatigue, several trends have been obvious. The first of these is toward a variety of diverse viewpoints. Much of this diversity has arisen from the variety of branches of science represented by the investigators. Fatigue, for the physiologist, was something pertaining to muscle and nerve activity. Fatigue, for the biochemist, also pertained to the tissues, but was studied in terms of chemistry. Fatigue, for the psychologist, had more varied interpretations, perhaps most commonly pertaining to performance, studied in terms of work output. Occasionally, in psychology, fatigue was seen as being somehow allied to the subjective. Fatigue for the physician, especially for the psychiatrist, was usually seen as subjective, although its basis was often sought in physiology. Thus instead of all branches of science actually studying component phases or aspects of a single phenomenon, many *kinds* of fatigue came to be assumed. In many instances these assumptions with such definitions as were made had little to do with each other. There was also a trend toward applying the term fatigue to all sorts of systems, and even to inanimate objects, such as metals.

Another decided trend in some kinds of fatigue studies has been toward vagueness and ambiguity. This does not mean that less precise measurement has been employed, but that fatigue has been taken as axiomatic—ultimately undefinable. It has been used more often as an explanation than as something to be explained. Fatigue has been subjected to less detailed analysis than have such concepts as inhibition, adaptation, and accommodation, from which it has been only vaguely distinguished.

Another feature applying to the investigation of fatigue is oversimplification. In the attempt to deal with tangible phenomena and to obtain precise data, highly specific types of performance have been chosen for study. The choice of performance for experimental study has been dictated by simplicity so as to minimize variations. The pertinence of the results of such study to answering the initial questions has been thus overlooked.

That "fatigue" has been studied in various scientific fields has already been pointed out. It was said that this diversified study had given rise to a number of somewhat unrelated kinds of "fatigue." First of all "general fatigue" has been studied. For this purpose the individual is subjected to conditions such as strenuous exertion and loss of sleep. "Central fatigue" has also been an object of study. It is fatigue that is assumed to occur in the central nervous system because it cannot be attributed to failure in the peripheral structures. Physiologists have used this concept to account for "fatigue" in voluntary performances. Another form of more or less localized phenomenon is called "perceptual fatigue." It is fatigue that is imputed to afferent pathways as evidenced by certain shifts in perceptual behavior (kinds of diminution of function). Functional changes and failures in the neuromuscular junction have been isolated, and these are sometimes called "transmission fatigue." In other cases, failure of muscle to perform is found to lie in changes within muscle itself. This phenomenon is called "contractile fatigue." Still another kind of failure to perform as usual is identified in the body and is sometimes called "enzyme fatigue."

From the foregoing survey of the diverse ways fatigue has been regarded, it becomes apparent that there has been no view in which fatigue is taken as a single over-all picture. This is seen as a definite lack, and the recognition of the need for such a view is one of the reasons for the present book. The treatment that follows is an attempt to satisfy this need.

In order that this be accomplished, the treatment stems from as consistent and adequate a view of the human organism as seems possible at present. It is believed that such a presentation must be a *personalistic* one rather than the more usual segmental treatment of the various phases and aspects of activity. There was no ready-made structure in existence in which our formulation of fatigue could be placed.

The present volume assumes that human activity is determined and regulated by other than purely energistic considerations. While it is recognized that there are such factors as metabolic limits, and that these may be imposed by the physical world, it is maintained that the organism plays a part in determining what conditions limit it. It is becoming more and more obvious that, in order to understand and account for human endeavor, terms and concepts other than those exclusively physiological or even narrowly "psychological" must be used.

Impairment is seen as referring to the condition of tissue, which is directly discovered only by physiological and biochemical analyses, whereas fatigue is seen as an expression of the organization of the whole organism, which can be described only in personalistic terms.

The plan of this book is dictated by this distinction between fatigue and impairment, as well as by the fact that fatigue has been customarily so diversely viewed and studied. Considerable space has been devoted to matters of impairment, which often involve what are called limiting conditions for action. The chapters reflect that the data of both fatigue and impairment are highly varied. It will be obvious that the style and choice of terms differ from chapter to chapter, in keeping with the field of science involved. Although this is hardly avoidable, it has the advantage of making the book useful to a more diverse group of readers. While each chapter by no means stands alone, the selection of chapters in accordance with taste, interest, and background is quite possible. What will most interest and be most intelligible to one reader will, doubtless, be of less help to another.

A motivating factor in the production of this book is the belief that fatigue merits more serious consideration as a factor in human affairs. As a liability to human welfare, it deserves the same direct attack as do identified diseases, for example. Hence, although the dominant character of the book is technical, it is hoped that at least some of the material covered will be of interest and benefit to individuals who are not particularly versed in the special fields involved.

Chapter II

VARIOUS VIEWS ON FATIGUE

THIS CHAPTER should not be read straight through, but rather used as reference material, particularly in connection with Chap. III. Its purpose is to provide documentation for our assertion that views of fatigue, up to the present, have been varied, fragmentary, and highly inconsistent. The numerous quotations also demonstrate the uniqueness of the systematic view of fatigue presented in Chap. III and maintained throughout the book.

Five sources have been used: (1) general textbooks on psychology, (2) general texts on physiology, (3) monographs on the subject of exercise and fatigue, (4) articles in the scientific and medical journals, and (5) remarks from a Symposium on Visual Fatigue sponsored by the Committee on Scientific Aids to Learning.

FATIGUE AS DEFINED IN PSYCHOLOGY TEXTS

Thirty texts in general psychology written during the decade of 1933–1943, and several other more specialized volumes, were consulted. They were found to differ considerably both in the amount of space devoted to fatigue, and in the directness with which they dealt with it. Some of the texts contain whole sections on fatigue, whereas others do not even allude to the subject. Among the books in which fatigue is discussed, some give no direct definitions, some quote definitions, and some include formal definitions in the author's own words. The excerpts given in this section were chosen from texts that contain sufficiently concrete and concise statements for the purpose.

Such agreement as there is among the 18 sources quoted exists primarily by implication. The amount of agreement that occurs pertains to the phenomena known to occur in the general area of work or activity rather than to what fatigue is. A tendency not to define fatigue, but rather to state that certain symptoms arise from it, represent it, or are due to it, is characteristic. There are said to be three classes of pertinent phenomena: the work done, the physiological effects, and the conscious

5

experiences. Most of the statements recognize these either by direct statement or by logical implication.

Three authors state directly that fatigue has three aspects: the work decrement, the physiological effects, and the feelings of weariness. Six authors state two of these three aspects, and two or them imply the third. Four of the remaining word their statements as though fatigue were only one of the three: the work decrement, the physiological effects, or the subjective experience. Three authors stress characteristic ways of dealing with fatigue, or discuss its relation to some other factor such as "will," or motivation. One author introduces the problem of organization by depicting muscular antagonisms and conflicts.

In many cases the quotations embody able descriptions of work or activity situations and the subjective consequences. None of them, however, represents what could be called adequate systematic stances with regard to the situation in general.

Viteles, in Guilford's[1] "Fields of Psychology," specifically mentions the three aspects of a work situation and states that fatigue is *characterized* by them. He does not state that fatigue *is* all these three. He says that feelings of weariness, the third type of phenomenon, are a subjective *sign* of bodily changes and lessened capacity for work. Fatigue, itself, is not defined, and it is impossible to say just what the author regards it to be.

To quote from Viteles:

Fatigue is characterized by (1) a decreased capacity for work, known as *work decrement;* (2) *modifications in the physiological state* of the individual; and (3) a *feeling of weariness.*

Fatigue is also accompanied by a feeling of weariness which appears with prolonged work. This is the subjective sign of deep-seated bodily changes and decreased capacity for work which characterize fatigue. The feeling of fatigue may be accompanied by irritability, anxiety, excessive worry, disturbed emotional states of all kinds which lead to disturbance in social relationships both inside and outside the plant. Unfortunately laboratory studies of the type early reported by Poffenberger show that there is no consistent relationship between decrease in output, changes in physiological state, and the feeling of fatigue. Because of this it has been found impracticable in laboratory and industrial experiments to employ the feeling of fatigue as the index of fatigue. However, particularly in English experiments and to some extent in experiments recently conducted in the U.S.S.R., this factor in industrial adjustment has been assigned its proper weight by the use of introspective reports along with measures of energy expenditure and changes in output in evaluating the fatigue status of the individual worker.

[1] Guilford, J. P., and others: "Fields of Psychology," pp. 498–499, D. Van Nostrand Company, Inc., New York, 1940. Pp. 695.

The second excerpt from Starch and coauthors,[2] which follows, indicates adherence to the three-part classification of fatigue.

The physiological effect of work is fatigue. Control of fatigue and recovery of energy for further work are not only physiological problems but very important psychological ones.[3]

Studies of fatigue are concerned with three phenomena. First, the changes in level of performance expressed in decreased capacity for work, which might be called *objective fatigue*. The finger ergograph measures this type of muscular fatigue. Second, the physiological changes due to the chemical products of fatigue, which might be called *physiological fatigue*. The metabolic rate of energy consumption measures this real basis of physical fatigue and also mental fatigue in so far as it can be determined physiologically. Third, the feeling of fatigue in ennui, bodily weariness, tiredness, disssatisfaction or boredom, which might be referred to as *subjective fatigue*.

Objective fatigue, or variation in output, may have little or no relation to subjective fatigue, or the person's report of his feeling of fatigue. And neither output nor subjective feelings may correlate closely with the physiological condition. When a person's report of tiredness coincides with deep-seated bodily changes causing a decrease in work, the subjective feeling will then serve as a means of control and protection in preventing exhaustion. This control may easily fail, however, in intense emotional situations, such as intense grief, where no discernible feeling of fatigue serves as a warning even though there is exhaustion at the end of the period. Intense concentration in creative work, such as scientific research or composing a symphony, which seems to possess one through many hours of steady work, may give one no fatigue warning.[4]

Work and fatigue involve the whole organism and interact in definitely organized patterns when the individual raises or lowers his levels of accomplishment. The physiological changes in the body which occur in fatigue involve not only the muscular and skeletal systems but the respiratory system, nervous system, digestive tract, endocrine and other glands. Less energy is available when waste products in muscles and blood stream are not liberated as fast as they accumulate. The accumulation of lactic acid in the muscles produces fatigue and a certain amount of oxygen is essential to reconvert lactic acid into glycogen, the energy-producing material. When muscular tension continues in the absence of oxygen, the body incurs an "oxygen debt," overtly experienced in breathlessness.[5]

These authors name three kinds of fatigue, based on the three types of phenomena inherent in the situation. Objective fatigue is measured by decrement in work output, implying that reduced work output and reduced capacity for work are parallel and that the one can be used to deduce the other. This makes "objective fatigue" objective only in terms of a *measurement* of an external indicator. It would seem that "physio-

[2] Starch, D., H. M. Stanton, and W. Koerth: "Controlling Human Behavior," 1936. Pp. 638. By permission of The Macmillan Company, publishers.

[3] *Ibid.*, p. 197.

[4] *Ibid.*, p. 202.

[5] *Ibid.*, p. 198.

logical fatigue" is the basis for objective fatigue; hence in actuality literal fatigues that pertain to the individual as an active agent reduce to *two* of the original three kinds mentioned. Work decrement is simply work decrement and is used as a sign of something happening within the individual which is either subjective fatigue or physiological fatigue.

The view of Bills[6] may be represented in the following statement:

> Studies of fatigue have attacked the problem from three quite different angles. Some have defined fatigue in terms of the subjectively observed feelings of fatigue as these show themselves in ennui, boredom, dissatisfaction with the task, and feelings of bodily weariness and an unpleasant affective tone. All these can be grouped under the term Subjective Fatigue. Others have been concerned with changes in the level of performance or output as a result of continuous work. This can be called Objective Fatigue. Still others have taken the position that physiological changes within the organs constitute the real basis of fatigue, and that the term should be applied to them. This can be spoken of as Physiological Fatigue. If any two of these three variables were correlated with one another the problem would be simplified, but as a matter of fact, each one is to a certain extent independent of every other. Neither subjective feeling nor output is highly correlated with physiological condition; nor are subjective feeling and output closely related. Output has a much less rapid decrement than subjective feeling. As a result of these discrepancies some psychologists, notably Muscio and Watson, have argued that the term fatigue is essentially ambiguous and should be eliminated from discussions of work and fatigue. Certainly there is no entity *fatigue* which is independent of these various criteria; but the term is so well established that it seems more practicable to continue to use it with a careful definition of exactly what is implied, than to try to eliminate it.

The view represented in this statement denies that fatigue is an entity. Bills suggests that fatigue is merely a convenient label for phenomena that fall into three categories through the criteria mentioned. It is only usage, he says, that makes saving it as a label preferable to eliminating it. This has important implications that the reader should examine later in the light of the view presented in the next chapter.

The following statements are from Gilliland, Morgan, and Stevens.[7]

> The ordinary mechanical device has to undergo repairs at various stages and usually, during the periods of repair, cannot function. The human machine also has to be continually repaired, but it is equipped with a device which enables much of this repair work to be accomplished while work is continued. When the human being becomes fatigued, his speed, or quantity of work, is diminished and the organism has an opportunity to recuperate. Fatigue really has two components. One is the feeling of fatigue, the subjective experience which makes the person feel as though he must slow down or stop work. The second is the actual incapacity of the organism to function efficiently.[8]

[6] Bills, A. G.: "General Experimental Psychology," p. 416, Longmans, Green and Company, New York, 1934. Pp. 620.

[7] Gilliland, A. R., J. J. B. Morgan, and S. N. Stevens: "General Psychology," D. C. Heath and Company, Boston, 1935. Pp. 462.

[8] *Ibid.*, p. 414.

Because muscular fatigue is so easily demonstrated, one is tempted to assume that nerve tissue may become fatigued in the same manner. Experimental tests have failed to demonstrate any neural fatigue which is as complete or extensive as muscular fatigue. One can easily get the tired feeling from mental work, but the physiological deterioration resulting from such work has been very hard to demonstrate. There have been a few changes in nerve cells as a result of extreme stimulation, but these were in an experimental situation and the stimulus was stronger than any that would occur in ordinary life. Miss Arai, a Japanese student, did a heroic task in mental multiplication for long periods with very little specific loss in efficiency.

Mental work will produce physical fatigue of muscles which are held tense during such work, and it is quite likely that much that has been called mental fatigue has really been this physical fatigue.[9]

These authors consider that "mental fatigue" reduces to "physical or physiological fatigue." The fact that long-continued mental operations can occur signifies to them that one does not really tire mentally. They believe that mental fatigue can be spoken of only when physical fatigue occurs during mental work.

Cattell[10] also posits two basic aspects to fatigue, the physiological and the subjective.

In retrospect two riddles remain to tease us concerning work and fatigue. First is the discrepancy between objective symptoms of fatigue and subjective sensations. In many activities objective collapse comes long after the feeling of weariness has reached a maximum, passed off and been succeeded by a feeling of well being. The line between fatigue and boredom is a slight one, yet we can defy the latter with good conscience and the former only at our cost. Nature seems not to have adjusted the real danger signs of fatigue to our understanding.

The second enigma is the apparently small cost of mental work. Here the work decrement is often very small; the expenditure in calories is negligible compared with physical work and the effect on pulse rate and breathing is often scarcely detectable. True, there are some indications that mental fatigue is relatively long lived and difficult to eradicate when established; but the belief that mental work is highly fatiguing, indeed more fatiguing than physical activity, rests largely on the subjective sense of effort.

Mental work that proceeds smoothly and with the full enthusiasm of the subject apparently causes little direct fatigue. It is fatiguing in proportion to the sense of conflict, worry or emotional upset. The high cost of mental conflict in terms of energy is well known from the marked physical and mental exhaustion of the neuroses. Yet all juggling with ideas and even fine physical adjustments involve a conflict of impulses, with censorship and critical control. Smooth mental work is habitual work: creative work means conflict and relative exhaustion. The well-integrated person may perform mental work with least fatigue; but he may not be able to perform the work of the artist at all.

Usually one of the first consequences of the fatigue of mental work, after increasing errors, is increasing emotionality, and a shifting of fatigue from cortical

[9] *Ibid.,* p. 416.

[10] Cattell, R. B.: "General Psychology," p. 410, Sci-Art Publishers, Cambridge, Mass., 1941. Pp. 624

to subcortical activities. When the roots of emotion and conation are themselves fatigued, mental work is impossible; but critical mental performances may fall off while emotional drives are still relatively intact. Fatigue must be traced down in the end to the sources of energy. Attempts to make comprehensive laws of mechanical kind about the work curve itself have proved abortive. In work and fatigue, as in learning, we must invoke in the end the concept of purpose. There is no fatigue as long as a purpose itself is not fatigued.

The final riddle perhaps is why work, *i.e.*, continuous externally directed activity as distinct from the spontaneity of play or instinctive activity, should be so distasteful. Men will go to a great deal of trouble to avoid work. Some will risk their lives rather than face it. And though many will tolerate physical work few will put up with mental labor. A great number of people will walk a mile rather than write a letter, and, as history shows, most people will rather die than think something new.

Like others, Cattell is faced with distinguishing between *work* and *effort*. Work is a physical concept defined in terms of activity, such as foot-pounds. Effort is a psychological concept dealing with feelings, generally arising in activity. Effort arises at least in part from a kinesthetic basis and is not necessarily proportional to energy expended. Fatigue and effort are related in a different way than fatigue and work. Cattell, it will be noted, introduces *purpose* into his view of fatigue. He also distinguishes between *work* and *play*.

Freeman,[11] like Cattell, points out the discrepancies between fatigue and work, between feelings and overt behavior.

Studies of fatigue and its influence on the decrement in speed and accuracy of performance have a bearing upon the relationship between feelings and behavior. Thorndike has dealt with experiments on arduous intellectual work carried on for several hours, in which the subjects reported at different stages of the assignment on the degree of satisfaction or pleasantness of the task as it developed. The results showed that the speed and accuracy of performance varied but little during the assignment, but that the pleasantness decreased steadily and markedly. Even when it became unbearable, it showed but little drop in efficiency. Similar investigations by Poffenberger gave the same results. The Robinsons carried out experiments which also showed little decrement in efficiency of performance following a night of sleeplessness, but it was accompanied by a similar loss of pleasantness.

We should pause to comment upon the peculiarity in all these investigations of the maintenance of efficiency of output under conditions which could well be supposed to impair it. The reason is obscure. It might well be suggested that the measurement was such that the loss of efficiency through boredom and discomfort was concealed by the improvement in methods which might have accompanied continuous and prolonged effort in a routine endeavor. Thus a spuriously constant level of performance might have appeared in the results. The invariable increment in boredom and dissatisfaction would suggest a loss that might have become unsuspectedly compensated.

[11] Freeman, Ellis: "Principles of General Psychology," p. 202, Henry Holt and Company, Inc., New York, 1939. Pp. 530.

It will be seen that Freeman includes *compensatory* behavior to account for the discrepancy between fatigue and performance in the work situation.

Stroud's[12] view on mental fatigue is somewhat different from that of others:

The use of the term *mental fatigue* implies that there is another kind. There is a distinct psychological advantage in distinguishing mental fatigue from fatigue in the sense in which the physiologist uses the concept. Neither concept, mental fatigue or physiological fatigue, is free from ambiguity. The term *physiological fatigue* is sometimes used to denote certain toxic chemicals that accumulate in bodily tissue as a by-product of work. These toxins, as they accumulate, operate to lower the efficiency of the nerve and muscle cells. The term is also used in a more general sense simply to denote fatigue, in the sense of decrement, in physiological work. Nothing is implied as to the cause of the decrement.

In studying fatigue, the physiologist isolates a nerve-muscle preparation and observes the muscular responses, activated by succcessive stimulations of the nerve, until they no longer occur. The resulting exhaustion is known as physiological fatigue. Note, especially, that *the voluntary element is entirely eliminated from the response.* Since the mental factor is not present, we have here, if anywhere, a case of pure physiological work and physiological fatigue. This is the sense in which the term *physiological fatigue* is used here.

Mental fatigue occurs only in a situation in which mental factors are free to operate. The term is sometimes used to denote the fatigue that arises from so-called mental tasks, such as solving mathematical problems, studying, or delivering an address. The latter usage is untenable on two grounds: (1) These tasks are quite as much physiological as are such tasks as forging a piece of steel or playing tackle on a football team; (2) the nature of the resulting fatigue in the former tasks is not different, except in degree, from that in the latter tasks.

Let it be said that, theoretically, there is some approach, however slight, to physiological fatigue—the using up of energy, or the accumulating of toxins that prevent the utilization of energy—in every task, whatsoever its nature, if it be continued sufficiently long. Upon this score there is no difference in fatigue resulting from so-called mental and so-called physiological work. On the other hand, mental fatigue can arise only in tasks that are voluntarily performed, or that the organism may voluntarily stop, or of the performance of which the organism is conscious. Any attempt to apply the term to fatigue of the heart or other vegetative process is meaningless. Mental fatigue can arise only in mental situations. It may be encountered in the continued performance of any task which fulfills the conditions just stated. These conditions are so all-inclusive as to warrant the statement that mental fatigue may occur in any practical situation. It may be eliminated from consideration in the purely vegetative processes, as stated above, and in the nerve-muscle preparations of the physiological laboratory.

Mental fatigue, as we have chosen to use the term, is a particular kind of fatigue, not that fatigue that arises from a particular kind of work. It arises, theoretically, as readily from mountain climbing or paddling a canoe as from multiplying two

[12] Stroud, James B.: "Introduction to General Psychology," p. 574, Prentice-Hall, Inc., New York, 1938. Pp. 681.

2-place numbers or reading a treatise on the French Revolution. The two concepts of fatigue are contrasted further in the statement that limitation in capacity is closely correlated with the onset of physiological fatigue; whereas, the association between incapacity to work and mental fatigue is not close. Thorndike has aptly said: "An animal would seem likely to discontinue or decrease mental work because continuing it annoys him rather than because some inner fund of impulsion, which might be likened to physical potential energy, was running low." He further states that "Work without rest becomes less satisfying (1) by losing the zest of novelty; (2) by producing ennui, a certain intellectual nausea, sensory pains, and even headache; and (3) by imposing certain deprivations—for instance, from physical exercise, social intercourse, or sleep."

Stroud points out that mental fatigue arises only when mental factors are allowed to operate and is not a kind of fatigue dependent upon a peculiar kind of work. Many others take the stand that mental fatigue arises from doing mental work (*i.e.*, such tasks as doing arithmetic without the aid of pencil and paper).

It would seem from the statements below that Murphy[13] makes fatigue a physiological process and relabels the subjective states in connection with work as lack of interest, etc.

The result is that most persons doing physical work really suffer mental as well as physical fatigue in the sense that their brains are more or less clogged with waste substances. Part of this can be avoided by properly spaced rest periods: some factories give a five-minute rest period every half hour.

Another method of studying work is through the *metabolism,* or rate at which body energy is used.

In psychology we are not of course concerned only with the effects of the heavier forms of manual labor. Our problem is with subtler and more troublesome matters. For one thing, the sustained tension of certain muscles may give a sense of weariness or even depression which may not represent generalized fatigue at all. Finding a more relaxed posture or frequently changing one's posture may make all the difference in the world. What seems to be mental fatigue turns out to be physical fatigue.

Even so, is there no such thing as actual fatigue of the brain itself as it works? The answer is difficult to find. Delicate measurements of the amounts of energy used up in the brain show that these are slight as compared with the amounts used in physical work. For example, copying this page on the typewriter would use at least ten to twenty times as much energy as the brain would use in a concentrated study of it. Of course the brain, being a delicate organ, *may* be fatigued, that is, partially incapacitated, even through such exceedingly slight loss of energy, but the chemistry of the matter is complicated, and "loss of energy" does not describe all the facts.[14]

There is every reason to believe that most of the fluctuations in everyday work capacity are not really due to fatigue, but are a matter of *interest* and of other factors involving incentives. In fact, stating this somewhat more broadly, we may

[13] Murphy, Gardner: "A Briefer General Psychology," Harper & Brothers, New York, 1935. Pp. 572.

[14] *Ibid.,* p. 421.

say there is evidence that most of what we call fatigue is really inattention or boredom. We say that we simply cannot go on. What we mean is that we do not want to go on.[15]

In the following statements of Conklin and Freeman,[16] we again find the two-part classification of fatigue and the acknowledgment of a discrepancy between the two when quantification is attempted.

One of the most troublesome disturbers of human efficiency is fatigue. It is a common experience. Most people know what it is to be tired. And most people suppose that the study of fatigue is a relatively simple matter. But it has not proved to be such. Even the definition of fatigue has been difficult and it has proved to be a peculiarly difficult item to subject to measurement. That there are two aspects of fatigue to be considered everyone who studies the subject recognizes. There is the loss of functional capacity as the consequence of actual work done. This is conceived physiologically as the consumption of energy-producing compounds stored in the nerve cells. For the restoration of these compounds prolonged rest and sleep are necessary. There is also another aspect of fatigue. That is the effect of the presence in the body of the products of metabolism, fatigue products as they are sometimes called. These are partially known. There are carbon dioxide, lactic acid and probably other things. These probably produce the fatigue sensations with which we are all familiar. It is the effect of these which can be canceled by some drugs but their removal and the restoration of the energy-producing substances are not produced by taking a little caffein or other drug. These can be removed and the others restored only by rest and normal sleep.

Ordinarily we now think of fatigue as the reduction of the capacity for function through the actual effects of activity. The ratio between the two is not simple and direct. At least so far as we know it is not. There may be no apparent reduction of capacity after considerable activity. And there may appear to be considerable reduction of capacity after very little activity. Why this should all be is not clear. But the facts are as they have been stated.

In the following, Woodworth[17] includes a number of the features already brought out in previous quotations. He speaks in particular of the discrepancy between certain conscious qualities and the capacity to continue work.

As an example of a doctrine which owes its currency to superficial observation, and which, nevertheless, has been used extensively in the explanation of mental phenomena, we may take the view that the brain is very liable to fatigue. Common observation seemed to show that fatigue comes on very quickly in mental work, and this apparent fact has done duty in many psychological explanations. "Constant errors" in sense perception, shiftings and fluctuations of attention, changes in the efficiency of mental work, have been regarded as sufficiently accounted for

[15] *Ibid.*, p. 425.

[16] Conklin, E. S., and F. S. Freeman: "Introductory Psychology for Students of Education," p. 406, Henry Holt and Company, Inc., New York, 1939. Pp. 557.

[17] Woodworth, R. S.: "Psychological Issues," pp. 169–170, 1939. Pp. 421. Reprinted by permission of the Columbia University Press.

by appealing to mental fatigue. The brain was supposed to fatigue so much more rapidly than the muscles that what was apparently muscular fatigue has been explained as more probably brain fatigue. It was even suggested that the nervous system, by its capacity for quick fatigue, served to protect the muscles from over-work, much as a fuse in an electric circuit, by burning out easily, protects the more valuable apparatus in the circuit from excessive currents that would damage them. There was a certain amount of inconclusive experimental observation behind this view, but for the most part it owed its acceptance to the common observation that people, or rather many people, grow tired quickly of mental work, and feel that they must stop. Experimental tests in prolonged mental work have, however, revealed a surprising degree of resistance to fatigue. . . .

In all probability, the central nervous system, like the peripheral nerves, so far from being quickly worked out, is capable of an enormous amount of con-tinued activity without serious loss of functional power. How, then, are we to explain away the common observation of quick fatigue in brain work? Experi-ment shows pretty conclusively that this familiar form of fatigue is a sensory or emotional affair, a feeling of fatigue, not a true.fatigue in the sense of incapacity. In case of the fatigue that appears early in muscular exertion, at a time when the muscles are still demonstrably in good condition for work, the fatigue is really composed of unpleasant *sensations* that come in from the active members. The tendency of these sensations is to make us stop the activity that is causing them; but if we resist this tendency, and continue the muscular effort, we find that we are not incapacitated after all; we can still keep on, almost if not quite as well as before, in spite of the sensations of fatigue, which indeed usually dis-appear with the further continuance of the muscular activity. Similar remarks apply to the fatigue that is apt to come on early in mental work; it is composed partly of *ennui*—a mere emotion—partly of tendencies to do something more agreeable to the natural man, partly to sensations of strain arising from the eyes, neck, and various parts of the body, which dislike being held fixed in a cramped position. Let the mental worker resist this medley of incentives to stop work, let him determine to stick to it for a while longer, and he will usually find that his brain is still in good working order, that the feeling of fatigue passes away, and very likely that his best work is done after rather than before the time when his feelings told him he was played out.

In the following, Pillsbury[18] by implication makes fatigue the physio-logical effect of activity, or, in other words, impairment. Yet the physiologi-cal effects that are only collateral to reduced output do not seem to be con-sidered a part of fatigue.

Fatigue is to be referred to several different causes and may be simulated by various other conditions. Sometimes it is more specific, sometimes more general. Some men have insisted that what passes for fatigue is really merely disinclination to exertion. It is well to begin with the most specific evidence and to pass on to the more general. The most thoroughly studied phase of fatigue is of the muscles. Something of muscular fatigue must certainly be present in all the cases that are

18 Pillsbury, W. B.: "The Fundamentals of Psychology," 3d ed., 1934. Pp. 663. By permission of The Macmillan Company, publishers.

classed as fatigue. Some authors have argued that this is the only element in fatigue.[19]

The problem of fatigue is complicated in practice by the fact that it is not always directly evident when a man is fatigued and to what degree. This holds whether we deal with the subjective or the objective indications. On the subjective side it seems not infrequently that when the individual is not specially unfitted for work, he feels listless or even has a marked disinclination to exertion. Yet, when an incentive is given, he finds that he can accomplish more than usual. The output is also not a direct indication of the degree of exhaustion, for sometimes after long exertion the work is continuing with approximately the normal rate, but a breaking point is near. This is especially true of mental work, in which few muscles are involved. These facts make it essential to seek definitions of fatigue. They must include recognition of the capacity for work at the moment as measured by the output, latent capacity, which can be measured, if at all, by some physiological index, and the later after-effects of the work as shown by the quickness of recovery and in severe cases by the effects upon later health. Fatigue then is an effect of work which shows itself immediately in reduced output. It reduces the capacity for work at periods closely or more remotely following upon the work.[20]

Poffenberger[21] gives the following definition of fatigue:

Fatigue is the reduction in the output of work as the result of work, and which is recoverable by rest.

Goodenough[22] defines fatigue in sensory terms:

Fatigue is a general sensation, which is felt in the muscles and joints all over the body. It is believed to be due to the accumulation of waste products in the blood.

Higginson[23] refers to the "perception of fatigue" as phychological and suggests that fatigue is due to a neural condition.

A human being also perceives kinesthetically such psychological properties of himself as fatigue, strain, and pain. When he is fatigued, he usually observes that his arms and legs have actually become very heavy and that they cannot be moved as readily and easily as when he is rested. He observes, moreover, the increased effort and strain involved in maintaining an erect posture or in carrying a load. He wishes to rest. He finds increasing difficulty in continuing whatever task he has to do. He is no longer able to function—perceive, imagine, think—as efficiently as previously. He may be forced to read or hear something several times before he understands it. Situations, objects, take on new meanings or lose old meanings. In short, he behaves differently. Scott wrote in his journal of an incident

[19] *Ibid.*, p. 593.

[20] *Ibid.*, p. 596.

[21] Poffenberger, A. T.: "Principles of Applied Psychology," p. 134, D. Appleton-Century Company, Inc., New York, 1942. Pp. 655.

[22] Goodenough, F. L.: "Developmental Psychology," p. 86, D. Appleton-Century Company, Inc., New York, 1934. Pp. 619.

[23] Higginson, G. De V.: "Psychology," p. 222, 1936. Pp. 646. By permission of The Macmillan Company, publishers.

that occurred during the return trip from the South Pole. He had turned back to aid one of his men who through exhaustion had fallen in the snow. Scott gently encouraged him to get up and continue with the rest of the party. But the man, kneeling in the snow, stared stupidly at Scott without understanding what he was saying.

Neither precise stimulus conditions (physical and chemical energy) nor receptive structures which are sufficient to account for fatigue have ever been discovered. That is, no adequate description of fatigue has ever been given in terms of such factors as physicochemical energy (stimulus) and specialized fatigue sense organs. It is a psychological property which unquestionably appears at times in human beings. It is an inherent characteristic of life that clearly emerges under various conditions—some of which are better understood than others. The presence in the body of certain products of the metabolic functions, such as carbon dioxide and lactic acid, may be shown in certain cases of fatigue. These may possibly serve, in some manner, as stimulus conditions. But particular or specialized end organs which such substances might possibly affect to produce fatigue *have not been isolated*. Perhaps there are no such structures and perhaps there is no stimulus, in the sense of some form of physical and chemical energy which is *distinct* and separate from the organism. Fatigue may possibly arise as a direct result of a change in the normal mode in which protoplasm functions. An increase or a decrease in some one necessary substance or condition, thereby disturbing the innately determined life balance within the protoplasm itself, may be wholly sufficient.

In this connection, we must not neglect the experimental evidence derived from studies of certain functions of muscle tissues which have been removed from the body and electrically stimulated. The data indicate under such conditions that fatigue is possibly due more to *physical* than to *chemical* causes. This is to say that muscle tissue which has ceased to function—contract—after a prolonged period of functioning may be immediately restored to a functional condition by being washed in a saline solution. It is quite like saying that the fuel in a stove cannot burn so strongly when the ashes of previous burning have accumulated.

We must recognize, of course, when we speak of fatigue in an isolated muscle, that we are definitely in the field of physiology. Whether the perception of fatigue, which is psychological, depends upon conditions identical with those of the isolated muscle or upon other causal conditions remains an open question.

The observable weariness that characterizes fatigue may be a property of the whole organism. It is as much a part of fatigue as the general lowering of the efficiency of the whole organism. The student must recognize, furthermore, that both the weariness as well as the inability to function efficiently may occur in the complete absence of such substances as lactic acid and carbon dioxide. In such cases, the individual may be very weary and unable to do much, but there is nothing discoverably wrong with his muscles. Chemical tests, moreover, do not show the presence of waste products in the blood stream. The primary cause in such cases is to be referred again to the nervous system (brain) of the individual. We suggest that all normal fatigue is really due largely to a neural condition. It is based primarily upon a change (decrease) in the functional level of the central nervous system. When emergencies appear, the individual may actually arise instantly to a new functional level.

Cole[24] has much to say on the topic of fatigue and impairment. He speaks of muscle conflicts and thus introduces the problem of organization. Only a small part of his discussion is reproduced here.

Continuous or rapidly repeated contraction of a muscle alters its irritability. If curves of successive contractions are superimposed, four changes will be noted: (1) an initial spurt showing increase in strength of the contractions, (2) subsequent decline in strength, and an increase in latent time, and (3) in the later responses a slower return to the original length. Although inexcitable, the muscle is not "exhausted" and may remain in a state of partial contraction for a considerable time.[25]

"Fatigue" has been related to the chemical products released by the contraction process (CO_2, lactic acid, acid phosphates, etc.).[26]

Certain questions arise at once. Obviously we cannot look upon fatigue as a simple exhaustion phenomenon, for the action-current studies show clearly that the muscle is far from being in a resting state.

We should remember, too, that the intact organism presents additional complications. Fatiguing a reflex and fatiguing nerve-muscle preparation are not identical processes. Sherrington showed that when the "flexion reflex" (evoked by stimulation of a toe pad of the spinal dog) has been reduced to an irregular phasic tremor, the flexor muscles contracted promptly to the stimulus for the "scratch reflex." Or, a fatigued scratch reflex promptly reappeared when the stimulating electrode was moved to a point 2 cm. away. Thus a muscle which refuses to respond to one stimulus may still be accessible to another.

When fatigued, we can perform routine intellectual activities but fail at the more complicated and variable ones. Our conversation may employ the same speech mechanism, but its descent to banalities, clichés, and automatic verbal sequences distinguishes it from our better performance. These observations prompt one to present the fatigue problem in terms of "levels" ranging from chemical changes in muscle to a disintegration of our most complex habits.

Do these seemingly diverse types have a common basis? Does the chemical change in the muscle, induced by repeated stimulation, lie back of all these phenomena? The generalization is tempting, and certain facts persuasive. For example, the metabolic changes in nerve are minute and neural fatigue is negligible. Long before the conductors fail, the "fuse" at the neuromuscular junction fails. In fact, neither nerve nor muscle is depleted. It is, rather, a change in the relationship between the parts, such that transmission from one to the other is no longer possible, a failure in resonance rather than exhaustion. The effects are simply less available.[27]

Many fatigue phenomena are clarified when we recall the arrangement and functioning of antagonistic muscles. In the properly timed movement the antagonists clear for each other and our strokes are freely flung, without opposition. The novice who has not acquired the skill (and the timing), on the other hand, sets one antagonist pushing against the other. His work requires more energy

[24] Cole, L. E.: "General Psychology," McGraw-Hill Book Company, Inc., New York, 1939. Pp. 688.
[25] *Ibid.*, p. 139.
[26] *Ibid.*, p. 140.
[27] *Ibid.*, p. 141.

and is more fatiguing. Hence it is that the teacher of piano must strive to get loose wrists, elbows, shoulders; otherwise the performance will be stiff, arhythmic, and if practice is intensive, the pupil will develop persistent, fatiguing (and even painful) contractures (piano arm). Similarly, the industrial engineer, the instructor in golf, in fact, anyone who is concerned with efficient performance in a skill, will find sources of fatigue as well as faults of style of execution in the timing of opposed muscles; and whatever he can accomplish in the direction of converting the slow, tense movements, where one antagonist contracts against another, into the rapid, freely thrown, ballistic movements will be in the direction of efficiency.

On a social level, by an extension of the same logic, we may describe the so-called conflict situation, which all will agree is exhausting, as occasions in which each line of action has to be worked out against a musculature that is also mobilized for opposite actions. The person with divided loyalties finds living a difficult task, and actions which would be easy for another are for him energy consuming. On the other hand, when he has reached a decision, and has finally thrown his lot upon the side of the issue, he experiences a release of energy and may speak figuratively of an "oppressing weight" that has been lifted. He speaks of "breathing more freely," and if our view of the matter is correct, his subjective account of the matter has a solid muscular basis.[28]

Young,[29] in dealing with motivation of behavior, makes brief reference to fatigue.

If there is a true "will" factor in the nexus of motives, it has yet to be found. The unsophisticated is certain that sheer *will power* keeps him going in the face of obstacles and fatigue. The transatlantic flight of a Lindbergh, the polar expedition of a Byrd, the many foot races, fights, and struggles which occur in warfare—all bear witness to the fact that "will" dominates human behavior despite great odds.[30]

The experiment points to the existence of two motivating factors or factor groups which operated side by side: (1) the determination or attitude of the subject, described as *will* to do well on the tests, and (2) fatigue. The hypothesis is reasonable that the increments from the first offset the decrements of the second. This hypothesis at least fits the belief of everyday life that a fixed determination to act can offset fatigue.[31]

Husband[32] alludes to several factors that are significant in the fatigue situation.

Fatigue follows prolonged exertion and requires rest, preferably sleep. Its effect upon motivation is negative; the more tired a person is the less he desires to do anything. But fatigue itself is in turn partially dependent upon motivation. Boring tasks tire one much more quickly than interesting activities. We may play tennis for hours, but a half hour spent in weeding the garden leaves us exhausted.

[28] *Ibid.*, p. 143.

[29] Young, P. T.: "Motivation of Behavior," John Wiley & Sons, Inc., New York, 1936. Pp. 562.

[30] *Ibid.*, p. 210.

[31] *Ibid.*, p. 213.

[32] Husband, R. W.: "General Psychology," p. 134, Farrar & Rinehart, Inc., New York, 1940. Pp. 513.

Moore[33] not only states his own position but epitomizes those of several other writers.

What fatigue is, no one knows; the word is of the nature of such terms as intelligence, emotion, and instinct: a name that is glibly used to cover a multitude of states, for some of which there may be objective correlates, while for others there is no conceivable relation between the subjective experience and the objective expression. In fact, so much confusion has resulted from the use of the term that some (Muscio, for example) , suggest that it should be banished from precise scientific discussion. In common usage, "fatigue" is confused with nearly every other related or similar condition. The one with which it is identified most frequently is boredom; some of the objective results of the two states are the same: decreased output, increased inaccuracies, and general lack of expression of either interest or enthusiasm. In both cases, the subjective reports of feelings and experiences are the same; and yet, any casual observer can distinguish between the type of decreased production that results from decreased capacity and the type that results from a lack of desire to do the work or from an aversion to it.

Definitions of fatigue abound; like many other commonly used, yet uncomprehended, terms, its vagueness provokes efforts at clarification, and these usually take the form of concise definitions. Samples of such attempts are:

A decrease in the capacity to do work—a loss of efficiency.

"A decrease in interest in or willingness to work—a feeling of ennui or weariness (Starch) ."

"A more or less complete loss of irritability and responsiveness of a tissue (Freeman) ."

"A condition of mind resulting from prolonged mental activity (Wilson) ."

"A failure to maintain physiological or organic equilibrium (Dill) ."

"A condition caused by activity, in which the output produced by that activity tends to be relatively poor; and the degree of fatigue tends to vary directly with the poorness of ouput (Muscio) ."

"Not an entity but a convenient word to describe a variety of phenomena (Dill) ."

The suggestion given by Dill that fatigue is not an entity, but a word describing a variety of phenomena, is a convenient starting point for a discussion of the subject. What phenomena are present when a person says he is fatigued? What causes them? What effects do they have? and How can they be removed?—these are the issues that any person must face when confronted with a factor militating against efficiency and productive of discontent.

FATIGUE AS DEFINED IN PHYSIOLOGY TEXTS

Six tests in physiology provided sample statements about fatigue. The tendency in physiology texts seem to be to use fatigue as a perfectly well-known category into which various phenomena are placed, rather than to define it. Various changes in muscular and neural properties are specified, though not in such a way as to make them anything more than evidence of fatigue.

[33] Moore, H.: "Psychology for Business and Industry," p. 384, 2d ed. rev., McGraw-Hill Book Company, Inc., New York, 1942. Pp. 527.

In the main, fatigue is taken to be something that happens during activity in muscle and in nerve to diminish its activity. This something pertains mostly to the tissue itself (we should call this "impairment"), although the functional interaction between structural elements is mentioned in some cases. The factors determining functional interrelations between elements are less well understood, and changes in them giving rise to fatigue phenomena may not belong in the same category as the changes in tissue elements.

Bard[34] makes the following statements about fatigue:

Fatigue is due, in part at least, to the fact that after prolonged activity each fiber in the muscle is able to develop less tension when it contracts.[35]

In contrast to peripheral nerves reflex arcs are strikingly susceptible to fatigue. A nerve trunk stimulated at a rate of 40 to 50 times a second will continue to conduct impulses at this rate for hours. In the spinal cat the flexor reflex may fail within thirty seconds when afferent impulses are set up at this rate of stimulation.[36]

Best and Taylor,[37] after stating the usual viewpoint with regard to muscle fatigue, bring up the difference between fatigue and adaptation without clarifying the difference. In fact, the cases they cite do not seem even to illustrate the difference.

If the muscle be stimulated repeatedly in an atmosphere of nitrogen it contracts forcibly at first, but soon becomes fatigued.[38]

When the ear is fatigued by a tone, let us say of 800 c.p.s., the end organs which are accustomed to respond to this frequency fail to do so or do so inadequately, while those on either side are little affected.[39]

The olfactory receptors adapt fairly rapidly. It is a common experience that a disagreeable odor which when first smelt is almost overpowering soon becomes imperceptible. But though lost for one particular odor smell is retained for others; the phenomenon is not due to fatigue of the olfactory mechanism, but is an example of sensory adaptation.[40]

In a statement in Starling's[41] "Principles of Physiology," fatigue is used only as an axiomatic term.

34 Bard, P., *et al.*: "MacLeod's Physiology in Modern Medicine," 9th ed., C. V. Mosby Company, Medical Publishers, St. Louis, 1941. Pp. 1256.

35 *Ibid.*, p. 20.

36 *Ibid.*, p. 109.

37 Best, C. H., and N. B. Taylor: "The Physiological Basis of Medical Practice," 3d ed., The Williams & Wilkins Company, Baltimore, 1943. Pp. 1942.

38 *Ibid.*, p. 1029.

39 *Ibid.*, p. 1733.

40 *Ibid.*, p. 1780.

41 Evans, C. A. L.: Starling's "Principles of Human Physiology," 6th ed., Lea & Febiger, Philadelphia, 1933. Pp. 1122.

The following quotations express the views of Bainbridge and Menzies:[42]

If by means of an induction coil we stimulate the motor nerve to a muscle we find that it fairly rapidly exhibits evidence of fatigue.[43]

Until we understand completely the chemistry of the muscular contraction we shall not be in a position to explain either fatigue or rigor mortis. Nevertheless there are certain features which are known to us which will now be described. The fatigue which is observed experimentally in an isolated frog's muscle may be due either to exhaustion of the glycogen, hexone phosphate or creatin phosphate, or to the accumulation of acids.

The feelings of fatigue which we ourselves experience when we are tired may be due to the painful stimuli aroused in our muscles by the decreased alkalinity produced by the rise in the lactic acid content.[44]

If a muscle be repeatedly stimulated, the latent period gets longer, the height of the contraction diminishes, and the time taken for relaxation to occur is prolonged.[45]

The following is taken from Wright's "Applied Physiology."[46] Wright gives a more or less common statement about activity-reducing properties of muscle.

One of the reasons why a nerve fiber can respond to continuous stimulation for hours without showing signs of fatigue is that the fiber is conducting not continuously but intermittently; any stimulus falling during the refractory period is ineffective, and the fiber only responds again when it has recovered to some extent.[47]

Myasthenia gravis is a rare disease, characterized by great muscular weakness and rapid onset of fatigue, without any recognizable changes in the nervous system or in the muscles themselves.[48]

Wiggers[49] provides the fullest as well as the longest statement pertaining to fatigue.

The term fatigue is frequently used to express a sensation or even a psychic state rather than the objective manifestations with which we are now concerned. It may be noted that the sense of fatigue is often a fallacious index of working capacity. Muscular fatigue, as an objective phenomenon, is best defined as a transitory decrease in the working power of the muscle from which recovery takes place after shorter or longer periods of rest.[50]

[42] Hartridge, H.: Bainbridge and Menzies' "Essentials of Physiology," 9th ed., Longmans, Green and Company, New York, 1940. Pp. 651.

[43] *Ibid.*, p. 328.

[44] *Ibid.*, p. 295.

[45] *Ibid.*, p. 285.

[46] Wright, S.: "Applied Physiology," 7th ed., Oxford University Press, New York, 1940. Pp. 787.

[47] *Ibid.*, p. 19.

[48] *Ibid.*, p. 27.

[49] Wiggers, C. J.: "Physiology in Health and Disease," 4th ed., Lea & Febiger, Philadelphia, 1944. Pp. 1174.

[50] *Ibid.*, p. 77.

Fatigue is a state of diminished capacity for performance of work associated with feelings of tiredness, weariness, and disinclination to continue. The fatigue of muscular origin is determined by the speed and intensity of work. Physical fatigue may be local or general; it may be temporary or chronic. Two types are generally recognized—one originating entirely in the central nervous system and the other partly within the central nervous system and partly in active muscles. The former occurs most commonly in industry and is chiefly responsible for work decrement, loss of interest or boredom, except in so-called heavy industries which require hard labor. These manifestations of fatigue are closely related to accidents and absenteeism. Central nervous fatigue also develops after prolonged strenuous mental efforts and various emotional stresses.

The nervous component, responsible for the disagreeable sensations and weariness, is partly of peripheral and partly of central origin. Fatigue sensations are probably mediated through stimulation by waste products of sensory nerve endings within muscles, and represent biological warning signals against overuse. As sensory end organs fatigue, the rate at which impulses are discharged decreases progressively. This seems to be related to the degree of oxygen deficit which exists, but anaerobic stimulation, as in cardiac pain, has not been fully excluded. The sensations of fatigue are frequently referred to joints and tendons in which the effects of anoxia or waste products could not be significant. The central component involves changes in the functions of the spinal cord and various parts of the brain. The latter appears especially vulnerable to hypoxia and other changes in the blood (Gellhorn). In general the symptoms resemble those which occur in chronic anoxia (Barcroft). Broadly the central nervous changes consist in development of increased synaptic resistances. In the spinal cord it results in less perfect coordination of the many reflexes involved in muscular actions. In the cerebral cortex facilitation and integration between areas is depressed and conditioned reflexes are often annulled. This depression extends also to subcortical structures, and involvement of the hypothalamus may modify visceral functions adversely.[51]

FATIGUE AS DEFINED IN CERTAIN MONOGRAPHS

A number of separate publications bear more or less directly on the subject of fatigue. They have to do either with the physiology of exercise, or the work output in industrial situations, hence like the texts lie in the fields of psychology and physiology.

Schneider[52] writes as follows in dealing with the physiology of muscular fatigue:

The claim is constantly made that there are two types of fatigue, one arising entirely within the central nervous system and the other largely in the muscles themselves. We are told that fatigue among industrial workers has its origin entirely within the central nervous system and with that statement goes the implication that we are dealing with a problem outside the field of physiology. It is true that the physiologist has all too frequently emphasized the effects of fatigue as seen in the working organ but he ordinarily recognizes a twofold participation

[51] *Ibid.*, pp. 918–919.

[52] Schneider, E. C.: "Physiology of Muscular Activity," 2d ed. rev., W. B. Saunders Company, Philadelphia, 1939. Pp. 428.

in fatigue. This he does when he speaks of "neuromuscular fatigue," which at once indicates the respective share of muscular and nervous elements.[53]

It is quite generally recognized that excessive muscular work may cause mental weariness, but that excessive mental work may cause muscular weariness seems to be a new thought to many people. That such a relationship exists was demonstrated by Maggiora by the use of an ergograph. He stimulated the flexor muscles of his middle finger by an electric current applied directly to them, thus securing involuntary contractions. He found these muscles ordinarily were capable of lifting a certain weight 53 times before exhaustion appeared, but that immediately after three and a half hours of a hard oral mental examination the same muscles were capable of only 12 contractions with the same weight.

It is difficult, if not impossible, to separate wholly these two types of fatigue. Mental concentration and emotions are factors in much of the so-called "industrial fatigue" and they enter also into athletic activity.

It must be admitted that fatigue is a very indefinite and inexact expression. Hill early pointed out that there are many types of fatigue and that only a few concern the physiologist.[54]

Dill makes a distinction between the fatigue of moderate work, hard work, and maximal work. He believes the first of these is of rather remote interest to the physiologist in that it includes the rather large type described as boredom. Here the expenditure throughout an eight-hour work day is relatively small, so much so that when the day's work is done the worker enjoys such physical activities as gardening, strenuous games, and dancing. He points out that with ideal social conditions, outside as well as inside the factory, work is carried on happily and at a uniform rate without the appearance of fatigue and boredom.

The distinction between moderate and hard work is made on the basis of metabolism, which, of course, relates these to the capacity of the individual for supplying oxygen to his tissues. Moderate work is defined as that amount of activity which uses energy at a rate of three times or less that of the basal metabolic rate. With hard work the use of energy ranges between three and eight times the basal rate. It is said that a mean metabolic rate of about eight times the basal rate is as much as can be maintained for eight hours. Up to this rate the circulatory and respiratory systems effectively provide the body with the necessary oxygen. . . .

In maximal work, Dill's third type, the worker enters the "overload" zone, in which a steady state cannot be maintained and breakdown is not far off.

Some of the symptoms of fatigue are subjective and others objective in character. If it be accepted that the outward manifestation of fatigue is a diminished capacity for doing effective work, then it must be recognized that the subjective sense of fatigue is often a very fallacious index; since one frequently feels quite tired and yet finds, if he goes to work, that his capacity for performance is large and that the tired feelings disappear as he warms up to his task.[55]

The subjective feeling of fatigue is really a great complex of sensations, differing in some degree according to the character of the work, whether it be mental or physical. One author finds there may be a feeling of local tiredness in the active muscles, a general bodily sensation of tiredness, or a feeling of sleepiness. There

[53] *Ibid.*, p. 286.
[54] *Ibid.*, p. 287.
[55] *Ibid.*, p. 288.

may be a tired feeling in the head, obscure and poorly localized pains in the back of the head, pain and soreness in the muscles, stiffness in the joints, and swelling of the hands and feet.

Subjective symptoms of brain fatigue are sometimes clearly recognized by the subject. He complains of inability to keep attention fixed, of impaired memory, of failure to grasp new ideas, and of difficulty and slowness in reasoning. Arithmetical calculations and the like are slowed and inaccurate.[56]

Collier,[57] in his treatment of industrial fatigue, writes as follows:

Many unsuccessful attempts have been made to produce, experimentally, a condition of "neural" fatigue of the brain cells. It has been shown that hours can be spent in adding columns of figures, in reading, in copying, in doing intelligence tests or in performing other kinds of essentially mental work without the occurrence of manifest fatigue. In these experiments fatigue was produced as soon as interest in the task was lost and whenever boredom supervened.

In practice, it is found that nearly all of the practical problems of industrial fatigue, and not a few of the problems of industrial unrest, are emotional or psychological rather than physical in origin.

The next important point to emphasize is that industrial fatigue is a "transition state" (so to say) between health and disease. It has been shown that artificially fatigued animals are thereby rendered more susceptible to infection by the pneumococcus. It is a matter of common observation that many so-called physical illnesses are aggravated, if they are not caused, by precedent fatigue-states. The condition of being "run-down" is a fatigue-state and it is commonly a precursor of illness of some kind. Again, the intimate connection between fatigue and accident liability is universally recognized. It follows, therefore, that industrial fatigue is more peculiarly a medical problem than is usually supposed.[58]

It still happens occasionally that overwork or uncomplicated physical fatigue occurs in modern industry. . . .

Temporary fatigue is characterized by a sudden and sharp drop in output as fatigue comes on. Both the feeling of fatigue, and the diminution of efficiency associated with it, form defense mechanisms of the psyche-soma which, like pain, are designed to protect the integrity of the individual.

The feeling of fatigue is designed to prevent a dangerous depletion of the energy reserves. In a nerve-muscle preparation, "fatigue," or rather, the cessation of response to the stimulus, occurs first in the muscle end-plate. That is to say, it is the nervous element in the mechanism governing muscular activity that becomes fatigued before, and not after, the muscular element. In the same way we begin to feel tired long before muscular exhaustion renders us unable to continue at active work. A feeling of tiredness after prolonged work is, therefore, not a pathological but a protective physiological state, provided that the tiredness has not been produced by a totally inadequate exertion of mind or of body. The tiredness of the myasthenic or neurasthenic patient is pathological, but a hard day's work should be expected to leave the worker tired whether he has been engaged at muscular or mental work. The characteristic that separates normal

---

[56] *Ibid.,* p. 289.

[57] Collier, H. E.: "Outlines of Industrial Medical Practice," The Williams & Wilkins Company, Baltimore, 1943. Pp. 440.

[58] *Ibid.,* pp. 177–178.

tiredness or temporary fatigue from the other types is the rapidity with which the effects of each of them pass off. After a short rest, normal tiredness passes off and the original work can be resumed without any considerable deterioration in efficiency. A short rest, however, will not abolish the effects of established fatigue. Tiredness that is relieved by an ordinary night's rest is a normal physiological condition and should be clearly distinguished from fatigue.[59]

That "practice makes perfect" is true of both physical and mental work. The beginner and the unskilled worker soon grow tired. Physiologists have shown that anyone engaged in muscular work grows increasingly proficient with practice, and that, as proficiency increases, the length of time required to produce fatigue (when performing a standard piece of work) progressively increases with learning. After a while a "steady state" of maximum efficiency is reached and proficiency is attained. The trained athlete and the experienced workman are in a "steady state" in respect to their special work. It follows, therefore, that during the period required to learn a new skill or to "get into training" for a race or to become used to any kind of heavy manual employment, there is an initial period, during which fatigue states—both of body and of mind—are easily produced. Not only is the learner's work performed with relative inefficiency but his muscles, and still more, his central coordinating mechanisms are also inefficient."[60]

These are the points we gain from Collier:

1. Nearly all the everyday problems of industrial fatigue are psychological rather than physical.

2. Industrial fatigue is a transitional state between health and disease.

3. An intimate relation exists between fatigue and accident proneness.

4. Industrial fatigue is divided into five types: (1) physical fatigue, (2) temporary fatigue, (3) learner's fatigue, (4) subacute fatigue, and (5) chronic industrial fatigue.

"Physical fatigue" is said to be the impairment arising out of heavy muscular exertion as distinguished from the other types mentioned. A mixture of the subjective and physiological is involved in the remaining four kinds of fatigue given by Collier. Temporary fatigue is more transient. It involves both feelings of tiredness and lessened efficiency and serves as a warning signal against additional exertion. Learner's fatigue is the outcome of incoordination of the neuromuscular system while skill (efficiency) is being developed. Subacute and chronic industrial fatigues represent two degrees in which fatigue is accumulating.

Myers,[61] who studied fatigue in England for many years, states the following:

From what has been said in this chapter, the impossibility will have been already realized of defining industrial fatigue in a way which will warrant the

[59] *Ibid.,* pp. 178–179.

[60] *Ibid., pp.* 179–180.

[61] Myers, C. S.: "Industrial Psychology in Great Britain," The People's Institute Publishing Company, Inc., New York, 1925. Pp. 164. By permission of W. W. Norton & Company, Inc.

application of any of the various tests that have from time to time been devised to measure it.[62]

If we coninue to use (and it is almost impossible to avoid using) the term "fatigue" in industrial conditions, let us remember how complex is its character, how ignorant we are of its full nature, and how impossible it is in the intact organism to distinguish lower from higher fatigue and fatigue from inhibition, to separate the fatigue of explosive "acts" from the fatigue of maintaining "attitudes," or to eliminate the effects of varying interest, of excitement, suggestion and the like.[63]

Moreover, the problem of whether, and if so how far, fatigue at a given occupation is local or general has been too often overlooked. And the degree of correlation between industrial fatigue and the evidence of fatigue revealed by the tests is unknown and apparently unknowable.[64]

Elton Mayo,[65] connected with the study of fatigue (1929) at the Western Electric Company's Hawthorn plant, recognizes some difficulties in the use of the term fatigue.

One begins to wonder at this point whether the word "fatigue" is not itself in serious danger of being overworked; it seems to be used to describe a wide variety of situations.[66]

One might say, for example, that all physiological "work" consumes fuel reserves and that after a working day such reserves are at least in some degree depleted. The objection to this is that it does not in any sense represent the problems actually encountered in industry or in the physiological laboratory. The physiologist—Hill or Vernon, Henderson or Dill—is describing and measuring, a situation in which some defect of external relation is giving rise to an organic unbalance in the individual "worker." This unbalance is not "fatigue" in the sense that it is the same organic ill in all situations. On the contrary, its nature depends upon both the external condition and the individual. Of the infinitude of such maladaptations, we have looked at three—muscular activity in an untrained subject and "oxygen debt," insufficient air movement in a hot room and heart inefficiency in exercise, excessive loss of sodium chloride in perspiration and muscular "cramps." In every instance there is some "interference" with the balanced relation of the variables involved in bodily activity. And the disaster is not slowly continuous as the wage theory implies; once it has appeared, the individual is rapidly forced to stop work.

On the other hand, the physiologists equally describe and measure situations in which the individual continues to perform the task set him—even under the experimental conditions. In such instances, they point out, he achieves a "steady state." He is equal to the task, his inner equilibrium is maintained at the higher expenditure of energy.[67]

We cannot be surprised, then, that the English Research Board has dropped

[62] *Ibid.*, p. 71.

[63] *Ibid.*, p. 74.

[64] *Ibid.*, p. 73.

[65] Mayo, E.: "The Human Problems of an Industrial Civilization," 1933. Pp. 194. By permission of The Macmillan Company, publishers.

[66] *Ibid.*, pp. 8-9.

[67] *Ibid.*, pp. 22-23.

the word "fatigue" from its title. It is too fatally easy to conclude that because we have a word "fatigue" there must be a simple thing or fact that corresponds with it—a common fallacy discussed by Henderson in his studies of Pareto. The industrial investigator is constantly forced in his inquiries to take account of many factors in a complex situation; wherever the general effect is unsatisfactory to the worker and to industry he sets himself to discover the nature of the disequilibrium and the nature of the interference. The monographs published by the scientific workers under the Fatigue Board do not discuss fatigue directly; they inquire into hours of work and rest pauses, atmospheric conditions, vision and lighting, vocational selection (*i.e.*, individual differences with respect to a particular task), posture and physique and so on.[68]

Like many others, Mayo regards that which is psychological as accessory to that which is physiological. The "factors in the complex situation" seem to be more or less independent and cannot be seen as members in an integral system. The outcome of such a dualistic approach is bound to be that described by Mayo.

Ash,[69] who published his findings many years ago in the form of an archive, presents his general orientation in the subject very comprehensively. The whole introduction should be read by everyone interested in fatigue.

Fatigue is a comprehensive term which in its widest application embraces all those immediate and temporary changes, whether of a functional or organic character, which take place within an organism or any of its constituent parts as a direct result of its own exertions, and which tend to interfere with or inhibit the organism's further activities. Its principal effect is loss of efficiency, a lessening of the capacity to do work or to sustain activity; its most obvious sign is depression,—a lowering of sensitivity so that a given stimulus calls forth a response of less magnitude and intensity after exertion than before.

If, however, efficiency and sensitivity to stimuli were always inversely proportional to the amount of work done, *i.e.*, if particular units of activity always represented a definite loss of efficiency, the problem of measuring efficiency, or its opposite, fatigue, would be a relatively simple one. The amount and quality of work which an individual can accomplish at any time is determined by a large number of factors. Temperature, light, atmospheric conditions, time of day, distractions, mental attitude, practice and familiarity, health and nutrition all exercise a very decided influence upon the state of one's energies and his ability to direct them to the accomplishment of a specific task. Therefore, since fatigue is dependent, not only on amount of work done and the physical and mental state of the worker, the fatigue state will have to be estimated on the basis of changes within the organism rather than on the basis of what it has actually accomplished.[70]

In natural fatigue, we should have present the conflicting tendencies: First, there would be the tendency for the impulses to be shunted off by the resistances

[68] *Ibid.*, pp. 26–27.
[69] Ash, I. E.: Fatigue and Its Effect upon Control, *Arch. Psychol.*, No. 31, pp. 1–61, 1914.
[70] *Ibid.*, p. 1.

raised by fatigue in nervous tracts whether at the synapses or in the motor end-plates; and the second, the tendency of the organism to try to control the direction of impulses by voluntary inhibitions in adjacent nerve tracts.

If, then, fatigue represents a conflict between two opposing tendencies in the organism respecting the course which motor impulses shall take, we should expect the first symptoms of fatigue to be a loss of control in directing activities and in executing movements so as to make them coordinate with volitions. The effects of fatigue, according to this conception of it, are similar to those of a number of other discouraging agencies and influences which affect an individual's efficiency. They simply set one back, so to speak, in his process of development, and in the acquisition of efficiency for particular kinds of accomplishments. And since control in coordinating activities and directing movements is acquired last in the process of developing efficiency it will be the first to fall away under the influence of those disorganizing factors which interfere with efficiency. In other words, the ability to execute movements will remain after one has lost the power to control and coordinate them.[71]

"Loss of control" is seen by Ash as one of the significant features of the fatigue state. This view is quite different from the usual one in which energy expenditure and "fatigue products" are resorted to for explanations.

FATIGUE AS DEFINED IN PERIODICAL LITERATURE

The viewpoints represented in the 18 quotations from scientific and medical journals are those of physiologists, psychologists, psychophysiologists, and medical men. The first excerpt, from von Brücke, Early, and Forbes, embodies a clear statement from nerve physiology. The second quotation, from Dill, gives the standard physiological viewpoint. The next six quotations were taken from psychologists. The excerpts from Bartley indicate a psychophysiological viewpoint. Two quotations from Muscio and Garner represent industrial interests, and the remainder give the point of view of medical men, particularly as regards chronic fatigue.

Von Brücke, Early, and Forbes[72] view fatigue as encompassing all varieties of diminution in activity.

To avoid confusion between the lasting effects of prolonged stimulation and the transient refractory phase following a single response, we shall speak of the former as "fatigue" and shall use the word "conditioned" to denote the effect of a single preceding impulse.[73]

The depression in excitability due to prolonged stimulation is the main and often the only symptom of the condition that is generally called "fatigue" in nerve. Since this condition affects and prolongs the subnormal period, which is assumed to be the same as the old "refractory" period, it is merely a matter of

[71] *Ibid.*, pp. 14–15.

[72] Von Brücke, E. Th., M. Early, and A. Forbes: Fatigue and Refractoriness in Nerve, courtesy of the *Journal of Neurophysiology, 4:* 456–472, 1941.

[73] *Ibid.*, p. 457.

nomenclature whether we speak of a state of fatigue or of a prolongation of the refractory period. The delay of recovery during the "second" refractory state may be the first detectable sign of fatigue. But in going one step further we might also assume that not only is *prolonged* refractoriness a symptom of fatigue in nerve but also that the short refractory state itself following a single impulse in resting nerve is the elementary manifestation of fatigue.[74]

These authors make any kind of diminished sensitivity, or reduced activity, even of the tissue unit, for example, a case of fatigue. It has generally been held in physiology that refractoriness and fatigue are not equivalent, although the logic of this was never made clear. From our standpoint, refractoriness is a type of impairment. Since always some fraction of the structural units of the nervous system are in a refractory phase, impairment in this sense is always present.

The following excerpts are from Dill,[75] who has been studying the physiological cost of exertion for a number of years:

We say that fatigue is a state in which the organism has lost its capacity to carry on. It has a limited capacity for work. In the isolated muscle we can tell pretty well what some of these changes are. If the work has been carried on, for example, in an atmosphere of nitrogen, chemical changes can be detected by analysis which depend on the use of the energy reserves of that particular system anaerobically. If the system has been in an atmosphere of oxygen, work will be carried on longer, and the nature of the breakdown will be different. In the intact organism the the picture is more complicated, but we can produce a state in the sprinter, for example, similar to the state seen in the isolated muscle. The sprinter is called upon to transform an enormous quantity of energy within a very short time. He has supplied nearly all of the energy from certain reserves that can be used without oxygen. When the work is done, there is a period of recovery in which extra oxygen is used, and eventually the original state of the organism is restored.

Another type of breakdown is one in which there is less heavy stress, but one of much longer duration.[76]

The third type of stress to which attention must be paid is that of moderate degrees of exertion carried on for a very much longer time.[77]

Another type of stress involves very little in the way of physical effort but does involve mental or emotional stress of various sorts.[78]

Thorndike[79] describes certain aspects of fatigue. His emphasis on right *kind* of activity as compared with *amount* is important.

Fatigue of a muscle is a definite thing, viz., relative inability to overcome resistance, but fatigue of the mind means inability to do the right *kind* as well as

[74] *Ibid.*, pp. 470–471.

[75] Dill, D. B.: Physiology of Fatigue: Factors and Criteria of Endurance, *J. Lab. & Clin. Med.*, *28*: 596–601, 1942–43. Reprinted from Lecture XIX, *Collected Lectures* of the Metropolitan State Hospital, Waltham, Mass., 1942.

[76] *Ibid.*, p. 596.

[77] *Ibid.*, p. 597.

[78] *Ibid.*, p. 598.

[79] Thorndike, E.: Mental Fatigue, *Psychol. Rev.*, *7*: 466–482, 1900.

the right quantity of work, and may refer to sonnet-writing, logical theorizing, sharpness of observation or a hundred other different sorts of things.

So much for the *fact* of fatigue. Our second conclusion that there was no pure feeling of general mental incompetency is, of course, the result of personal intro-spection, though under test conditions. When I tried to analyze my feelings during states which in accord with the social consciousness I called feelings of mental fatigue, of inability to do mental work, I found in them emotions of repugnance at the thought of certain forms of mental activity, amounting some-times to a sort of mental nausea; feelings of dullness or stupidity (by which names I mean a state of unsuggestiveness, of insipidity), cravings for certain familiar forms of mental relaxation, feelings of sleepiness, heavy feelings in the head, pains in the chest or back (from leaning against a table and sitting upright during work), and sometimes a feeling best characterized by the awkward phrase mental "goneness," which reminds one of the feeling of physical faintness This last is most likely the supposed feeling of incompetency, but I get it only very rarely and not necessarily after especially hard mental work. I fancy that it has some direct physical cause. I was constantly surprised to find myself when feeling, as I would certainly have said, "mentally tired," unable to demonstrate in the feel-ing anything more than an emotional repugnance to the idea of doing mental work. On at least half the occasions this seemed to be all there was.[80]

The gist of this whole article, then, is the claim that certain current ideas about the fact and the feeling of mental fatigue, and the relation between them, are naïve abstractions based on a simple-minded analogy, a failure to carefully analyze certain mental states, and a confusion in the case of experimental investi-gations between lack of *desire* and lack of *ability* to work.[81]

Dodge[82] points out that competition occurs between tendencies and ele-ments in an action situation.

However long a mental process may be continued and however insignificant the decrement in returns, there comes a moment when it stops. It may be inter-rupted by demands for food, for sleep, or by some competing task. It may be interrupted by the gradually increasing insistence of inhibiting sensations like thirst, eyestrain, muscle pains, or pressure pains from sitting still. In any case, the work decrement of the consequent break can never be fully understood if we regard it as a direct product of fatigue, but only in connection with the inter-current competing tendencies. Fatigue may be a contributing factor, but the apparent decrement of the break will bear no regular relation to the degree of absolute fatigue in the tissues which performed the discontinued task.[83]

But in the complex of competing tendencies a little relative fatigue becomes the occasion for an entirely disproportionate result. . . .[84]

Relative fatigue, then, is not a mere limitation of human efficiency. It is not exhaustion, but prevents it. It is a conservator of organic equilibrium, as well as a condition of organic development. The incapacity of the young child for long-continued monotonous tasks may be a symptom of an active, developing

---

80 *Ibid.*, pp. 480–481.
81 *Ibid.*, p. 482.
82 Dodge, R.: The Laws of Relative Fatigue, *Psychol. Rev., 24:* 89–113, 1917.
83 *Ibid.*, p. 110.
84 *Ibid.*, pp. 111–112.

mind. Lack of competition would result in mental deformity, or absolute exhaustion, just as truly as the lack of stable reinforcing systems in the adult would mean perpetual infantilism. Thus it seems to me that the principles of relative fatigue have a direct bearing on the practical problems of education which the traditional doctrine of fatigue as apparent work decrement entirely missed.[85]

Whiting and English[86] make a distinction between fatigue and impairment similar to the one that we shall later show to be so necessary.

The hypothesis is advanced that fatigue is a negative emotional appetite. As such it is to be differentiated from the physiological phenomenon of exhaustion of which it is a concomitant. As an emotion in the broader sense, fatigue is a conscious (if negative) motive to action. Fatigue does not directly cause work decrement, but raises the threshold at which work motives are effective. But if such positive motives are adequate at all, the fatigue—as distinguished from the accompanying exhaustion—has no effect upon work efficiency. This hypothesis deserves experimental investigation since it seems to explain many otherwise puzzling facts.[87]

While exhaustion is thus primarily a physiological or specific and local phenomenon, we believe that fatigue is chiefly a "subjective" phenomenon. Like exhaustion, it is a function of exertion. But unlike exhaustion, fatigue is not symptomatic of inability to do work. The relation of fatigue to work is more complex.[88]

For Johnson,[89] fatigue is primarily what we refer to as impairment.

A rational attitude toward fatigue and its social consequences demands a better understanding of the condition itself. Essentially it is an impairment produced by exercise, of present performance, or of preparedness for future performance. With feelings of "tiredness" and with complaints thereof, it has less to do than we might suppose.[90]

We often hear and sometimes speak of the "toxins of fatigue." It may help to consider how these poisons are generated. The vital activities of the bodily cells are made possible by the burning within the cell, of certain fuels which it manufactures from raw materials taken from the blood stream. These fuels are about as unstable as nitroglycerin, and burn at explosive speeds, though in minute quantities at once. When the cell is "irritated" some of these highly explosive fuel molecules split into smaller fragments, which are then burned from either end. In case the process of splitting should go more rapidly than the burning of the split fragments, the cell is left with an excess of the latter. Some of these products of splitting are poisonous . . .

There are three ways in which this condition may be brought about. The first is by asphyxiation . . .

The second way is by narcosis . . .

[85] *Ibid.,* p. 112.
[86] Whiting, H. F., and H. B. English: Fatigue Tests and Incentives, *J. Exper. Psychol., 8:* 33–49, 1925.
[87] *Ibid.,* p. 49.
[88] *Ibid.,* p. 47.
[89] Johnson, H. M.: The Real Meaning of Fatigue, *Harper's, 158:* 186–193, 1929.
[90] *Ibid.,* p. 186.

The third way is by fatigue . . .[91]

Collier[92] points out some of the numerous ways the term fatigue is used. He employs it as a term for a condition in which decrement in movements appears.

The variety of ways in which the term fatigue has been used not only in common speech but also in scientific writing necessitates considerable caution in the use of the concept. The term may be found to indicate decrements in muscular activity, raised sensory thresholds, adaptation, refractory states of nerve and muscle, reduced capacities for work either mental or physical, effects of accumulated toxins, sensations from overworked muscles, boredom, distractibility, and almost any unanalyzed hindrance to effective work. The term fatigue will be used in this discussion to denote a condition developed within the organism coincident with prolonged muscular activity which operates as a decrement either to the total movement or to components of the movement.[93]

It is important in relation to the present experiments to note that a condition recognized as fatigue may apparently produce either excitatory or inhibitory effects.[94]

One of the most insightful discussions of fatigue in recent years is the short note of Bentley,[95] which we quote in full.

Is fatigue tiring? The word "fatigue" stands within a fairly long list of terms which accept with like facility the adjectives "mental" and "physical." Other words in the list are "habit," "practice," "skill," "drive," "reward," "pain," "health," and "disease." When set before any one of these terms, either adjective makes sense, sense not only in common speech, but sense also (and all too often) in the phraseology of the sciences. If you will begin a sentence with such "mental" words and phrases as I feel, put forth, am, accomplish, enjoy or suffer, you will find that these ambidextrous terms fit in, and that they also fit in just as naturally into a "physical" context, either organic or inorganic. As everyone knows, this double use harks back to the old-age division of substances into material and spiritual, bodily and mental, physical and psychical. Most of these words seem to derive their color and flavor, however, from the circumstance that they profess to combine, or intimately to relate, things and states which stand, by almost common consent, in complete opposition, an opposition as uncompromising as life-and-lifeless, north-and-south, heaven-and-hell, black-and-white, good-and-evil. That is to say that one and the same living man may suffer mental fatigue and physical fatigue, may be skilled in mind and body, may enjoy mental health or physical, and so on. When we consider, therefore, the deep interest of psychologists in combining, by all sorts of fantastic speculations and doctrines, the two beings within man, still better of merging them (psychophysical), or of denying one member of the troublesome pair (man-the-machine, body-responding-to-energy,

91 Ibid., p. 187.

92 Collier, R. M.: The Crossed Effect upon Voluntary Movements of a Unilaterally Induced Fatigue, J. Exper. Psychol., 23: 26–44, 1938.

93 Ibid., p. 26.

94 Ibid., p. 27.

95 Bentley, M.: Tools and Terms in Recent Researches, Am. J. Psychol., 57: 264–269, 1944.

neural-organization), or, best of all, melting them down into one (psychosomatic, organismic, whole-organism), we should not wonder at the volumes and volumes devoted by psychologists of many schools and professions to these innocent vehicles of *double entendre*.

Now the main embarrassment arising from the technical employment of these ambiguous words is that each *changes its basal significance* as it passes back and forth. Is mental work the same *work*, possessed of the same *dimensions*, as physical work? Is the habituated muscle group the same thing as the mentally habituated man? Is a jumping toothache the same *genus* of pain as the "painful situation" of the animal behaviorist? Watch disease change its coloring, its intent, its quale, as you pass from physical disease to mental disease, of from the one sort of health to the other.

With respect to fatigue the curious investigator does not have to proceed far in our current researches or through summarizing reviews before he sees whither this confusion tends. In most of the reviews, indeed, he will find a separate section devoted to mental fatigue; "mental" often in half-quotes but with no definition. Within this single periodical the last half-dozen volumes will show several contexts in which the term has been used; sometimes as mental, sometimes as bodily. Last year, H. M. Johnson (*56*, 1943, 552*ff.*), criticized the numerological definition of "fatigue," maintaining that a statistical result of tests (as of driver's skill and road accidents) is at times identified "wholly by presupposition" (p. 558) with something illicitly called "fatigue." The criticism is both pointed and timely. An interested reader may, for example, apply it to H. L. Valentine's inference (1943, pp. 381*ff.*) that an observed improvement in certain tests using various vitamin-B ingredients may safely be laid to this same undefined factor. In fact, throughout a half-century of "mental testing," fatigue has been regarded (usually without sufficient attestation) as one of the standard determinants of accomplishment. Is it not now time to ask whether "fatigue" is not properly to be used (if at all) in a generic sense, as including two or more species? It is more than possible that the "species" will—when once they have been distinguished and described by careful experimental means—return the term "fatigue" to the dictionaries for less technical and precise uses than it now enjoys in the physical and biological disciplines.[96]

Bartley,[97] in a preliminary study of the relation of ocular discomfort to fatigue, disclosed intrareflex conflict. At this time his statement on fatigue was as follows:

Vision, though primarily a function of a specific visual pathway, involves the participation of the whole organism. Since vision depends upon so many diverse components, visual fatigue is so complex a phenomenon as to be variously understood and diversely defined, or to be dealt with without explicit definition.

The main symptoms of visual fatigue are generally localized in the eye or head region, although they may be much more diffuse. Although it has most usually been supposed that discomfort localized in the eyes must *originate* there, some evidence suggests that much of the localized discomfort is a function of the organism as a whole, becoming thus localized when visual achievement becomes, for any reason, unsatisfactory. This leaves us with two diverse conceptions. The one seeks

[96] *Ibid.*, p. 264.
[97] Bartley, S. H.: A Factor in Visual Fatigue, *Psychosomatic Med.*, *4*: 369-375, 1942.

explanation in the eye itself, as if the trouble there were a perfectly static condition, which when once corrected could be expected to banish the untoward symptoms. The other view, although fully attending to the state of the local mechanism, sees the local symptoms as not alone but as a part of the general behavior of the individual. It attempts to deduce the organism's success or failure in what the latter is trying to do and envisages local functions accordingly.

The present study was designed to test the idea that visual fatigue arises (1) from the attempt to inhibit certain inclinations inherent in the visual mechanism, or (2) in situations in which although conscious objectives are absent the eyes are induced to attempt certain contradictory actions simultaneously.[98]

Fatigue was not defined, but an attempt was made to state some of the conditions for the experimental qualities involved.

In a later article, Bartley[99] more nearly approached a formal definition.

Although fatigue is something we all believe to be ubiquitous and manifest in many forms, it has not yet been reduced to satisfactory definition and study. In fact, those who have best succeeded in simplifying the approach to fatigue problems (such as the measurement of work decrement or impairment), while obtaining perfectly useful information, have failed to answer some of the most pertinent questions.[100]

Fatigue arises out of conflict, either organic and physiological or that which is more directly and immediately motivational to start with. Irresolvable conflicts end in frustration. If the conflicts that happen to arise are not too suddenly imposed, or are not too great, the reactions themselves are something that develop more slowly. They constitute fatigue. On the other hand, it is conceivable that certain frustrations develop without a protracted history of conflict and thus through their suddenness induce very sharply drawn reactions such as have been described as aggression, regression and fixation. These represent the realignment of the whole organism. In such cases it would be expected that fatigue would be skipped in the train of consequences.

And yet, chronic fatigue is sometimes met with. This apparently is not all of one pattern. Some of it arises out of impairment and the constant recognition of it. But it is conceivable, that other cases of it may, upon investigation, turn out to be instances of fixation, or perhaps related in some way to regression. In other words, instead of skipping the fatigue stage, the responses may represent the development of a *fixed* attitude of fatigue.[101]

Muscio,[102] in an analysis of the problem of testing fatigue, begins his discussion by pointing out the need for a definition. As will be seen from the following quotations, certain logical requirements are made:

The conditions of experimentation with the purpose of finding a fatigue test

98 *Ibid.*, p. 369.

99 Bartley, S. H.: Conflict, Frustration and Fatigue, *Psychosomatic Med.*, 5: 160–163, 1943.

100 *Ibid.*, p. 160.

101 *Ibid.*, p. 162.

102 Muscio, B.: Is a Fatigue Test Possible? (A report to the Industrial Fatigue Research Board), *Brit. J. Psychol.*, 12: 31–46, 1921–22.

are two: (a) that we know what we mean by fatigue; (b) that we have some method *other than the use of a suggested fatigue test* by which we can *know* that different degrees of fatigue are present at certain different times.

(a) That the first of these conditions is necessary is self-evident: it is obviously absurd to set about finding a test of an undefined entity . . .

(b) If it be not known *before the application of a proposed fatigue test* in what degree fatigue is present, the result obtained from its application will be destitute of significance. The results of any proposed fatigue test, insofar as it is a fatigue test, must correspond exactly with the presence of different degrees of fatigue; and the determination of such correspondence requires a knowledge of *two series,* namely, *on the one hand,* a series consisting of results obtained from the the application of the test at different times, and *on the other hand,* a series consising of the different degrees of fatigue present when these results were obtained. The knowledge of this second series must be obtained by some other means than by the proposed test; otherwise we should have only one series.[103]

(1) In the present state of scientific knowledge, two definitions of the intrinsic nature of fatigue may be offered. When organic matter is "continuously" active, energy is transformed into heat and mechanical work, and there tend to accumulate chemical products of the activity, of the character of organic poisons. The nature of fatigue may be specified by reference to either of these two facts.

(a) Fatigue may be defined as that condition in which a certain percentage of available organic energy has been transformed into heat or work (the more energy transformed after this point has been reached, the greater the fatigue) . . .

(b) Fatigue may be defined as that condition in which certain chemical products of activity, of the nature of organic poisons, have accumulated in the organ that has been active; "different degrees of fatigue" meaning "different amounts of these activity products." As it is known that some at least of these products are in active muscle, it might seem that this definition would be satisfactory; but this is not the case.[104]

It is clear that fatigue in the present sense cannot be directly observed. There is, therefore, only one method by which its presence and its degree at any time can be known, namely, deduction from something else that is observed. Hence, everything depends, so far as our present purpose is concerned, upon whether or not there can be found some phenomenon from which this deduction can be made; and this resolves itself into *the possibility of finding some characteristic expression of fatigue. If such an expression cannot be found, fatigue test experimentation with reference to the intact organism has no sufficiently definite problem.*

(2) The *acceptance* of a characteristic expression of fatigue in the intact organism is included in that *general* definition of fatigue most usually adopted at the present time; according to which *fatigue is a condition caused by work, in which the capacity for work is diminished.* The characteristic expression of fatigue here accepted, and explicitly stated to be such in certain forms of the definition, is a *diminished capacity for work.* We have now to consider whether this is adequate for our purpose . . .

---

[103] *Ibid.,* p. 31.
[104] *Ibid.,* p. 33.

(a) The definition might be taken to mean that play, as distinct from work, could not produce fatigue. Such a conclusion would probably be denied by most of those who accept the definition: if capacity for work can be diminished by work, it seems certain that it *can* also be diminished by play. In any case, it is often difficult to determine whether a particular activity is play or work. It may be work in respect of the fact that it yields remuneration, and play so far as the performer's attitude is concerned. This ambiguity in the definition does not occur when the term *activity* is substituted for the term *work*.[105]

(b) The definition does not specify the *kind* of work for which capacity is diminished in fatigue. It could be taken to mean either that capacity for *every* kind of work is diminished, or that capacity for the particular kind of work that caused it is diminished . . .

(c) A statement of the "diminished capacity" definition of fatigue which would remove the above ambiguities would be as follows: *fatigue is a condition caused by activity, in which the capacity for repeating the activity that caused it is diminished.*[106]

Now, if diminished capacity is an "expression" of fatigue, any observable expression of diminished capacity can be considered simply as an expression of fatigue. We may therefore speak *as though any expression of diminished capacity due to prior activity were an expression of fatigue.*[107]

(d) The statement that the condition of diminished capacity expresses itself in relatively poor output must therefore be altered by substituting *tends to express* for *expresses* itself. This will mean that it expresses itself in this way *in the absence of interfering factors* . . .

(4) Having seen how the commonly accepted expression of diminished capacity must be modified if from its presence diminished capacity may be inferred, we must consider one other fundamental question. *Is it justifiable to accept diminished capacity as a characteristic expression of fatigue?* So far an affirmative answer to this question has been *assumed*.[108]

The definition of *fatigue* would then be as follows: *fatigue is a condition* (partly specifiable by reference to accumulation of metabolites and blocking in impulse paths) *caused by activity, in which the output produced by that activity tends to be relatively poor; and the degree of fatigue tends to vary directly with poorness of output* . . .

The possibility of finding a fatigue test thus depends upon the possibility of eliminating or of determining the precise effects of all interfering factors (among which are included factors tending to produce the accepted characteristic expression of fatigue in the absence of the fatigued condition). Among these factors are (a) incitement, (b) practice, (c) spurts, (d) illness, (e) diurnal rhythm, (f) incentives to a given kind of activity, and (g) competing incentives. It seems possible to control the first five of these, but impossible to control the two last. Whether it is possible to determine the precise effects upon output of ineliminable interfering factors, is a highly problematical question. The mere discovery that *any*

105 *Ibid.,* p. 34.
106 *Ibid.,* p. 35.
107 *Ibid.,* p. 36.
108 *Ibid.,* p. 39.

factor influences output is very important here; and the elimination or determination of the precise effects of each such factor is in itself a considerable experimental problem. This work, however, *must precede* the application of proposed fatigue tests: that is, *the first requirement is a* technique *for determining independently of a proposed test in what degree fatigue is present at certain times.* For the carrying out of this work, the interfering factors must be under the control of the experimenter, and this condition cannot generally be realized in industry. Once this work has been done, the next question concerns the actual fatigue tests to be used.[109]

Most proposed tests of fatigue are performance tests.[110]

In view of the foregoing considerations it is recommended that the whole fatigue test problem be stated in a form the nature of which may be indicated by the following suggestions:

(a) That the term *fatigue* be absolutely banished from precise scientific discussion, and consequently that attempts to obtain a fatigue *test* be abandoned.[111]

After stating the requirements of a fatigue test, Muscio comes to the definite conclusion that the term fatigue should be abandoned. He suggests that, in the place of fatigue tests, investigations be made of the effects of various kinds of work on mental and physiological function. These conclusions are rational within limits, but as will be seen more clearly as the reader progresses through the present book, certain very important considerations were neglected. Muscio's view with regard to human behavior is inadequate to handle what he calls "mental" and "physiological." Without benefit of recent advances in organismic or holistic thinking, we should be forced to agree with Muscio. As it is, the assumption that the existence of a function or phenomenon rests on a quantitative test for it cannot be accepted.

Garner,[112] interested in fatigue in relation to practical situations, writes the following:

Fatigue has been described as being a physiological condition of the cells or organs of the body which have undergone excessive activity with a resulting loss of power. More correctly speaking, however, fatigue should be considered from both the psychical and the physical aspect.

Psychically, one who has been active for a considerable time, either mentally, or physically, or both, develops a condition familiarly described as a "tired feeling"; this sensation being one of weariness is truly a psychical phenomenon conveying no comprehension of any physical changes in the body tissues although important material changes have, in fact, taken place. Physiologists have been giving much concern in their endeavor to determine in just what these changes really consist, and even yet some are not fully understood.[113]

109 *Ibid.,* p. 40.

110 *Ibid.,* p. 41.

111 *Ibid.,* p. 45.

112 Garner, J. R.: Fatigue in Its Relation to Accident Prevention, *Indust. Med., 6:* 665–668, 1937.

113 *Ibid.,* p. 665.

Seham,[114] in dealing with fatigue and nervousness in children, regards fatigue as follows:

Fatigue and nervousness are probably the most frequently overused and misused terms in medicine. The layman applies them interchangeably to his everyday life and the physician finds them short cuts to diagnosis.

Since the term fatigue is so often applied and since there seems to exist a great difference of opinion as to just what is meant by it let us say at once what we understand by chronic fatigue. By fatigability, which often appears as one of many symptoms in organic disease, we do not mean acute fatigue which can be artificially produced in normal persons, or which is the inevitable result of overwork at the time, and from which immediate recuperation is possible through adequate rest. What we have in mind is a psychobiological syndrome, which may be primary, but often is secondary, in which more than one organ and more than one system is involved and in which the signs and symptoms of subefficiency are usually widespread. The symptoms, implicit and overt in character, are varied, differing at times even in one and the same individual. In some people the subjective, in others the objective symptoms may predominate.[115]

One of the chief obstacles to the study of fatigue is the different connotation employed by the many writers. On the one hand they speak of a decreased capacity for work which is known as objective fatigue and on the other of various sensations, usually of unpleasant character. Unfortunately the concept of objective fatigue is not itself very clear even in its empirical acceptation. This is true because the measurement of fatigue on the basis of work done is liable to grave error, due to the fact that fatigue can be counterbalanced by voluntary effort. Fatigue is not uniformly revealed in the decrease of work accomplished.[116]

The feeling of fatigue is a complex state, consisting not only of fatigue sensations referred to different organs but also of a feeling of inertia, shown in a disinclination to begin new work and to continue it. Lassitude, limpness, laziness, changes in emotional attitude and a desire for rest are also common sensations. Because of the absence of methods for the analysis of subjective complaints, the study of subjective fatigue has been almost entirely neglected.[117]

Although the feeling of fatigue plays a protective role in preventing exhaustion and generally increases in intensity more rapidly than the decrease in the rate or amount of work, it may not serve as an index of the physiological state of the body or of its capacity for continued work. A short walk, involving actually little use of muscles, may produce a pronounced feeling of fatigue to an individual who may dance all night without a complaint. Another may be on the verge of complete exhaustion, as a result of overwork, without feeling fatigued. Laboratory investigations have shown that a given task may be done as rapidly and as accurately when the subject reports a feeling of fatigue as when consciousness of fatigue is altogether absent. Particularly in mental work, the feeling of fatigue may be experienced when objective measures of production show progressive increase in the amount of work.[118]

[114] Seham, M.: Fatigue and Nervousness in Childhood, *Internat. Clin.*, 2: 105–121, 1935.

[115] *Ibid.*, pp. 105–106.

[116] *Ibid.*, p. 106.

[117] *Ibid.*, p. 107.

[118] *Ibid.*, pp. 107–108.

Wharton[119] refers to the fatigue syndrome as follows:

By fatigue syndrome we mean that group of symptoms complained of by patients who experience mental or physical depletion, or both. In this discussion we do not propose to restrict ourselves to those who reveal chronic nervous exhaustion, but will discuss that group of cases with chronic fatigue which is not relieved by average rest. We include, also, the patients whose fatigue is so masked by overactivity that they themselves are unaware of it. Work of itself seldom leads to this chronic condition we are calling fatigue. It is axiomatic that worry, not work, kills. Overwork, therefore, is not a condition to be considered merely for itself but as a symptom of maladjustment. Usually it is not overwork that leads to a nervous breakdown but the nervous breakdown drives the individual to overwork. Frequently overwork is suggestive of a mental conflict. Insomnia is another instance in which the result is often mistaken for the cause.

Various symptoms that result under stress of war conditions tend to be labeled fatigue. The following statement, by Tillisch and Walsh,[120] emphasizes the importance of the understanding of fatigue in military personnel.

Armstrong was the first to call attention to the chronic functional nervous disturbances seen in pilots, which he termed aeroneurosis. The symptoms he described are more or less identical with those of the syndrome variously called "situational neurosis," "chronic exhaustion state," "anxiety state," "anxiety neurosis," or "chronic nervous exhaustion." We use the term chronic exhaustion state because we do not believe the functional disturbances encountered in a pilot are any different from the functional disturbances encountered in any other hightensioned person subjected to overwork and prolonged emotional strain. The human nervous system, in common with the nervous systems of other animals, behaves as if it were a storehouse of potential energy. When its store becomes depleted, symptoms of exhaustion make their appearance. In a person subjected to long-continued mental fatigue recuperative processes do not have the opportunity fully to restore the nervous energy that has been utilized, so that the person is forced to rely on a special reserve store, which may be called the "nervous energy reserve" and which is intended to be used only for emergency.

Kepler[121] in a discussion of chronic fatigue, states as follows:

In the main, chronic fatigue is a disease of the intelligentsia. Its victims include doctors, lawyers, ministers of the gospel and their wives, nuns, artists, musicians, students, school teachers, big and little businessmen, executives and white-collar workers in general. Numskulls rarely are afflicted. People who use their muscles rather than their wits seem to escape, possibly because they expect to be tired. In any event, it is unusual for the day laborer or the charwoman to seek advice because of fatigue. Equally significant is the fact that patients having serious organic disease rarely mention fatigue as their outstanding or only complaint. There are, of course, a certain set of exceptions to this general principle, notably

119 Wharton, G. K.: The Fatigue Syndrome, *Canad. M. A. J., 38:* 339–342, 1938.
120 Tillisch, J. H., and M. N. Walsh: Chronic Exhaustion State in Test Pilots, *War Med., 2:* 917–922, 1942.
121 Kepler, E. J.: Chronic Fatigue, *Proc. Staff Meet., Mayo Clin., 17:* 340–344, 1942.

patients who have far-advanced hypertension. Both youngsters and oldsters seem to be relatively immune. The greatest incidence is in early adult and middle life before recuperative powers are on the decline. Likewise, it is significant that some patients who were always tired during their earlier years feel better as they approach old age.

Usually the examination of patients who complain of chronic fatigue does not disclose anything significantly abnormal. The blood pressure may be slightly less than what is considered normal, slight hypochromic anemia may be present and, not infrequently, the basal metabolic rate is moderately depressed. On the whole, however, the results of examination are disappointing, disappointing to the doctor because he is left without anything specific to treat and disappointing to the patient because a cause for his complaints has not been found.

Muncie[122] presents some insightful classifications of the fatigue situation.

A large share of the internist's clientele presents complaints which in the final analysis reduce (1) to such terms as emotions and affects, some more or less closely linked with, and expressive of basic physiologic states of malaise, and (2) to attitudes toward life, in general, or in some particular aspect . . .

In my experience the three most important conditions of the sort under discussion are (1) anxiety-tension states, (2) depressions, and (3) chronic fatigue. It is the last that I wish to discuss.

Patients suffering from chronic fatigue complain of being "tired," or "weak," or "exhausted." These terms, used rather loosely, are not synonymous, as can be easily shown by careful history taking. They roughly divide into two categories: (1) those in which there is a paralysis of initiative, with a variable degree of fatigability on effort, either mental or physical; (2) those in which spontaneity and desire still persist, but in which there appears to the patient to be an inadequate peripheral effectiveness. "I want to do things, but my body won't perform," is the usual statement. Common experience differentiates tiredness, the result of effort, from weakness, the forestaller of effort. Practically speaking, however, the terms do become interchangeable, because if tiredness exists or relentlessly recurs over some while, then effort is forestalled because of its sure anticipation and is consequently avoided.

Metts[123] writes as follows on chronic fatigue:

Chronic fatigue states represent no definite clinical entity, and a definition cannot be compressed into a few words. In this paper I shall attempt to discuss the symptom complex presented by people who complain of mental and physical depletion, or both; including those who are chronically nervously exhausted, as well as that group with chronic fatigue who do not recover with ordinary rest. Fatigue has been variously defined by physiologists as a diminished capacity for work, other conditions remaining constant, a break in organic equilibrium, and to use the terminology of Cannon, "a deficiency of homeostatic force." Many excellent papers on the subject have been published by physiologists; the group working at the fatigue laboratories at Harvard University, and by our industrial

---

[122] Muncie, W.: Chronic Fatigue, *Psychosomatic Med., 3:* 277–283, 1941.

[123] Metts, J. C.: Chronic Fatigue States, in Symposium of Psychoses and Psycho-neuroses, *J. Med. Assoc. Georgia, 31:* 308–312, 1942.

surgeons. A common conclusion of all is that there is no definite physiologic basis for chronic fatigue. The increase in lactic acid formation in the muscles which follows strenuous physical effort is absent, nor are there any other physiologic or chemical changes present to differentiate it from the normal state. There is a very definite psychologic factor. Familiar to most of you is the disappearance of that tired feeling when the dogs locate a "sundown covey" of quail; or that pickup in your golf when contemplating the nineteenth hole on a hot summer day.

Here, fatigue as a concept has not reached the stage of systematic treatment, although Metts, like many physicians, recognizes that the individual's attitude plays an important role.

Alexander and Portis[124] make these remarks in dealing with hypoglycemic fatigue.

Another constant feature is fatigue, chronic or appearing in acute attacks. The fatigue has certainly fairly constant features. It is present as a rule on awakening, slightly more severe in the mid-morning, temporarily improved after luncheon, and most marked in the mid-afternoon. There is practically always a complete relief after the heavy evening meal. The patients may awaken with a severe headache which is also manifest during the mid-afternoon fatigue. Along with this more chronic fatigue there may be acute attacks of extreme weakness, tremulousness, sweating, and vertigo. At times a feeling of "light-headedness" may be manifest. The acute attacks may be associated with anxiety of fainting or free floating anxiety.[125]

Not the absolute lowering of the sugar concentration but the inability of the organism to raise the sugar concentration of the blood as it is required during activity (particularly during mental activity, because the exclusive fuel of the brain cells is sugar) is the immediate cause of the subjective feelings of fatigue and exhaustion as well as in the acute cases of tremulousness, light-headedness, and weakness. The occasional anxiety state, which sometimes accompanies the attacks, is a subjective reaction to the acute feeling of weakness and has no specific etiological significance.[126]

Alexander and Portis describe the hypoglycemic syndrome, with the implication that when the term fatigue is used the reader will know what is meant.

A CONCERTED EFFORT ON VISUAL FATIGUE

An important attempt to understand fatigue, in recent times, was one made through the avenue of *visual fatigue*. Since this attempt represented the combined efforts of a number of scientists, the reader should be appraised of it through quotations that are relevant to the present chapter in which views on fatigue are being stated.

---

[124] Alexander, F., and S. A. Portis: A Psychosomatic Study of Hypoglycaemic Fatigue, *Psychosomatic Med., 6:* 191–206, 1944.

[125] *Ibid.,* p. 191.

[126] *Ibid.,* p. 205.

In 1938, the Committee on Scientific Aids to Learning, of the National Research Council, became interested in the possibility of the general use of projected microfilm in libraries in place of books. The question was raised whether such use of the film would induce an undue amount of visual fatigue. To answer this question, an Advisory Committee on Visual Fatigue was appointed. The members of this committee were Adelbert Ames, Jr., Walter F. Dearborn, and Wallace Fenn, who were to recommend the necessary kind of investigation. In 1939, the Advisory Committee on Visual Fatigue reported as follows:

> In general, therefore, your subcommittee sees no promise of an easy answer to the question of visual fatigue which has been asked. The inclusive psychological or performance tests might provide a quick but incomplete and unsatisfactory answer. Tests involving measurement of one or more of the visual functions are not sufficiently reliable.
>
> The committee recommends a thorough survey of the whole field of visual fatigue, with a view of establishing conclusively reliable tests to measure fatigue which could thereafter be used with confidence under the optimal conditions for the reading of projected films.

Accordingly, the Committee on Scientific Aids to Learning arranged for an expanded committee. Those present for its first meeting were Walter R. Miles, chairman, Adelbert Ames, Jr., Percy W. Cobb, D. B. Dill, Brian O'Brien, Irvin Stewart, and Francis Adler. After preliminary remarks giving the new committee the history following the initial interest of one of the large foundations in the possible fatigue from reading projected microfilm, plans were begun for a Symposium of Visual Fatigue.

The program of the symposium, which was held in Washington, D. C., in May, consisted in papers given by Walter R. Miles, George Wald, Clarence H. Graham, Selig Hecht, Brian O'Brien, P. C. Nutting, Jr., Alfred Bielschowsky, F. K. Moss, Ross A. McFarland, Miles A. Tinker, Walter F. Dearborn, Robert K. Lambert, and Harry M. Johnson.

The following quotations were taken from the discussion following the papers. Professor Johnson's paper being the last one prior to discussion, it seemed that it furnished a starting point for remarks from those present.

Among other things, George Wald said:

> We seem to have reached the following point. One group of scientists is equipped by temperament and training to search out what we may class as optimal conditions for visual performance, and has devised techniques for measuring such conditions accurately. Unfortunately these procedures do not measure what is commonly meant by visual fatigue. In addition we have a group of psychologists motivated by more complicated objectives and using a different type of procedure to attain them. It seems adequately indicated by Dr. Johnson's discussion that they also are not measuring visual fatigue. Dr. Johnson defined fatigue as a con-

dition of decrement in performance. But he describes experiments in which long series of psychological tests applied to persons suffering extreme fatigue—using the word in its colloquial sense—fail to demonstrate such decrements reliably. He suggests that this is due to compensation since we cannot measure fatigue. But surely we know less about compensation than we do about fatigue itself; there is no present indication that we can recognize it with certainty, much less measure it. It is significant that Dr. Johnson ended his description of certain fatigue experiments in which psychological tests had failed to demonstrate decrement, by assuring us that the subjects really were fatigued, as evidenced by a recognizable behavior pattern which we are accustomed to associate with extreme fatigue. It seems to me that we have little choice but to accept this situation as it stands. Fatigue seems to be one of those phenomena containing a complicated social component which we cannot reliably *measure,* but which we have no difficulty in *recognizing.* A subject's simple statement that he is fatigued is a primary datum, and very much more reliable than any measurement yet suggested in this symposium. This forces us back upon a formulation of the problem which we are equipped to handle; measurement of the conditions of visual performance, and of those optimal conditions which most delay the appearance of visual fatigue.

Professor Ames said:

It seems to me that in view of the general haziness of our ideas as to what fatigue is and especially in view of the role that compensations play in the picture, from an ideal point of view, the experimental setup should be such as to make it possible to determine the compensations at the same time that the variations of functions, which are considered evidence of fatigue, are measured. I do not know whether tests exist by which compensations can be determined but it would seem that unless the nature and extent of the compensations that might be in operation were known it would be difficult to determine the amount of fatigue.

Professor Miles, in summing up the symposium, said:

In coming to the close of this conference we all realize, perhaps more vividly than ever before, that visual fatigue as a psychophysiological state at present lacks scientific reports. As a concept it has currency by reason of our community of experience. When a person says, "My eyes are tired," the statement seems qualitatively meaningful and acceptable as a bit of self-description. If we ask him, "Why are your eyes tired?" he has only to tell what kind of visual task he has been doing and for how long he did it to give what is usually considered a complete answer. In reply we very likely say, "Yes, that kind of work is very fatiguing on the eyes, especially if you have to do a lot of it."

Socially we find ourselves on familiar territory in talking about this experience of visual fatigue but scientifically we seem to be lost in the woods. Generally speaking and in the physiological sense we regard visual fatigue as a temporary impairment of function following continued activity. Specifically we may, for example, think of it as a state of or the result of maladjustment between the amount of convergence, accommodation and the size of the pupil. Tests have been reported on and proposed by members of this conference relating to retinal functions, as for example, acuity and flicker-fusion threshold; to muscles of the refraction mechanism (to the extrinsic ocular motor mechanism) , for example, fusion amplitude, eye movements in reading; and to the more general musculature of the organism as a whole. Each test appeared to have certain things that recommend it for this study. At present we are not ready to go on record as unanimously approving any one of the tests as a standard test for visual fatigue.

The subject of visual fatigue while remaining scientifically hazy and perhaps rather unattractive is forced on our attention by certain practical considerations. In terms of specific practical problems, such as the reading of microfilm, research can possibly be undertaken.

A number of rather promising tests and methods have been presented in our symposium of yesterday and discussed in today's conference. Our consensus of opinion seems to be that several of these methods should be combined into a test battery for use in any single investigation that undertakes to measure visual fatigue in connection with any particular work task. We need comparative results on different tests applied to the same subject personnel following visual work routines. The general picture obtained from a battery of tests by being more comprehensive and sampling the performance of various types of eye mechanisms should provide the basis for later evaluation of the efficacy of individual tests. Experimentation in this field should not neglect the important datum of subjective report and it must be remembered that motivation is a crucial element in most visual work that is continued for long periods of time. We cannot afford to neglect the fact that mental fatigue of the work detriment type seems from previous research to be mostly fatigue of the inner stimuli rather than of the physiological capacity to react.

The following November, another meeting of the expanded Advisory Committee on Visual Fatigue was held in New York City. At this time, Prof. Ames, as chairman, said:

At the symposium in Washington there was a group of individuals who together knew as much, if not more, about fatigue than is known by anyone else.

Yet, I think it is fair to say that probably the most outstanding thing about the meeting was the general uncertainty, not only as to how to determine the presence of fatigue, but even as to just what visual fatigue was.

When such lack of certainty and agreement is found among a group of experts in any field, it is safe to presume that there are some basic misunderstandings floating around somewhere. In general this may be because either some important factor or factors have not been taken into account or because the philosophical background from which the matter is approached is at fault. I rather suspect that both causes are present in our fatigue problem.

Following his introductory remarks, Prof. Ames read a short paper giving his views on fatigue. The following is taken from the paper:

These impinging radiations are arranged in the form of patterns. Each part of the pattern is differentiated from every other part by (1) the particular wave length of the radiations and (2) their amplitude.

That is all that is given us, and these patterns, in the form in which they are received, do not reach consciousness. Before we become conscious of them, they have to be translated and interpreted. The different wave lengths of the incoming radiations are translated into color differences. The difference in their amplitudes is translated into brightness differences.

The relative positions of one part of the pattern to another are translated into particular relative sizes and directional values. In monocular vision, the various parts of the pattern are assigned particular relative distances to each other in accordance with the observer's empirical knowledge of the relative sizes of the objects within his field of view. In binocular vision, the directional patterns from each eye are combined. The disparity between the patterns of the two eyes gives data from which three-dimensional spatial relationships can be assigned to the various parts of the pattern. The exact nature of these spatial values is determined by the innate relations of corresponding receptors in the two eyes and the interconnections in the brain.

Having translated the given patterns into color, brightness and spatial relationships, we construct a picture in consciousness which is projected outward. It is this picture which we *see*—not the reality itself.

We are conscious not of what comes in, but of what we project out. The act of seeing, depending as it does upon translating, interpreting and projecting, is not simply a receiving process but is more akin to thinking processes marginal to consciousness.

In general, whether or not the function of vision is performing adequately depends upon how closely the picture we project outward conforms to reality.

In general, there are two principal questions that the function of vision must answer for us: (1) *what* is it? and (2) *where* is it?

What a thing is is made known to us primarily by the detail of the incoming pattern, *i.e.*, by the differentiations in boundaries and intensities of incoming bundles of wave lengths. This detail in the incoming pattern is produced by the optical system of the eye and the particular nature of the retinal reaction to light. It is broadly described by the term "visual acuity."

Where a thing is is made known to us primarily by the relationships of the different parts of the pattern and is broadly described by the term "spatial localization." In monocular vision, this is based upon the relative disposition and sizes of the different parts of a single pattern *received* through *one station point*. In binocular vision, it is based upon the differences in the relative disposition and sizes of corresponding parts of two different patterns *received* through two *separated station points*.

If the picture which is projected conforms with the reality before us, we are, so to speak, in tune with our environment, just as when our conceptual thought processes are in conformity with reality.

On the other hand, and insofar as our projected visual picture is not in conformity with what is about us, we are in conflict with our environment. When our conceptual thought processes are in conflict with reality, we become subject to frustration, compensation, aggression and fatigue. Similar results are to be expected when our projected visual picture is not in conformity with what is about us.

It might be stated that "insofar as our projected visual picture does not conform to what is about us, there exists a basis for visual fatigue."

In general, the amount of fatigue would depend (1) on the nature of the lack of conformity, for example, color blindness would probably cause less fatigue than incapacity to see detail which in turn would cause much less fatigue than false localization; and (2) on the motivation behind the particular situation, for example, a color-blind person who had to make a living at a ribbon counter would probably become much more fatigued than a near-sighted professor.

If the above be true, visual fatigue is mental in its nature. It should be treated and analyzed by the same methods that are used in treating and analyzing mental fatigue which would bring into the picture a consideration of frustration and its associated phenomena.

Chapter III

FATIGUE AND ALLIED CONCEPTS

It is the purpose of this chapter to present the formulations of fatigue and related concepts that constitute the viewpoint of this book. These formulations differ essentially from those in the quotations of the preceding chapter.

The assumptions underlying the view presented are the following:

1. The everyday experience of something that is commonly called fatigue is real, identifiable, and a legitimate starting point for precise inquiry and systematic formulation.

2. Fatigue, even though a ubiquitous experience, requires scientific analysis. It cannot be used as a vague axiomatic category. As yet fatigue has not been fully or clearly defined, and confusion over the term is obvious, particularly in technical usage. It is our purpose to analyze and to define fatigue.

3. Since fatigue is taken to be an *experience,* it is an expression of the whole person. Theory, then, must attempt to handle it as such.

4. We assume the organism to be a unity and not a plurality. As psychology is not rightfully handled except in the light of physiology, physiology cannot be all it ought except in the light of psychology or whatever discipline it is that provides for the personal in its logic. Operationism cannot rightly be used to justify the excursion onto tangents of interest that leave the organism fragmented into a plurality.

5. Once the logical framework has been chosen, the next task of the theorizer is the examination of existing terms to determine what they connote, what actual phenomena they refer to, and what they imply about the organism's behavior and its relation to the physical world. A theoretical formulation of fatigue must be self-consistent. Both the use of synonyms and the use of multiple meanings for single terms critical to the viewpoint must be abolished.

6. In the present formulation, fatigue is regarded as an experiential pattern arising in a conflict situation in which the general alignment of the individual may be described as aversion. This particular pattern involves feelings of limpness and bodily discomfort which, besides being

47

undesirable in themselves, are frequently taken as tokens of inadequacy for activity. The subjective constituents of this fatigue pattern are not to be taken as epiphenomena, or as symptoms of fatigue, but as fatigue itself.

7. Adequate handling of fatique requires a science *of* the person, *i.e.,* a science over and above disciplines merely *related to* the person. This science would require new facts. The study of fatigue cannot await that day. The process of initial defining of terms, or the redefining of those already in use, need not await the possession of more information than we now have. Systematization does not grow so much from the multiplication of facts and items as it does from viewing them in a new light. What is required is the construction of a tentative framework within which the details that are now available may be related.

In the previous chapter some of the varied uses of the term fatigue itself were illustrated. Two other terms have played especially large roles in the present scientific confusion. These are *impairment* and *work output,* both of which represent concepts undoubtedly related to fatigue. Clarification of impairment and of work output, both as terms and as concepts, is essential in any formation of fatigue.

The term *impairment* has been applied to performance, the criterion then being external to the organism. In spite of this, measures of work output are sometimes imputed to be quantitative indications of impairment of the organism. Impairment has also been used synonymously with injury, when injury refers to certain irreversible changes in structure or function. A third use of the term impairment has arisen from physiological studies in which tissue activity was the direct object of inquiry. Here impairment is deduced directly from tissue activity, the criteria being such changes as the failure of the neuromuscular junction or the accumulation of lactic acid in the muscles. In addition to these uses, many authors employ the terms impairment and fatigue interchangeably. In such cases it is not often clear what implications are intended. If progress is to be made, the term impairment should be restricted to one of these several uses. In the present formulation, *impairment will be used to refer to specific tissue conditions.*

Impairment is a physiological change in tissue which reduces its ability to participate in the larger aspects of organic functioning. Impairment is identifiable only through the methods of physiology and biochemistry. Reduction in the ability of the organism as a whole to perform is no criterion for the presence of impairment.

Unlike fatigue, impairment is never directly experienced. The presence of impairment, like that of other physiological changes, cannot be deduced introspectively. It is well known that bodily functions may become diminished or distorted, and that even pain may arise, in the absence of tissue impairment. Despite this, it has been customary even among sophisticated individuals to deduce the presence of impairment from overt behavior or from bodily feelings. The bodily components that form a part of the experience of fatigue are no accurate sign of the presence of impairment.

The term *work output* has been identified both with impairment and with fatigue. Although there is little confusion about the meaning of the term itself, many difficulties lie in the broad applications of the concept. *Work output includes all overt activity that is measured* either in the laboratory or in industry.

Work output is of immediate interest only in practical situations. In studies of productivity, external conditions may be systematically varied and the changes in work output noted. However, inferences about the organism made from studies of this sort are not justified. In dealing with fatigue and impairment, we are attempting to come to a knowledge of the individual organism. Since work output can give little clue to what is happening within the organism, it is unfortunate that productivity has been used as a measure of fatigue and impairment. When the attempt is made to relate organismic behavior to external conditions, it must be recognized that the overt response of the moment may not be related to the physical world in any simple way.

Work output is the primary interest in industrial studies which are frequently labeled studies of fatigue. This interest is natural, for it is not fatigue as such, but fatigue as it relates to production, that is important to industry. Exclusive preoccupation with disclosing relations between "working conditions" and output, nevertheless, represents a much aborted insight into the full situation. Work output must always be viewed in terms of conditions lying within the individual who is called upon to perform.

Neither fatigue nor impairment can be measured by the work output of the intact organism. Activity may be used as a measure of impairment only when such systems as isolated nerve-muscle preparations are used. A given organ in the *intact individual* may not function owing to lack of innervation. Innervational deficiency is not in itself a sign of impairment, but rather a sign of disorganization. Tissue, especially that of the central nervous system, is called upon to function in numerous roles. Thus the innervational output to any specific peripheral tissue may vary greatly in accordance with principles that govern the system as a whole.

In order that fatigue be seen in the proper perspective, some discussion of what is meant by the terms *organization* and *personal* is in order at this point.

A primary feature of *organization* is interaction *within* a system. Matters of organization may be viewed in nonpersonal terms. It is not difficult to picture such concrete entities as muscles either cooperating or pulling against each other in a tug of war. It is also possible to conceive of organization in the nervous system.

In the study of personality, the items that are analyzed out are bound to be more than independent and unrelated fragments whether customarily considered so or not. Interactions can be seen only in the light of the behavior of the whole individual. An analysis of personality is therefore meaningless if it avoids the matter of organization. Organization may be dealt with in personal as well as in other terms.

The term *personal* has been chosen because, more than any other term, it signifies the uniqueness and oneness that an individual possesses. Personal suggests the coexistence of humanness with all the other properties it is possible to assign to the organism. To put it another way, the human organism is no less than a *person,* and there should be logical techniques for constantly recognizing this in scientific procedures. *Nominal* attributions are insufficient. The personal has been largely omitted from academic treatments of perception. One of the reasons for this is the conventional psychologist's fear of being "unscientific." It has been thought that in dealing with the personal the solid techniques and logic that have been developed in the other sciences would have to be abandoned. Fortunately, such a view is becoming less prevalent.

Angyal,[1] for example, has developed a scheme, as yet not well enough known, which handles the organism remarkably well by use of "system principles." This scheme provides a truly adequate way to deal with personality and serves to indicate what tremendous progress can be made, once we are willing to go beyond the limits of conventional pattern.

It is assumed that when analysis utilizes terms in such ways as to imply clearly that it is the whole organism that is performing the functions, we are dealing with the individual in personal terms. Technical analyses are rarely of this nature. Even if such a beginning is made, the unity of the organism tends to be lost when parts are dealt with. Neither in thinking nor in the use of language has a facile way been devised for dealing with finely particulate analysis of the individual so as to retain the reference to the whole.

The personal connotation is clearly present in such everyday remarks as "John was worried," "He felt hopeful," or "He ran away." There is no sign of cleavage of the individual into parts in these statements, since everything that was said pertained to the whole individual. Much may be said about a given person by the mere use of a noun or pronoun combined with a verb denoting existence or action. One can delve into the

[1] Angyal, A.: "Foundations for a Science of Personality," Commonwealth Fund, Division of Publication, New York, 1941. Pp. 381.

internal operations of the individual, as well as observe his more overt responses to his environment. One may perfect devices whereby the organization of the individual may be discovered and described and still retain the reference just stated. Just so long as this occurs there is no trouble in dealing in personal terms. If, however, we wish to reach down to functions that we have come to call physiological, we customarily forsake the over-all reference.

Whether or not one is talking in personal terms in dealing with some detail of analytical abstraction depends primarily upon whether the reasoning involved is from whole to part, or part to whole, or what is quite similar to the latter, part to part. Part to whole logic deals with a function in a form abstracted from the whole, assuming that its basic characteristics can be discovered under the limited conditions of the abstraction and that one can later assemble this knowledge and thereby derive a whole and integrated organism with all the properties that it must have. Whole to part reasoning recognizes that the conditions for activity when the tissue (part) is in and when it is out of the body are essentially different and that it is a fundamental and inescapable principle of nature that the whole is other than the mere summation of part properties. When the full significance of this is realized, the appreciation of what is personal will follow.

At this stage the products of analysis on the personal level are wishes, aversions, and the like. Angyal[2] has developed a system to deal with the personal, which employs "psychophysically neutral" terms. He points out that organismic action can be described in terms of "tensions" and that all tensions are not "elaborated symbolically" and "experienced psychologically." It would seem that the task before those who would successfully analyze personality is to employ some such system of neutral concepts. The first step in this direction is to make the need for such a system apparent.

To evolve a picture of the organism in terms of *system thinking,* concepts that are not only self-consistent but that aid in furthering understanding must be utilized. Our particular concern is with the conceptual character and arrangement of the numerous systems within the human organism which can be adequately considered only with respect to the whole organism. While we have chosen the natural, though arbitrary, bounds of the organism in order to study its complicated system make-up, the effect of other systems upon the organism cannot be completely overlooked. We do not propose to study the organism entirely divorced from the physical world, but to choose the organism as a base when organismic systems are to be studied.

[2] Angyal, *op. cit.*

It has been customary, especially in the older mechanistic thinking, to overlook the fact that some degree of self-regulation is characteristic of all living things. Certain features of organic behavior, however, necessitate recognizing the organism as initiating that behavior. The considerable lag that occurs between stimuli and the organic events that are construed to result from them provides a good example of the uniqueness of organismic activity. The behavior of the organism at one moment may be clearly related to outside events long past, or to those which will take place in the future. Another such aspect of behavior is the organic continuity manifested in the face of intermittent stimulation. The organism imposes self-determination upon external determination.

While of course not free from external influences, the organism is seen to initiate and direct its behavior at both physiological and psychological levels. In fact, no part of organic behavior can be understood without making central the concept of self-government. This may be done by taking the organism itself as the starting point and viewing it as having certain dynamic properties of its own. There are two directions thinking should take here. The first involves centering of attention on the organism rather than the physical world, assuming no simple casual relationships between the two. The second is to consider the organism from the point of view of its over-all functional organization, rather than as a mass of specialized structures. The details of behavior should fall naturally into such a framework.

Most words have a generic connotation and certain more or less restricted meanings. *Conflict* is a term that has become restricted in meaning by its use in attempts to describe what occurs *within the organism*. These delimitations have been vague. To our knowledge no real definition of conflict has been made, nor shall we attempt such a definition here. It is, however, necessary to say a few things about conflict in order to clarify the manner in which we view it.

Whether behavior involves conflict depends upon the reference point taken. The collision of two automobiles is not an accident viewed from the standpoint of physical laws, for example. It is an incident from the standpoint of social affairs because it was contrary to the purposes of the individuals involved. Thus it was an example of traffic disharmony, but not of physical disharmony. In the same way, any opposing processes, whether biochemical, neroumuscular, or psychological, may be seen as conflicting depending upon the reference used. The reference involved in seeing the processes as conflicting is some unitary frame that embodies the order of process considered.

When the attempt is made to describe an individual in personal terms, conflicts on various levels of organization are always found. All that is known about the organism comes through the process of abstraction. The organism's activity may be described on a number of levels, or, as one might say, through a number of kinds of abstraction. Conflict can be envisaged on virtually all these various levels.

To summarize our view, conflict is taken to be any clash or incompatibility occurring within the organism; conflicts occur on all levels of organismic activity; they lead directly to further disharmony, disorganization, and tend eventually to result in fatigue.

Fatigue may be thought of as one form of attempt to retreat or escape from a situation that has become too difficult to contend with. It is both a warning that escape is indicated and a kind of enhanced discomfort when escape is not immediately possible. Conflict first arouses general tension. If it is prolonged, fatigue nearly always follows. Since fatigue may arise from unresolved conflicts of all sorts, it is clearly *an over-all state* and must always be attributed to and considered in terms of *the person as a whole.*

The following items, in stating what fatigue is and is not, are intended as ways of defining the term, and also, by implication, as ways of stating the errors or shortcomings of the more conventional viewpoints. In many cases, our affirmative assertions imply that the negative is customarily taken for granted, and our negatives imply the existence of the affirmative in prevalent opinion.

1. *Fatigue and impairment are not identical. When both exist at once, they can be separated.* An individual may be fatigued without being impaired and impaired without being fatigued. There is no need to deduce impairment to account for fatigue. The necessity for distinguishing between fatigue and impairment has never been fully recognized. Various patterns of emphasis of either one or the other appear in the literature, but the two have remained indistinguishably intertwined. The failure to make this distinction has perhaps been primary in precluding a complete systematic treatment of fatigue.

2. *Fatigue is not to be measured by measuring impairment.* Since the two are not identical, the closest relation they might have is that of a one-to-one correspondence. Such a simple relation, however, does not exist. No fatigue can be deduced or imputed from a measure of impairment. Customary thinking has failed to recognize the discreteness of the two terms.

Frequently, either of two assumptions underlies studies of fatigue: (1) that fatigue is impairment as we defined it, or (2) that the impairment is a *sign* of fatigue. That fatigue is not impairment has already been shown. It is equally wrong to assume that impairment is a sign of fatigue. Even if it were, the two items would have to have a fixed relation for the sign to be of use, and this is not the case.

3. *Unlike impairment, fatigue is always directly experienced—i.e., it is an experience.*

4. *Fatigue is a part of the individual's stance* with reference to activity, whether the activity is vigorous exertion, the assumption of an attitude toward a proposition, the maintenance of posture, or merely the need for staying awake, etc. Fatigue involves aversion and a feeling of unwillingness and inadequacy for activity. This aversion, when analyzed, can be seen to arise out of personal conflict and to be an expression of frustration.

5. *Fatigue is a manifestation of personal continuity.* The immediate situation does not contain all the origins of the fatigue of a given moment. The conditions for present fatigue can be traced to previous occasions in which circumstances were more crucial and evoked responses that have led to the specific ways of acting exemplified in the present. Habit formation accounts in part for the character of present reactions, including not only the unpleasant experiential components, but also the systemic bodily reactions.

6. *Fatigue is personal.* Fatigue pertains to the individual as a whole. Fatigue is consistent with the individual's ideals, goals, etc., and with his evaluation of himself. Conditions for fatigue are unique to the individual. The dynamics of fatigue cannot be adequately described in other than personal terms.

7. *Fatigue is an outcome of conflict.* The organization of the individual is not so simple as to constitute singleness of desire or tendency. Conflicts are constantly developing, and at any one time many conflicts exist in an individual. Conflict cannot be avoided in active situations, and conflict thwarts action. Many conflicts find resolution in appropriate action, others are very poorly resolved, and still others fail to find resolution at all. Pervasive bodily discomfort is one of the most frequent outcomes. Following its onset the individual becomes increasingly certain of the appropriateness of changing his present behavior. When relief of bodily discomfort is prevented and action is thwarted, fatigue commonly develops.

At the termination of specific activity, fatigue may disappear suddenly or slowly. Whether or not the overt termination of activity represents the actual abandonment of the task determines the outcome. When fatigue has been induced, certain bodily readjustments are required in order that comfort be regained. If, while this transition is in progress, the individual remains concerned with the task, the fatigue remains. On the other hand, to the degree that the individual can forget the task and feel free of obligation to do anything requiring effort, the bodily feelings will not be experienced as inadequacies.

8. *Fatigue is not to be confused with boredom.* Frequently when fatigue is used synonymously with impairment, the experiential aspect of the individual's response to certain situations is termed "boredom." Introspection reveals that a bored individual attributes his state to environmental events, whereas a fatigued individual lays the blame for his condition on himself. It is felt that merely escaping the situation will alleviate boredom and that it is therefore more transient than fatigue. It might be said that both boredom and fatigue are stances taken by the individual toward situations confronted. Fatigue, however, is by far the broader term. While boredom may form a part of the fatigue picture, the reverse is not possible.

9. *Fatigue is cumulative.* Fatigue arises at a level of organization which must be dealt with in terms that reach beyond the immediate situation. Fatigue developed on one occasion is likely to be revived when a similar occasion arises.

10. *Fatigue's onset and recovery may be sudden.* While impairment is a condition that is more or less gradually reached and recovered from, this is not always the case with fatigue. It is common knowledge that individuals do suddenly feel tired and quite as quickly experience release from fatigue. Fatigue can come and go nearly as rapidly as an individual is able to shift from one frame of mind to a different one.

11. *The concept of fatigue pertains to organization.* What the organism does or fails to do can be largely accounted for on the basis of the principles of its organization. Fatigue is a kind of behavior of the organism which is to be understood primarily in terms of organization. One purpose of the analysis of fatigue is to further the understanding of the relations of different organismic functions to each other and to the environment. The factor of organization is particularly critical in the study of fatigue, since this stance always involves internal contradiction.

12. *Fatigue does not crucially depend upon energy expenditure.* Confusion of fatigue with impairment, and the common practice of comparing men and machines, have contributed to the perpetuation of the energy idea of fatigue. Fatigue, contrary to the usual understanding of it, is not to be considered in terms of energy. Energy of course is involved, but the crucial determinant of fatigue is organization.

13. *Fatigue is never specific to a given body member.* It, in other words, is never localized, but is general. Bodily sensations, such as feelings of discomfort, can, of course, be localized, but it is only the individual as such that can experience fatigue.

14. *Fatigue is not to be defined or analyzed in terms of its supposed*

origins, nor on the basis of function involved. It is very common for fatigue to be classified as "mental fatigue," "nervous fatigue," "muscular fatigue," "combat fatigue," "operational fatigue," "convoy fatigue," etc. These terms connote the situations under which fatigue is supposed to have developed, or the function or both that are supposedly overworked.

Occasions for the production of fatigue are, of course, endless, but fatigue produced in one situation has an essential similarity with fatigue produced in any other. Fatigue cannot be defined in terms of diversity of external situations in which it occurs. Although fatigue may arise in the course of many different kinds of activity, it retains its own unique identity. Fatigue occurring during muscular activity is *essentially* similar to fatigue occurring in the course of mental activity. Classification in terms of part function of the individual not only denies the unity of the organism, but also throws little if any light on the nature of fatigue.

Chapter IV

ELECTROPHYSIOLOGICAL STUDIES

PHYSIOLOGY as a scientific discipline has utilized the term fatigue as a descriptive category for certain miscellaneous effects accruing from the prolonged activity of physiological structures. This chapter in reviewing some of the features of nerve and muscle activity, including those which have been labeled fatigue, is in line with one of the general purposes of the book, *viz.*, to survey all the fields in which the term fatigue has been used. The studies presented here are also relevant because they often deal with impairment directly. The question of whether or not the information included contributes to the knowledge of how fatigue (as we define it) develops is secondary. The items discussed indicate one of the settings into which conventional ideas of fatigue are brought. Fatigue, as employed by these workers, is of little help in promoting an understanding of physiology, and even less in promoting an understanding of the individual.

Studies on the physiology of activity vary all the way from precise investigation on the minute changes that take place in the cells, through the consideration of what happens in organs and systems, to the behavior of the whole organism. The physiological studies on record represent an unparalleled variety in modes of inquiry.

There are two main ways of studying muscle physiology as a part of the general study of "fatigue." One is to study how nerve-muscle systems behave, giving particular attention to how the separate components participate in the over-all movements and postures involved. The possibility of discord and inefficiency among component functions is a primary feature. The other method is the study of how much work a muscle or muscle system may do, how much fuel it requires to do it, and what chemicophysical waste products are produced in the activity. These two methods are examples of methods in standard muscle physiology and biochemistry. The latter focuses on energy supply and expenditure, the former on neuromuscular organization as revealed in timing, etc. A tacit assumption of the metabolic viewpoint is that fatigue is to be studied through conditions that reveal intrinsic functional failures in specific and localized tissues. It is as though fatigue were envisaged primarily in terms of local tissues, and only secondarily in over-all organization. From our point of view, the over-all organization is of primary importance. We shall take up the behavior of elemental structures, not forgetting that in so doing it is actually impairment, rather than fatigue, that is being dealt with.

Features of nerve function. The study of nerve tissue includes many details, virtually all of which have to do with the character of its activity. These studies encompass the relation of strength of response to strength of standard stimuli, the duration of response, the rate at which a series of responses can be elicited, and the intervals during which no responses can be elicited and those during which only reduced responses are possible. This study therefore not only includes the character of activity, but also the nature of its "failure." Most of the characteristics that have been disclosed have been given specific names, but in some cases the word fatigue has been used, either to account for these processes or to label them.

Since no strict formulations of fatigue or impairment have been developed, what they are taken to be has been left to the vagaries of custom and the discretion of the experimenter. Fatigue has conventionally been taken as an axiomatic category into which any failure phenomenon can be pigeonholed.

The following are examples of the features which, with the addition of the alleged process of fatigue, comprise the electrical activity of nerve.

Excitation is the process in the nerve leading toward discharge (spike response, etc.), whether spontaneous, induced by surrounding nervous tissue, or by an experimentally applied stimulus. The discharge itself is the result of excitation. *Threshold* is attained when excitation reaches a critical level for the given state of the tissue, the level at which it discharges. *Excitability*[1] is the general state of the tissue as measured by the threshold stimulus producing response, the lower the threshold, the greater the excitability. *Responsiveness* is another property of nerve tissue and is not to be confused with excitability, or with excitation. It is the ability to discharge, measured by the size of the potential produced. Whereas the more excitable of two elements will respond at a lower threshold, the more responsive will be capable of a stronger discharge. This is best applied to single fibers which react in an all-or-none fashion. The response spike either does not appear, or when it does, it is of a given size for a given set of internal conditions. Responsiveness applied to nerve trunks or other multi-element systems is but a statistical matter. The size of threshold response is then more arbitrary and relative. *Refractoriness* is the opposite of excitability and is applied only to a raised threshold

---

[1] Excitability has apparently become a specific term to label irritability used as a generic term.

persisting after a response, and resulting from it, and until excitability first reaches prestimulus levels.

Stimuli may be so ineffective that no spike discharge develops. Though they induce no response, they set up some degree of excitation. When the excitation does not reach threshold for response, it gradually decreases. During this decrease a second stimulus would find a state of excitation as a residual effect of the first stimulus. Excitability is greater than it was prior to the application of the first stimulus. A weaker stimulus than before may now produce a response. This is to say, two subthreshold stimuli, the second of which reaches the tissue during this short period, will together produce a response. The period during which this is possible is called the *summation period* or *period of latent addition*. The principle of summation finds its greatest use in describing behavior at the synapses.

Accommodation is another another feature of nerve function. If a subthreshold stimulus as applied to the axon for a prolonged period (*e.g.*, $\frac{1}{3}$ to $\frac{1}{2}$ second), the extinction process in the axon builds up rapidly and then diminishes during the continuation of the stimulus. To do this, a galvanic current is applied to the nerve and at chosen instants short faradic shocks are superimposed. In each trial the interval elapsing between the onset of the galvanic current and the faradic shock is altered. The height of these responses when plotted against the interval between the beginning of the current and the shock results in a curve, the height of which is a function of two variables, excitability and responsiveness. The typical drop in the curve from the original peak is the demonstration of accommodation.

Although the greater the strength of stimulation (polarizing current),[2] the greater the degree of accommodation, no constant relation exists between the threshold for a single shock and the amount of accommodation manifested by the usual technique for measuring it.[3] Initial excitability and accommodation are not related in a simple manner. In states of depression, such as strychninization, insulinization, or anesthesia, accommodation bears no simple relation to threshold.[4] In general, however, depression does increase accommodation. Continued stimulation of nerve at high frequency results in a reduction in the size of the action potential— a reduction in responsiveness. This would customarily be called fatigue.

The electrical response of the axon consists in a transitory wave of

[2] Blair, E. A., and J. Erlanger: Temporal Summation in Peripheral Nerve Fibres, *Am. J. Physiol.*, 117: 355–365, 1936.

[3] Heinbecker, P., and S. H. Bartley: Manner of Strychnine Action on the Nervous System, *Am. J. Physiol.*, 125: 172–187, 1939.

[4] Heinbecker, P., and S. H. Bartley: Action of Ether and Nembutal on the Nervous System, *J. Neurophysiol.*, 3: 219–236, 1940.

negativity called the "spike" and one or more afterpotentials. Whereas the major portion of the spike is completed in 0.4 to 0.5 msec., the duration of afterpotentials may be a matter of seconds or minutes.

If the excitability of the fiber is considered during the period prior to its full return to the original steady state, the following rough stages may be delineated. During the fraction of a millisecond consumed by the spike itself, no additional activity can be induced by a shock of any strength. This means that the excitability of the fiber is zero. Responsiveness is thus likewise zero. This stage is called the *absolute refractory period*. Refractoriness does not end here but continues, usually a matter of milliseconds. The period of refractoriness following the absolute refractory period is called *the relative refractory period*.[5] Unless the relative refractory period is to include a much longer time, these two refractory periods are only part of the *recovery period*—the period required for full return to the original steady state.

One way[6] of stating the sequence of events is as follows. These are (1) the absolute refractory period, (2) the start of recovery, (3) supernormality, (4) subnormality, and (5) return to the initial state. Occasionally a few further oscillations are involved. The outstanding difference between nerves and between the same nerve at different times is manifested in their time characteristics. When supernormality is defined, some of these temporal differences will be stated.

Gasser[7] states that the threshold for the fastest (*A*) mammalian fibers in the normal condition in the body may return to normal in about 3 msec. In such cases it is supposed that both excitability and responsiveness have returned to normal in this short time. In some nerves, 85 to 90 per cent of such recovery is reached in 1 msec. (see Fig. 1).

According to the customary viewpoint, the termination of the relative refractory period is reached when the spike height, conduction time, and excitability *first* return to normal. Since the end of the relative refractory period does not represent the steady resting state, it is only an arbitrary point in the full recovery of nerve. The relative refractory period in the isolated nerves is followed by a *supernormal phase,* which is represented by the negative afterpotential. The time elapsing between the start of response and the peak of the supernormal phase differs in different kinds of nerves. This interval is about 7 msec. in mammalian *A* fibers, 5 to 10 msec. in

5 Sometimes the terms *relatively* and *absolutely* are used instead of *relative* and *absolute* in referring to refractory periods. This is true in the writings of some of the St. Louis school of neurophysiologists, for example.

6 von Brücke, E. Th., M. Early, and A. Forbes: Fatigue and Refractoriness in Nerve, *J. Neurophysiol., 4:* 456–472, 1941.

7 Gasser, H. S., and J. Erlanger: In "Electrical Signs of Nervous Activity," University of Pennsylvania Press, Philadelphia, 1937. Pp. 221.

frog *A* fibers, 25 msec. in sympathetic fibers of the frog's heart, and 50 msec. in sympathetic fibers of the cat's pupils. The state of the nerve determines the height of the afterpotential and the degree of supernormality. As excised nerves change state during experimentation, the negative after-potential may grow and the relative refractory state may shorten. During the sequence of changes, two time aspects tend to remain relatively constant, *viz.*, the absolute refractory period and the time needed to reach maximum excitability. It is inferred that, since the spike tends to retain

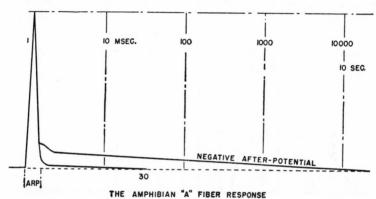

THE AMPHIBIAN "A" FIBER RESPONSE

Fig. 1.—The amphibian *A* fiber response with indication of the spike and the negative afterpotential. The latter is shown under two different conditions: the more usual, in which the afterpotential is in the neighborhood of 30 msec., and a special condition under which it is very much longer. The purpose of this diagram is to show that the fiber does not reach *status quo ante* for a considerable time after the onset of activity (the nerve impulse). *ARP* indicates the absolutely refractory period.

a nearly constant shape, the process responsible for it is the one underlying the two nearly constant features just mentioned. Ordinarily, the maximum excitability and the maximum negative afterpotential do not correspond. From this it is supposed that the variable afterpotential process underlies the shortening of the relative refractory phase and the prolongation of the supernormal period.

Under some conditions (*e.g.*, following a tetanus), nerve exhibits a period of *subnormality*[8] following supernormality. In such cases the supernormality is shortened. Subnormality is associated with the *positive afterpotential*.[9] Although slowed conduction exists under such conditions,

[8] Graham, H. T.: The Subnormal Period of Nerve Response, *Am. J. Physiol., 111:* 452–465, 1935.

[9] Graham, H. T., and H. S. Gasser: Augmentation of the Positive Afterpotential of Nerves by Yohimibine, *Proc. Soc. Exper. Biol. & Med., 32:* 553–556, 1934–1935.

the spike remains full size, thus presuming full responsiveness. In the characteristics just mentiond the *C* fibers, for example, do not compare in all respects with *A* fibers. A description of the differences between types of fibers is, however, beyond the scope of the present discussion (see Fig. 2).

What should be called fatigue (impairment) in connection with the various changes of nerve tissue has not been settled among neurophysiologists. Gasser[10] states, for example, that none of the features of the subnormal period can be rightly said to be caused by fatigue of the nerve.

THE AMPHIBIAN "C" FIBER RESPONSE

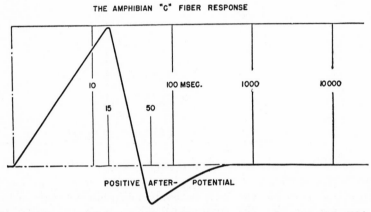

Fig. 2.—The amphibian *C* fiber with the positive afterpotential. This diagram, like Fig. 1, is to show that most events occur before *status quo ante* is resumed.

This is based on the fact that, during the subnormal period after tetanic stimulation, a shock of at least threshold strength will raise excitability to temporary supernormality during the negative afterpotential of the response. He says the fact that this can occur indicates the existence of ability to exhibit supernormal responsiveness.

Von Brücke, Early, and Forbes[11] hold a seemingly opposite view. They state that "the depression in excitability due to prolonged stimulation is the main and often the only symptom of the condition that is generally called 'fatigue' in nerve. Since this condition affects and prolongs the subnormal period, which is assumed to be the same as the old 'refractory period,' it is merely a matter of nomenclature whether we speak of a state of fatigue or a prolongation of the refractory period."

Von Brücke, Early, and Forbes suggest dividing the recovery or restora-

10 Gasser, *op. cit.*
11 von Brücke, Early, and Forbes, *op. cit.*

tion period into two parts (see also Graham and Lorente de Nó[12]). The *first* part is characterized by complete recovery of spike height and velocity (1.5 to 2.0 msec.) and about an 80 per cent recovery of excitability. The *second* part, the period during which the completion of the recovery occurs, is greatly influenced by rhythmic activity and several other factors. They suggest calling the first the relative refractory period, and the second, the subnormal period. They also say that the difference between the recovery rates for the two parts of the restoration period (relative refractory and subnormal) is heightened in the "fatigued" nerve. In other words, fatigue presumably heightens the difference between the rates of regaining responsiveness and excitability. They state that the delay in recovery during the second refractory period may be the first identifiable indication of fatigue, and finally suggest that the mere refractoriness itself may be the primitive expression of fatigue (impairment).

As one examines the literature, various grades or kinds of separation between what is called fatigue (impairment) and what is otherwise thought of are confronted. It would seem that, with a full ideational divorcement of fatigue and impairment, accompanied by the riddance of the idea that either of them necessarily implies the exceptional or the pathological, we would be led to von Brücke, Early, and Forbes's view. All examples of tissues' temporary diminution in, or absence of, ability to function would then fall into one broad category.

Equilibrium. Gerard[13] has shown that nerve stimulated for long periods at a given frequency does not show decline to exhaustion. A level is reached at which reduced activity can be maintained. This, he calls "equilibration fatigue." With changed stimulus conditions, the level is either raised or lowered, depending upon frequency rate of stimulation.

Chronaxie in nerve. The two great classes of irritable tissues are nerve and muscle. Insight into their excitable properties is made possible by comparisons. It is obvious that a common mode for measuring their several properties, or even a single one of them, would be very helpful.

One such mode does exist, in the form of a time-intensity relation for excitation, called *chronaxie.* Since the time-intensity relation is represented by a hyperbolic curve, a slight drop in intensity involves a considerable increase in time. With weaker and weaker stimuli the time curve becomes asymptotic, theoretically ever approaching but never quite reach-

[12] Graham, H. T., and R. Lorente de Nó: Recovery of Blood-perfused Mammalian Nerves, *Am. J. Physiol., 123:* 326–340, 1938.

[13] Gerard, R. W.: Studies on Nerve Metabolism. II. Respiration in Oxygen and Nitrogen, *Am. J. Physiol., 82:* 381–404, 1927.

Gerard, R. W., and A. Forbes: "Fatigue" of the Flexion Reflex. A Note on Action Currents and "Equilibration" in the Cat's Peroneal Nerve, *Am. J. Physiol., 86:* 178–205, 1928.

ing infinity. For all practical purposes, durations of current that are somewhat greater than those prior to the inflexion of the curve are spoken of as "infinite." Hence all such stimuli are customarily said to be continued "indefinitely." Chronaxie then is said to be the duration of the electrical stimulus required to excite a tissue when the strength of the stimulus is twice the value of a rheobasic current, or in other words the value of a suddenly applied constant current that will excite it if continued indefinitely. Occasionally, relatively inert tissues will respond to weak intensities of galvanic current when stronger intensities of faradic current are not effectual even for more excitable tissue. Some tissues fail to respond to faradic current of any intensity. Tissues seem to be distinguished from each other on the basis of duration of current rather than on threshold intensity. Thus it will be seen that chronaxie is a measure that takes this into account. Chronaxie derives its value from its relations to other tissue properties, such as conduction rate of excitation, development rate of action current, summation interval for subliminal stimuli, refractory period, latent period in muscle, and the duration of the isometric twitch in muscle. Measures of all these properties suggesting heightened excitability are positively related to short chronaxie.

The facts of nerve stimulation, conduction, etc., are complex. A full portrayal of the usages of the word fatigue as applied to nerve would be almost equivalent to an exposition of the entire subject of nerve activity. This is not necessary here. What is necessary is the answer to each of the following questions. Do the extreme changes in nerve properties that are brought about in the laboratory occur in everyday life in the fatigued individual? What properties of nerve are radically or significantly altered in the day's activity so as to constitute impairment?

The frequent assertion that nerve as a conductor is practically "unfatigable"[14] would lead us to believe that impairment does not account for everyday fatigue.

Features of muscle function.   Muscle and nerve have certain properties in common. Both are irritable and conductile. One of the chief differences is that muscle is contractile and performs mechanical work. Large amounts of energy are transformed not only into motion, but also into heat. The four usual approaches to the study of muscle activity are the electrical, the thermal, the mechanical, and the more strictly metabolic. Of these, the electrical plays a spectacular role in demonstrating the similarity of muscle and nerve.

"Excessive" stimulation, which in conventional parlance is equivalent

14 Fulton, J. F.: "Muscular Contraction and the Reflex Control of Movement," The Williams & Wilkins Company, Baltimore, 1926. Pp. 644.

to fatigue, tends to increase chronaxie without changing rheobase,[15] whereas impoverished blood supply may reduce chronaxie and increase rheobase.[16]

The time between initiation of stimulation at some point in the nervous system and actual muscle contraction is the *latent period*. This interval may be divided into four phases: (1) the conduction time of the impulse to the neuromuscular junction; (2) *end-plate delay*, or the time required for the activity to develop on the muscle side of the juncture; (3) the *true latency;* and (4) the period of rigidity.

For our purpose end-plate delay is the first item that really pertains to muscle behavior. It is about 3 msec. in duration. Fatigue, imputed from repeated or constant stimulation, increases this delay noticeably. True latency is very short (about 1.5 msec.) and is apparently unaffected by prolonged activity. The period of rigidity is abrupt and tends with activity and dissection age to become much less so.

Muscle is likewise abrupt in ending its contraction, and in fresh tissues the "angle" caused in the contraction record is pronounced. The initial point in relaxation is easily measurable, for the angle is steep. Prolonged activity (fatigue) is accompanied by a rounding off of the angle, even to the point of total masking.

The shape of the curve beyond the angle is significant also. Ordinarily it is composed of a long concave sweep in the record, while an initial convexity, or so-called "nose," indicates fatigue, since it characteristically appears after prolonged activity. Occluded circulation, however, produces the same effect.

Muscle exhibits an action current as well as mechanical activity. The electrical response begins prior to the mechanical by a period represented in the true latency. In fatigued muscle, the duration of the rising phase of the action current is prolonged, and presumably this and end-plate delay vary together. Since both nerve and muscle exhibit electrical variations, these exist in the records taken of intact muscle during voluntary contraction.

Features of nerve-complex activity. Studies of preparations in which a number of neural elements work together add instances of what is conventionally called fatigue. Since such complexes possess functional properties that do not exist in single elements, the opportunity for diminished or distorted function is different. If the point of reference is the single element, certain changes in function tend to be labeled fatigue; if the system being described is a working group of elements, still other func-

---

[15] Lapique, L., et M.: Modification de l'excitabilité musculaire par la fatigue, *Soc. de biol., 82:* 772–774, 1919.

[16] Bourguignon, G.: "La chronaxie chez l'homme," Masson et Cie., Paris, 1923. Pp. 417.

tional changes are thought of as fatigue. Assertions about nerve complexes sometimes imply denials of what is said about single fibers.

"Central fatigue" is often referred to. Sherrington[17] early made a number of distinctions between the behavior of reflex arcs (a kind of nerve complex) and conduction in nerve trunks (conduction in nerve fibers). The great difference in the degree of "fatigability" was one of the features pointed out. Reflexes were said to fatigue relatively quickly. Sherrington stated that reflexes were much more variable in function, much more independent of quantitative features of the stimulus, much more fragile, and thus much more easily impaired than nerve fibers. Analytical experiments showing what happens to functioning nerve complexes to make them less efficient or to impair them have been scarce. Most of what has been done pertains to neuromuscular function, rather than to nerve-to-nerve behavior.

"Central nervous fatigue" is often resorted to as an explanation for various effects that cannot be specifically and concretely assigned to local peripheral tissue. This concept tacitly assumes that impairment is at the basis of diminished activity (generally called fatigue). If no impairment can be discovered in the periphery, it is assumed to exist centrally. This reasoning does not take into account that modification of activity in complex systems can occur through shifts in organization, as well as through tissue impairment. The concept of central nervous fatigue is also used to explain "mental fatigue."

Such reasoning is exemplified in the following: Hofstetter,[18] in his ergographic study of ocular accommodation, was unable to assign impairment to the ciliary muscles. He therefore proceeded step by step toward the higher centers, passing the neuromuscular junction, the ciliary ganglion, and the nucleus of the third nerve, in a search for a locus for fatigue. Blatt[19] specifically suggested toxic effects on the accommodation centers in the brain to explain accommodation fatigue.

Bock and Dill[20] state that fatigue as it develops in industrial workers originates entirely within the central nervous system. Although they admit that under the stress of heavy muscular exertion muscle fatigue supervenes, they say that as a rule fatigue after muscular exertion is essentially a nervous affair. This is because metabolic products are generally taken to be, at least in part, responsible for inducing central nervous fatigue. These

[17] Sherrington, C. S.: "The Integrative Action of the Nervous System," Charles Scribner's Sons, New York, 1906. Pp. 411.

[18] Hofstetter, H. W.: An Ergographic Analysis of Fatigue of Accommodation, Am. J. Optom. Arch. Am. Acad. Optom., 20: 115135, 1943.

[19] Blatt, N.: Weakness of Accommodation, Arch. Ophth., 5: 363–373, 1931.

[20] Bock, A. V., and D. B. Dill: "The Physiology of Muscular Exercise," Longmans, Green and Company, New York, 1931. Pp. 272.

authors, then, conclude that central nervous fatigue is a toxic affair affecting tissue elements themselves. When we can be sure that sizable amounts of toxins are produced in the body, they might well be expected to have some effect on the central nervous system, changing certain constants and thus bringing about reduced efficiency and even over-all qualitative changes in personal behavior. But putting the local changes, such as shifts in ocular accommodative behavior after a few trials on an ergograph, in the same category with impairment in nervous tissue is not to be entertained.

Features of neuromuscular function. In nerve-muscle preparations, the point of attention is the muscle's ability to contract in response to innervation through the nerve trunk. Two arrangements provide this: the nerve-muscle preparation and the intact organism in which voluntary contraction is induced. In the latter, the whole nervous system is connected with the muscle, and possible effects attributable to its influence should be recognized. In both cases, the behavior recorded is movement. The underlying mechanisms can be arrived at by deduction from the recorded behavior and the conditions inducing it.

In the examination of muscle, it is customary to consider the possible ways in which its functions may become reduced or obliterated. Since natural stimuli act first on nerve tissue, this tissue may be responsible for some of the end results expressed in muscle contraction. Precise studies have yielded information which indicates that muscle contraction is diminished or terminated by difficulties arising at one of three places (central nervous system, neuromuscular junction, or muscle). Two of these loci of fatigue lie outside the muscle fibers themselves.

The first of these is said to be *central*. In ergographic studies on the intact organism, motor failure in a muscle may occur long before it can be shown that the muscle itself is incapable of contracting. The efferent nerve supply for contraction under many conditions ceases and thus becomes accountable for cessation of muscle action. Phenomena of this kind were briefly discussed in the previous section on nerve-complex activity.

The second locus of fatigue in the system whose motor behavior is under study is the *neuromuscular junction*. Nerve-muscle preparations in which the muscle fails to contract after repeated nerve-trunk stimulation may not be totally inert. Direct stimulation of the muscle itself may continue to effect the contraction. On this account, the neuromuscular junction is taken to be the seat of the difficulty. This type of fatigue is called "transmission fatigue." Rapidly repeated stimulation may induce transmission failure, and reduction of the stimulus frequency will witness the return of muscular contraction quite readily. This phenomenon has also been known as "Wedensky inhibition."

Luco and Rosenbleuth[21] have shown that "transmission fatigue is not dependent upon contraction for its induction. The chemical theory of transmission offered by Rosenbleuth and Morison,[22] rather than the older electrical theories, would seem to account for this. These authors also point out the distinction between fatigue and curarization. In both conditions, the concentrations of the chemical mediator at the neuromuscular junction are subthreshold. In fatigue the actual amount of acetylcholine is decreased, whereas in curarization the normal amount is insufficient for mediating transmission owing to a heightened requirement (raised threshold). A superabundance of acetylcholine at the juncture is said to lead to paralysis of some of the fibers. Rosenbleuth and Morison show that the type of Wedensky inhibition that occurs after narcotization of the nerve trunk must be ascribed to some mechanism not acting on the neuromuscular junction. They suggest postcathodal depression reported by Erlanger and Blair.[23]

When a motor nerve is stimulated at a high frequency, the muscle it activates responds with a sequence of tension changes. The first rise in tension is soon followed by a fall, and then a second rise. Rosenbleuth and Luco[24] designate the three phases just mentioned, the first, second, and third stages in neuromuscular transmission, assuming that these changes in tension are expressions of inherent changes in the tissue involved and are a product of activity. If the stimulation frequency is too low, the second phase (initial drop in tension) may be omitted. A fourth stage consisting of a slow decline sets in following the third, and it is spoken of as fatigue. If stimulation is continued some time after fatigue develops, a new stage of increased tension may develop, called the fifth stage. Stimulation for a matter of hours is required to demonstrate the complete sequence of the five stages. If stimulation is momentarily interrupted, the muscle begins to relax to the initial level of tension, but at a slower rate than fresh muscle. This, too, is taken as an expression of fatigue. The fourth and fifth stages are taken to be independent of each other, since they depend upon different factors. If the fourth stage is fatigue (impairment) brought about by continued contraction (activity), it would not be followed by a stage of increase in contraction unless some new factor comes into play. The

[21] Luco, J. V., and A. Rosenbleuth: Neuromuscular "Transmission-fatigue" Produced without Contraction during Curarization, Am. J. Physiol., 126: 58–65, 1939.

[22] Rosenbleuth, A., and R. S. Morison: Curarization, Fatigue and Wedensky Inhibition, Am. J. Physiol., 119: 236–256, 1937.

[23] Erlanger, J., and E. A. Blair: The Irritability Changes in Nerve in Response to Subthreshold Induction Shocks, and Related Phenomena Including the Relatively Refractory Phase, Am. J. Physiol., 99: 108–128, 1931.

[24] Rosenbleuth, A., and J. V. Luco: Fifth Stage of Neuromuscular Transmission, Am. J. Physiol., 126: 39–57, 1939.

fourth and fifth stages are taken to be synaptic phenomena, since the nerve action potentials and the mechanograms of the muscle do not show comparable quantitative changes. Both slow and fast muscles manifest the five stages.

The third locus of fatigue in the preparation being studied is in the *muscle* itself and is called "contractile fatigue." Conditions can be set up under which direct stimulation of the muscle will become ineffective in inducing contraction. The deduction is made that the reason for failure lies in muscle tissue.

The work of Reid[25] bears on the temporal and other relations of the three kinds of nerve-impulse transmission through the juncture to muscle by serial induction shocks when circulation is intact, but under ischemic conditions (in animals), excitation could almost completely exhaust transmission across the neuromuscular junction before any contractile diminution in muscle was demonstrated. Ischemia, in itself, at first does not greatly influence the contractile response to a *voluntary effort*. But finally a pronounced failure develops, peripheral stimulation suffering less change in effectiveness than voluntary effort. Neuromuscular depression is evidenced by the nerve trunk becoming less effective than the muscle excited directly. In a limb experimentally made ischemic, fatigue from serial contractions is also largely attributable to the central nervous system, but occurs much sooner than with intact circulation. This hastened "central failure" Reid attributes to the action of *afferent inhibitory impulses* from the working muscle, which he regards as taking place in nonischemic preparations as well. Prolonged faradization of the nerve trunk, however, induces junction failure before failure of the muscle, regardless of circulation conditions.

After "voluntary fatigue" has been produced, equal periods of rest and of perpiheral stimulation demonstrate marked differences in recovery of the strength and number of the voluntary contractions before fatigue again occurs. Recovery after the stimulation period is relatively slight as compared with the amount after rest, suggesting to Reid that the influence of local conditions developing in the muscle have an inhibiting effect, probably through afferent impulses on the central nervous system. Recovery after voluntary fatigue is aided by removing the load from the muscle. On the other hand, the fatigue of maintained ("static") voluntary contraction differs notably from fatigue from a series of voluntary efforts, in the effect of rest, peripheral stimulation, and ischemia. Recovery in "static fatigue" is similar after periods of rest and peripheral stimulation by faradic current.

25 Reid, C.: Mechanism of Voluntary Muscular Fatigue, *Quart. J. Exper. Physiol., 19:* 17–42, 1928.

It would seem from the evidence on hand that failure of the peripheral neuromuscular system is not an important factor in voluntary fatigue. Whether failure in the peripheral mechanism overlaps that of central fatigue depends upon whether a relatively rapid series of voluntary efforts are used to induce fatigue.

The two kinds of peripheral fatigue have also been studied by del Pozo,[26] who distinguished them by the rates of stimulation needed to produce them. Fatigue induced by frequencies above 30 per second, he interpreted as due to deficiency in transmission. Fatigue induced by stimulus frequencies below 20 per second, he attributed to contraction deficiency. "Subliminal transmission" effects were produced by 20 to 30 shocks per second. He found that recovery from "transmission fatigue" was relatively prompt, while it was slow in "contraction fatigue." The two kinds of fatigue were considered to be independent phenomena, as we would suppose. To account for transmission failure, he resorted to Rosenbleuth and Morison's theory of decrease in acetylcholine. The response failure due to contraction processes was attributed to metabolic changes in the muscle. Muscles were grouped into two classes, slow and fast, contraction failure being more pronounced in the fast than in the slow.

Sympathetic innervation and adrenalin action. Skeletal muscle fibers receive a dual innervation. In addition to the somatic motor innervation, there is an accessory sympathetic (autonomic) innervation. It was thought for a time that the latter was involved in the maintenance of tonus, but investigations later showed this was not the case. Orbeli, however, was able to show an important contribution of sympathetic innervation to muscle activity. It was demonstrated that stimulation of the sympathetic supply prevented diminution of muscle tension following intermittent somatic stimulation. In fact, early in the intermittent series, sympathetic stimulation even augmented the tension already developed. Used alone, however, it produced no tension. This has been taken to mean that sympathetic activity retards the onset of fatigue.

Sympathetic stimulation and adrenalin act quite similarly on muscle. Cannon and Nice[27] and Gruber[28] showed that when adrenalin was applied to excised muscle it diminished fatigue. This action is thought to be due to the power of adrenalin to aid in removal of metabolites.

[26] del Pozo, E. C.: Transmission Fatigue and Contraction Fatigue, *Am. J. Physiol.,* *135:* 763–771, 1942.

[27] Cannon, W. B., and L. B. Nice: The Effect of Adrenal Secretion on Muscular Fatigue, *Am. J. Physiol., 32:* 44–60, 1913.

[28] Gruber, C. M.: Studies in Fatigue. XI. The Effect of Intravenous Injection of Massive Doses of Adrenalin upon Skeletal Muscle at Rest and undergoing Fatigue, *Am. J. Physiol., 61:* 475–492, 1922.

Chapter V

ANOXIA AND RELATED LIMITING CONDITIONS

PERFORMANCE may be thought of as being limited by the specific conditions under which it occurs. For "normal" performance certain ranges of conditions are required. If the conditions are altered toward the extremes of lack or oversupply, behavior changes accordingly. Common examples of these extremes are lack of oxygen, heat, carbohydrate, water, salt, etc., and oversupply of heat, carbohydrate, etc. Many extreme conditions have been studied intensively owing both to their frequent occurrence and to their spectacular effects.

OXYGEN AND RESPIRATION

The organism's intake of oxygen is highly variable from moment to moment. Oxygen intake is an integral part of the process of energy transformation in the body. It depends upon a number of factors, including the supply of air to the lungs, the diffusion of oxygen through the lung capillaries, its uptake by the blood, and its transportation to the sites of oxidative reactions. Since the amount needed is so critically connected with muscular exertion, and no considerable storage can occur, as in the case of the food fuels, the securing of enough oxygen for exertion often becomes crucial. Under normal demands there is a linear relation between volume of air expired and level of oxygen consumption, but with excessive demands, lung ventilation increases out of proportion to added oxygen utilization. With lowered partial oxygen pressures in the blood, two critical organs, the heart and the brain, which require oxygen constantly, are particularly affected.

In addition to oxygen intake, other factors play important roles in the respiratory process. The respiratory center is even more sensitive to the concentration of *carbon dioxide* in the blood than to that of oxygen. Although carbon dioxide is a product of oxidation, and is thought of as a waste product, it is far from that alone. Along with oxygen regulation, the maintenance of a steady carbon dioxide level is necessary.

Hemoglobin plays an indispensable role in respiration. This substance, the pigment in the red corpuscles, is an iron-containing material able to

71

combine with oxygen under some circumstances and to release it just as readily under others. Under ordinary near-sea-level conditions, hemoglobin becomes 95 per cent saturated and is able to give up all oxygen when the partial pressure of the oxygen is reduced to zero. The union of oxygen with hemoglobin is dependent upon the pH: the more alkaline, the higher the attraction for oxygen. As the blood carries carbon dioxide from tissues to be released in the lungs, the blood becomes more alkaline and has a greater affinity for oxygen. The separation of oxygen and hemoglobin is favored as temperature rises, being more marked in cold-blooded than in warm-blooded animals. Getting loaded hemoglobin from the lungs to the rest of the body where it is divested of its oxygen depends upon the perpetual action of the heart as a pump. With the individual at rest, the heart provides the body with about 4 l. of blood per minute in which 240 cc. of oxygen are carried.

Aeroembolism. When atmospheric pressure is reduced relatively rapidly, an effect known as "aeroembolism" is induced. When atmospheric pressure is reduced, the pressure of nitrogen in the body is also reduced. Nitrogen tends to be released from the body solutions, and since it is a gas, its release is in the form of bubbles. During quietude at sea level, according to Dill, the blood and other body fluids will absorb about 14 cc. of nitrogen. At an altitude of 18,000 ft. the atmospheric pressure is one-half that at sea level, and at 40,000 ft. it is only one-fifth. Behnke[1] states that an aviator's ascent from sea level to 33,800 ft. (barometric pressure one-fourth that at sea level) is comparable to a diver's ascent from a depth of 100 ft. (pressure 4 atm.) to the surface in salt water.

Aeroembolism obviously constitutes a hazard to life and a limiting condition for action. Armstrong[2] lists the ill effects of aeroembolism as pertaining to (1) gross structure (joints, etc.), (2) skin, (3) cerebrospinal system, and (4) respiratory system. Fatal coma arising from embolization of the cerebral circulation and the presence of gas in the cardiac chambers may ensue. All but the more severe consequences of aeroembolism may be relieved by recompression.

There is a great deal concerning the production of aeroembolism that is not yet understood, for the average individual does not immediately develop symptoms even at 25,000 ft. Dill suggests this may be due to the production of bubbles too tiny to be immediately harmful and that, finally, symptoms develop from the coalescence of numerous bubbles

[1] Behnke, A. R., Jr.: High Atmospheric Pressures; Physiological Effects of Increased and Decreased Pressure; Application of These Findings to Clinical Medicine, *Ann. Int. Med.*, *13*: 2217-2228, 1940.

[2] Armstrong, H. G.: "Principles and Practice of Aviation Medicine," 2d ed., The Williams & Wilkins Company, Baltimore, 1943. Pp. 514.

into larger ones. The difficulties encountered in the behavior of nitrogen within the body at high altitudes are somewhat the same as those encountered when divers return to sea level.

ANOXIA

Anoxia is the state resulting from a lack of oxygen in the blood and other tissues. Although it is generally studied as a metabolic state, the various personal manifestations that arise during oxygen lack will be included in this consideration. In fact they, rather than the tissue impairment itself, are the main objects of our interest. Holders of conventional views which confuse fatigue with impairment would assume much of anoxic impairment and fatigue to be identical. It is known that personal activity during oxygen lack varies considerably. Investigations show that on many occasions when extreme tissue impairment is known to exist the subjects report absence of fatigue.

Although anoxia has been studied for some time in connection with mountain climbing and balloon ascensions, it is one of the hazards that has been made more prominent in the recent trend of events. Both incidental and experimental anoxia, particularly the latter, have been of great interest to those studying both chemistry and physiology.

Altitudinal conditions for anoxia. Human metabolism is adapted to sea level and slightly above. Within this range the blood is nearly saturated with oxygen. Under such conditions, oxygen lack is rarely a problem. As altitude increases, oxygen saturation of the blood decreases because of reduced atmospheric pressure. For ages mountain climbing and permanent residence in high-altitude regions have presented difficulties. There are limits to the altitude at which exertion, such as climbing, can occur, and there are limits to which a person may be safely carried without his exertion. Naturally, individuals in passive states can endure higher altitudes better than those in exertion. Different limits pertain to the individual encountering high-altitude conditions for the first time and to the one who has become somewhat adjusted to them (acclimatized).

Slight anoxia symptoms may appear at or slightly below 6,000 ft. The peril of oxygen lack first arises between 10,000 and 20,000 ft. When an altitude of 37,000 ft. (7 miles) is reached, despite the use of a supply of pure oxygen, anoxia begins to develop owing to the reduced partial pressure. Breathing pure oxygen at 40,000 ft. saturates the blood no more than breathing air at just above 14,000 ft.[3] The limit of consciousness while breathing pure oxygen is not known but is not far above 45,000 ft. (a little above 8½ miles).

[3] Armstrong, *op. cit.*

Figure 3 indicates the calculated relation of both alveolar oxygen tension and arterial oxygen saturation in relation to altitude.

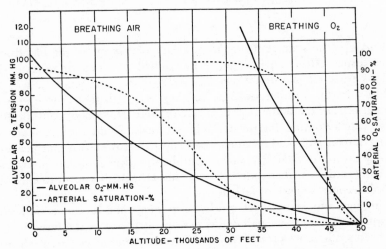

FIG. 3.—The alveolar oxygen tension and the calculated percentage oxygen saturation of arterial blood at various altitudes when breathing air and when breathing oxygen. (*Armstrong: "Principles and Practice of Aviation Medicine," 2d ed., The Williams & Wilkins Company.*)

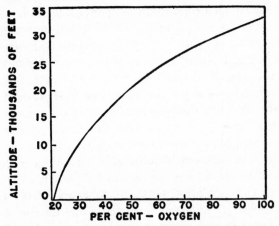

FIG. 4.—The relation between altitude and the required percentage of oxygen to maintain normal alveolar oxygen tension. (*Armstrong: "Principles and Practice of Aviation Medicine," 2d ed., The Williams & Wilkins Company.*)

From the information obtained from Armstrong's graph and from Armstrong's Fig. 42[4] (our Fig. 4), which gives the relation between oxygen

4 *Ibid.*, p. 327.

percentages and altitude while maintaining normal alveolar oxygen tensions, a family of curves can be drawn, as shown in Fig. 5. Each curve in the family represents a single alveolar tension and the percentage of oxygen required to provide it at various altitudes. Using the abscissa, one

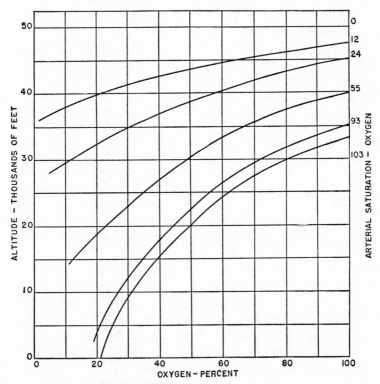

Fig. 5.—The relation of altitude and the percentage of oxygen supplied, to degree of arterial saturation. While the lowest curve in the family is identical to that in the previous figure, the other curves indicate the relation of percentage supplied and lesser degrees of arterial saturation. It will be noted that somewhere below 50,000 feet, pure oxygen will cease to maintain the saturation of the arterial blood above zero.

may choose a given arbitrary percentage and find the relation between altitude and alveolar tension. Or one may choose a given altitude and find what percentage will be required to provide one of the several indicated alveolar tensions.

The hazard first makes itself known in behavior imputed to the nervous system. Armstrong and Strughold[5] emphasize the insidiousness of the various symptoms because pain or various forms of discomfort or both are typically absent, and the ability to recognize impairment as it develops is lacking from the start. Brain tissue is the most sensitive to reduced oxygen supply, and not a great enough variety of delicate mental functions has as yet been studied to determine the altitudes at which detectable impairments first arise. In fact, no absolute levels may be stated, since impairment occurs for some individuals before others.

Anoxic effects may also arise from decreased tension of carbon dioxide in the blood. Inhalation of carbon dioxide is said to abolish Cheyne-Stokes breathing and to improve cerebral functions in aviators.[6] Also the increased oxygen consumption, typical during exposure to low atmospheric pressures, can be diminished by adding 2 to 4 per cent of carbon dioxide to the air intake.[7]

Hyperoxic anoxia or oxygen poisoning. Too much oxygen, a possibility only in rare situations, is a definite factor in impairment of performance and constitutes one of the limiting conditions for activity. When an animal is subjected to oxygen at high barometric pressures, certain untoward results occur that have long been known as oxygen poisoning.[8] The effects have been studied mostly in animals, although the toxic effects of oxygen constitute a problem for divers and caisson workers and possibly for aviators.

The initial symptoms in man are nausea, substernal pain, and flushing of the face. These may appear after 6 or 7 hours of breathing pure oxygen, although some declare that pure oxygen can be used for as long as 2 days. It is possible that persons with anoxemia are less likely to develop toxic effects. Concentrations of oxygen below 60 per cent are harmless.

In oxygen poisoning, the consumption of oxygen is decreased presumably from faulty transportation of carbon dioxide and its consequent accumulation, the accumulation of excessive acidity in the tissues from the failure of the normal reduction of hemoglobin and also from a poisoning of the respiratory enzymes by the high oxygen pressure. Some authors[9]

[5] Strughold, H.: Die biologische Höhenwirkung vom Standpunkte der Luftfahrt, *Wien. klin. Wchnschr., 52:* 857–860, 1939.

[6] Bergeret, P. M.: L'hypocapnie de l'aviateur, *Rev. serv. de san. mil., 111:* 293–315, 1939.

[7] Rühl, A., and W. Kühn: Kohlensaüre und Stoffwechsel-regulation, *Ztschr. f. klin. Med., 135:* 704–717, 1939.

[8] Bert, P.: "Barometric Pressure," trans. by M. A. Hitchcock and F. A. Hitchcock, The College Book Co., Columbus, Ohio, 1943. Pp. 1055. ("La pression barométrique," Paris, 1878.)

[9] Bean, J. W., and D. F. Bohr: High Oxygen Effects on Isolated Striated Muscle, *Am. J. Physiol., 124:* 576–582, 1938.

have concluded that, unless central structures are more susceptible than peripheral, the toxicity resulting from inadequate reduction of hemoglobin is the more significant factor in both the initial and later symptoms of oxygen poisoning. These same authors[10] have been led to conclude, then, that anaerobic metabolism is at the base of oxygen poisoning and oxygen poisoning may be spoken of as *hyperoxic anoxia*. Contributing to this conclusion is the increase in blood lactate found in anesthetized animals subjected to oxygen at high pressures. Since considerable variation in dehydrogenase inactivation was found in oxygen poisoning in the laboratory, it has been suggested[11] that this might be the factor underlying the differences in susceptibility of intact animals to oxygen poisoning.

Oxygen poisoning, being a type of anoxia, might be expected to have some of the same effects as other forms of anoxia.

Autonomic adjustments in anoxia. The following will show how the organism compensates for the lack of oxygen in the intake resources. Since control of vital processes is an autonomic function, the phenomena enumerated are attributed to autonomic innervation, although the descriptions themselves pertain to circulation, respiration, temperature levels, etc.

The major autonomic adjustments in anoxia pertain to the respiration and circulation processes. Gellhorn[12] gives a good account of these and of the temperature adjustments involved. Mild degrees of anoxia are typically accompanied by an increase in respiratory volume without change in blood pressure. The respiratory adjustment raises the oxygen tension in the arterial blood, which in turn tends to take care of the oxygen need of the tissues. A rise in blood pressure, accompanied by acceleration of circulation in the heart and brain, is at first unnecessary. In more severe cases of anoxia, blood pressure rises in addition to the respiratory change.

The direct action of diminished oxygen supply on the respiratory center is apparently paralyzing. The enhanced respiratory response typically seen after inhalation of gases low in oxygen arises from reflex action of the carotid sinus receptors. The effect is more pronounced on the respiratory than on the vasomotor center. But since the vasomotor center is affected also by impulses originating in sino-aortic pressure receptors, depressor reflexes in anoxia are significant. This is well shown when the organism is put under sudden stress by shifts in posture when in this state.

[10] Bean, J. W., and D. F. Bohr: Anoxic Effects of High Oxygen Pressure on Smooth Muscle, *Am. J. Physiol., 130:* 445–453, 1940.

[11] Bohr, D. F., and J. W. Bean: Dehydrogenase Inactivation in Oxygen Poisoning, *Am. J. Physiol., 131:* 388–393, 1940.

[12] Gellhorn, E.: "Autonomic Regulations," Interscience Publishers, New York, 1943. Pp. 373.

The blood pressure of a subject in the erect posture inhaling 8.5 per cent oxygen (equivalent to about 23,000 ft., see Figs. 6 and 7) falls very rapidly, and complete collapse may ensue in a few minutes, whereas in the reclining position the inhalation of 8.5 per cent oxygen has practically no effect on the systemic blood pressure.

Two of the primary mechanisms in the maintenance of the blood pressure in the erect posture are the reflexes from the carotid sinus and those

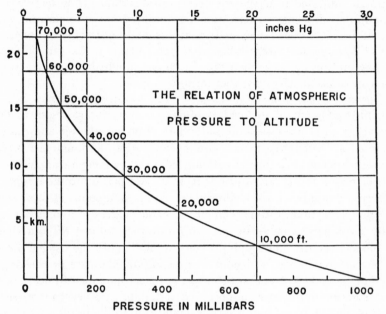

THE RELATION OF ATMOSPHERIC

PRESSURE TO ALTITUDE

PRESSURE IN MILLIBARS

Fig. 6.—The relation between pressure of the atmosphere and altitude given in thousands of feet and kilometers. The pressure is given both in inches of mercury and in millibars.

from the aorta, both activated by blood-pressure decline. The collapse could be accounted for if the inhalation of the low oxygen were found to diminish carotid sinus stimulation. "Tilting" experiments have shown that the blood pressure falls more in anoxia than under control conditions when the individual is in a nearly vertical position. A rise of the intra-sinusal pressure effects a much smaller blood-pressure fall during anoxia than in control periods, the general conclusion being that the carotid sinus depressor reflexes are greatly diminished in anoxia. In orthostatic hypotension the systemic blood pressure drops rapidly on standing, though it is normal in a reclining position.[13] Since anoxic effects parallel this,

[13] Alvarez, W. C., and G. Roth: Orthostatic Hypotension, *Proc. Staff Meet., Mayo Clin., 10:* 483–489, 1935.

experimental anoxia is a means of producing a syndrome closely resembling orthostatic hypotension.

In anoxia the variable blood flow through the extremities is a resultant of the constricting impulses originating in the vasomotor center and the local dilator effect of oxygen lack on the blood vessels. In marked anoxia, the central impulses predominate and vasoconstriction of the extremity ensues. On return to normal air intake, the blood flow does not return to normal but shows a marked compensatory phase, producing hyperemia. Apparently during the period of diminished circulation the oxygenation of the tissues was inadequate and is now compensated by an increased blood flow, paying off the oxygen debt incurred during the period of anoxia. In lesser degrees of anoxia with relatively weak central sympathetic activity, an actual increased circulation in the hand, for example, may be observed, compensating for the lowered oxygen tension. In such cases no oxygen debt is accumulated, and after readmission of air the blood flow is normal. Any reduction in the oxygenation of the tissues during anoxia, whether mild or severe, is accompanied by a compensatory increase in circulation, either during or after the period of anoxia.

What then takes care of the demands of the brain and heart? Cannon has called attention to the augmented sympathetic discharges in anoxia. Sympathetic nervous activity involves release of adrenalin, vasoconstriction, and rise in blood pressure. The supporting role of these discharges is obvious, for sympathectomized animals succumb more readily to anoxia than do normal controls.[14] Augmented secretion of adrenalin in anoxia has been demonstrated by examination of blood in the adrenal veins[15] and by sensitizing a pupil to adrenalin by removal of the superior cervical ganglion, in which case the denervated miotic pupil dilates more than the normal.[16]

Gellhorn points out that these types of reactions occurring in anoxia may be interpreted as attempts of the organism to improve the oxygenation of the tissues by facilitating the transport of oxygen by the blood. Lack of oxygen can be met also by decreasing the oxidative metabolism of the tissues through a fall in body temperature. Fall in body temperature may perhaps contribute to the adjustment to anoxia through alteration of the carotid sinus reflexes.

To summarize, the autonomic adjustments in anoxia consist largely in

[14] Sawyer, M. E. M., and T. I. Schlossberg: Studies of Homeostasis in Normal, Sympathectomized, and Ergotamized Animals. II. Effect of Anoxemia, *Am. J. Physiol., 104:* 172–183; 184–189, 1933.

[15] Houssay, B. A., and E. A. Molinelli: Adrenal Secretion Produced by Asphyxia, *Am. J. Physiol., 76:* 538–550, 1925.

[16] Kellaway, C. H.: The Hyperglycemia of Asphyxia and the Part Played Therein by the Suprarenals, *J. Physiol., 53:* 211–235, 1919.

changes dependent upon the degree and persistence of the oxygen lack. Respiratory adjustments increasing air intake are the first to occur. Blood pressure rise follows and enhances the transport of available oxygen to the tissues. Temperature may drop, in which case metabolism requires less oxygen, a result compensating for the diminished supply.

Manifestations of anoxia.   Anoxia is associated with four diverse situations: mountain climbing, aerial flight, decompression chamber, and breathing low-oxygen mixtures at normal pressures. In each of these many unpleasant symptoms develop, varying with amount of exertion, the particular person involved, the barometric pressure, the suddenness of subjection, the duration of exposure, and the broader conditions involving presence or absence of sensory stimulation.

In general, the most frequent manifestations of anoxia are irregular pulse, muscular weakness, frontal headaches, shortness of breath, cold hands and feet, disturbing dreams when asleep, and increased sensory irritability. Other frequent complaints are feeling of suffocation, difficulty in remembering and concentrating, restlessness and a tendency to "easy irritation," constantly recurring ideas involving anxiety, increased effort required in executing tasks, and the rapid development of fatigue on exertion.

These symptoms represent moderate stages of anoxia. With more severe involvement, psychomotor deterioration sets in, and were it not for the fact that the rate of involvement in the late stages is quite rapid, a greater array of symptoms might be expected. Cyanosis, muscular rigor, and a few such signs commonly develop before collapse occurs. The rapidity of oxygen starvation is in contrast to sugar starvation, in which the sequence of stages occupies a more extended time line and can be better observed.

McFarland,[17] using the breathing-bag method, gave his subjects concentrations of oxygen ranging from 12.28 to 7.68 per cent. According to his calculations, these concentrations are comparable to those encountered in flights at altitudes ranging from 15,000 to 28,000 ft. (see Fig. 7). The study involved several tests, the results of which were classifiable, although there was considerable variation from subject to subject.

The same deprivation affected one subject differently than another, although with repeated subjection to oxygen deprivation most individuals tended to act the same as on the first occasion. There appeared to be four different behavior outcomes, each representing a mode of reaction of a given individual in a single case. On most of the tests the subjects reacted in one or more of the following ways (1) with extreme amusement and

[17] McFarland, R. A.: Psychological Effects of Oxygen Deprivation (Anoxemia) on Human Behavior, *Arch. Psychol.*, No. 145, pp. 1-35, 1932.

fits of laughter, (2) with inordinate irritation and with roughness toward apparatus, (3) with unusual persistence and little apparent awareness or regard for poor performance, or (4) with fairly immediate abandonment of the task. When conditions were extreme enough, all the subjects exhibited a loss of psychomotor control.

McFarland[18] also reports studies on sensory and motor responses of individuals at high altitudes, arrived at by plane and by train. He points

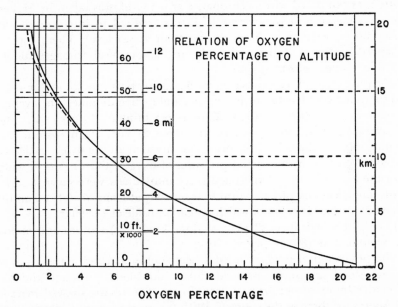

FIG. 7.—The relation of oxygen percentage in the atmosphere to altitude, given in thousands of feet, miles, and kilometers. The dotted line at the upper end of the curve indicates a necessary correction for shift in the proportions of oxygen and of the constituents of the atmosphere at higher altitudes.

out that tests conducted in plane cabins, as compared with those conducted in decompression chambers at sea level, are likely to involve (1) greater excitement, (2) nausea and sympathetic nervous disturbances brought on by sudden plane movements, and (3) greater distraction owing to vibration and engine noise.

The settings for McFarland's studies were the planes that cross the mountains between Santiago, Chile, and Mendoza, Argentina, in about 1 hour and 15 minutes. High altitudes are reached in 20 to 30 minutes. Under good flying conditions the altitude is about 14,000 ft., whereas under more unfavorable conditions it increases to about 17,000 or 18,000 ft.

[18] McFarland, R. A.: Psycho-physiological Studies at High Altitudes in the Andes. I and II, *J. Comp. Psychol.*, *23:* 191–225; 227–258, 1937.

The psychological tests that were used included the measurement of differences in perseverational lag and in latent periods of afterimages. The reasons for selecting these kinds of tests were the commonness with which individuals, suddenly exposed to oxygen lack, have difficulty in shifting from one intellectual (mental) task to another and the facts that intensely illuminated objects seem dim and afterimages persist longer than normally. The average loss of 9.3 to 11 per cent in number of symbols written, as compared with performance at sea level, was taken by McFarland as a measure of perseveration. Errors credited to interference and perseveration were three times greater than at sea level. There was an enhanced latency of 47 per cent in the appearance of afterimages and an added persistence of 34 per cent.

The physiological tests consisted in measuring pulse and blood pressure and sampling the alveolar air for oxygen and carbon dioxide. The average increase in pulse rate was about 32 beats per minute (48 per cent), and the average rise in blood pressure was about 21 mm. Hg in systolic and 11 mm. Hg in diastolic pressure. The alveolar-air analyses indicated marked decreases in the partial pressures of oxygen and carbon dioxide.

In the ascent-by-train experiments, six individuals were given a series of psychological and physiological tests one day at Lima (500 ft.) and the following day at Morochoca, which is at an altitude of 14,890 ft.

The "psychological tests" were of three kinds: (1) sensory and motor, (2) mental, and (3) complaint rating.

The physiological tests included a hemoglobin and red-cell analysis of venous blood, measures of basal pulse and blood pressure, and the Schneider Index of neurocirculatory fitness. The results showed marked differences for three of the subjects. With the exception of one individual, the percentage increase in pulse rate upon standing and after exertion was greater at high altitude than at sea level.

McFarland[19] reports two other high-altitude studies, one concerned with the effects when a few days at each of several stations on the ascent were allowed for the subjects' adjustment, and the other, tests on the residents at 17,500 ft.

Sensory, neurocirculatory, and biochemical measurements were obtained in the second study and compared with those of a group of workmen at sea level similar in age and race. Also, comparisons were made with members of the expedition. The residents at high altitudes were slower in simple and choice reaction times and less sensitive in hearing than workmen at sea level. The results were attributed to the reduced partial oxygen pressure at high altitudes, to unfamiliarity with the tests,

19 McFarland, R. A.: Psycho-physiological Studies at High Altitudes in the Andes. III and IV, J. Comp. Psychol., 24: 147–188; 189–220, 1937.

and to the effect of exposure to dry winds on the end organs. The residents were superior in neurocirculatory efficiency to the members of the expedition, as indicated by the Schneider Index. They also were more efficient than the workmen at sea level.

Anoxic states and vision. Several authors, including Wald and colleagues,[20] have pointed out that oxygen lack, carbon dioxide excess, etc., have their point of application somewhere beyond the receptor photochemical system. They reason that in the perfectly dark-adapted state the rod system is at rest, so that if it can be shown that changes in the level of the visual threshold occur, the effects must depend upon the central nervous system. Various investigators have reported that lowering oxygen tension to about 10 per cent, though not altering the course of dark adaptation, prevents the attainment of as low a threshold as normal.

McDonald and Adler[21] found the character of the dark-adaptation curve to be dissimilarly affected by anoxemia and vitamin A deficiency, from which they deduced that two different points of application were involved. Since it is known that the primary connection of vitamin A is with the rod photochemical system, the other effect on the dark-adaptation curve (that represented in anoxemia) must result from changes taking place elsewhere in the visual pathway. McDonald and Adler found that anoxemia raised the thresholds for both rods and cones without changing adaptation rate. For comparison, the intake of vitamin A was reduced, with the result that the adaptation curve was again changed. The effects, however, on the rods and cones were unequal. The rod threshold was raised more than the cone. The rises in threshold induced by anoxemia and vitamin A deficiency were simply additive.

Wald and colleagues[22] found a rise in threshold produced by anoxia. Under their conditions, threshold was doubled, and other investigators reported a similar or greater effect.[23] The former tested the effect of overbreathing on the threshold in connection with reduced oxygen pressure. They found rapid breathing was at first effective in countering the

[20] Wald, G., P. V. Harper, H. C. Goodman, and H. P. Krieger: Respiratory Effects upon Visual Threshold, *J. Gen. Physiol.*, *25:* 891–903, 1942.

[21] McDonald, R., and F. H. Adler: Effect of Anoxemia on the Dark Adaptation of the Normal and of the Vitamin A-deficient Sub ect, *Arch. Ophth.*, *22:* 980–988, 1939.

[22] Wald *et al., op. cit.*

[23] Bunge, E.: Verlauf der Dunkeladaptation bei Sauerstoffmangel, *Arch. f. Augenh.*, *110:* 189–197, 1936.

McDonald and Adler, *op. cit.*

McFarland, R. A., and W. H. Forbes: The Effects of Variations in the Concentrations of Oxygen and Glucose on Dark Adaptation, *J. Gen. Physiol.*, *24:* 69–98, 1940–1941.

effect of anoxia, but later this tendency vanished, leaving the threshold at supranormal levels.

The action produced by rapid breathing could not be attributed to increased oxygenation of the tissues, but rather to alkalosis. From the experiments, it could be said that respiratory alkalosis and acidosis have opposite effects on the visual threshold, the one depressing it and the other elevating it. These effects are analogous to those obtained in experiments[24] on the cerebral cortex in which decreasing pH elevates the excitation threshold. All the evidence favors the idea that visual disturbances caused by anoxia are central to the receptors themselves.

Gellhorn[25] found reversible diminution in visual discrimination of brightness under conditions of oxygen lack (8 to 10 per cent oxygen-nitrogen mixtures), carbon dioxide excess (6 per cent carbon dioxide-air mixtures), and hyperpnea. Under all three conditions, a supranormal phase was sometimes seen subsequent to return to normal intake. Impairment of hearing[26] is also produced by subjection to reduced oxygen for 10 to 30 minutes, depending upon the concentration, individual idiosyncrasy, etc. Carbon dioxide concentrations of 4 to 8 per cent, in air with normal oxygen content, also diminish auditory sensitivity, with quickly reversible results, whereas the anoxic effects last for several hours. Aften an interval of hyperpnea of 3 to 6 minutes, auditory threshold rises during the period of apnea.

The latency of negative afterimages[27] was also lengthened by oxygen lack (9 to 11 per cent oxygen), carbon dioxide excess (4 to 11 per cent), or voluntary overbreathing (2 to 5 minutes at 35 or more cycles per minute). As well as being delayed, the afterimages tended to be quite blurred and in some cases failed to appear at all. This effect on afterimages lasts as long as 12 minutes after the stress conditions.

Using red light (Wratten filter No. 70), McFarland and Halperin[28] tested the foveal visual acuity of 11 subjects with a black Landolt broken circle. When the logarithm of the illumination was plotted on the abscissa

[24] Dusser de Barenne, J. G., W. S. McCulloch, and L. F. Nims: Functional Activity and pH of the Cerebral Cortex, *J. Cell. & Comp. Physiol.*, *10:* 277–289, 1937.

[25] Gellhorn, E.: The Effect of O$_2$-lack, Variations in the CO$_2$-content of the Inspired Air, and Hyperpnea on Visual Intensity Discrimination, *Am. J. Physiol.*, *115:* 679–684, 1936.

[26] Gellhorn, E., and I. G. Spiesman: The Influence of Hyperpnea and of Variations of O$_2$- and CO$_2$-tension in the Inspired Air upon Hearing, *Am. J. Physiol.*, *112:* 519–528, 1935.

[27] Gellhorn, E., and I. G. Spiesman: The Influence of Hyperpnea and of Variations of the O$_2$- and CO$_2$-tension in the Inspired Air upon After-images, *Am. J. Physiol.*, *112:* 620–626, 1935.

[28] McFarland, R. A., and M. H. Halperin: Relation between Foveal Visual Acuity and Illumination under Reduced Oxygen Tension, *J. Gen. Physiol.*, *23:* 613–630, 1940.

and the logarithm of visual acuity on the ordinate, reduced oxygen tensions induced a shift to the right in the curves (along intensity axis) of about 0.24 log unit at an oxygen percentage of 14.3 (10,000 altitude) and 0.47 log unit at a percentage of 10.3 (18,000 ft. altitude). Inhaling pure oxygen for a few minutes completely reversed the effects. Owing to the shape of the curve, this shift represented a considerable decrease in visual acuity at the lower illuminations, but very little at the higher.

Evans and McFarland[29] failed to find any effect of oxygen deprivation on central visual acuity. On the other hand, they did find that angioscotoma widens as oxygen lack develops and obliterates the field except for a region 8 to 10 degrees surrounding the macula. There is a considerable difference in the degree and rate of widening of the angioscotoma both among individuals and between the two eyes of one person. These authors interpret the findings to mean that areas of the retina vary in their susceptibility to ill effects from anoxia. They point out that the loss of vision in glaucoma follows the course of the angioscotoma under oxygen lack very closely.

Recently, Halstead[30] reported results of what he calls a dynamic field test, under oxygen pressure conditions equivalent to an altitude of 10,000 ft., provided by a decompression chamber. Twenty subjects, ranging in age from 17 to 29 years, selected by the standards of the Service Air Corps, were used. These were exposed to the low oxygen pressure for 5 or 6 hours daily, for 6 days per week, for 4 to 6 weeks. The test required the subjects to determine the presence or absence of a small disk of light in the periphery of the uniocular visual field, while concurrently making a form and color discrimination at the center of the field. Both targets were exposed for only 20 msec. on a translucent screen. Serial presentation at the subject's own rate was provided by a built-in projection system controlled by a push-button switch.

Under these conditions, 13 of the 20 subjects developed a decided and progressive deterioration in performance on the test, after 3 weeks or more. This was measured in terms of the number of "perceptual errors" made in detecting the peripheral targets (see Figs. 8 and 9). Whereas the dynamic field test was primarily a peripheral vision test, central vision was also examined in the study. In some subjects, a concomitant deterioration in performance in using the central field developed, though in others deterioration based on the peripheral field appeared alone. When deterioration in performance did develop, "failure symptoms" were unde-

29 Evans, J. N., and R. A. McFarland: Effects of Oxygen Deprivation on Central Visual Field, *Am. J. Ophth., 21:* 968–980, 1938.

30 Halstead, W. C.: Chronic Intermittent Anoxia and the Dynamic Visual Field, *J. Psychol., 20:* 49–56, 1945.

tected by the subjects in the ordinary use of the eyes, although they were observed in the tests. When deterioration in the test performance reached an unquestionable stage, it could be obliterated at once by the inhalation of pure oxygen "at altitude." Performance deficiency could be detected not only in the decompression chamber, but under "ground" conditions on the same day. Persistent efforts to detect a deficiency by methods of campimetry and perimetry, the usual clinical methods, were unsuccessful.

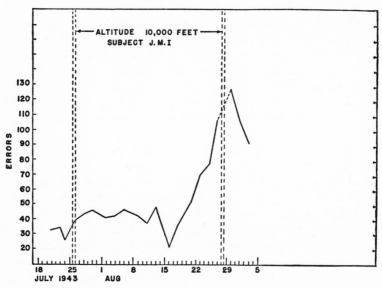

Fig. 8.—The number of errors in the dynamic field test relative to the continuance of intermittent exposure to low oxygen pressure for 5 or 6 hours daily 6 days per week. (*Halstead, W. C.: Chronic Intermittent Anoxia and the Dynamic Visual Field, Am. J. Psychol., 20: 49–56, 1945.*)

Retinoscopy failed to show any pathology. At the end of a 6 weeks' exposure period, several weeks were required before full return to original performance could be demonstrated. Both the retarded onset and the slow recovery are pictured in Fig. 8.

In subsequent experiments, Halstead found that a shorter delay in onset of performance deterioration followed exposures to oxygen pressures lower than in the original experiments. One subject exposed to pressures equivalent to altitudes of 18,000 ft. showed deterioration on the second day. This increased during further exposure, and one month following the last exposure it had not fully disappeared.

The special four subjects exposed to "equivalent altitudes" above

10,000 ft. were the same individuals used by Bryan and Ricketts[31] in their inquiry on the possible effects of chronic intermittent anoxia on the adrenal cortex. These individuals were kept on uniform weighed diets. Studies of glucose tolerance, urinary excretion of sodium, potassium, chloride, phosphorus, nitrogen, and 17-ketosteroids, showed largely negative results. The exceptions were a slight increase in potassium excretion

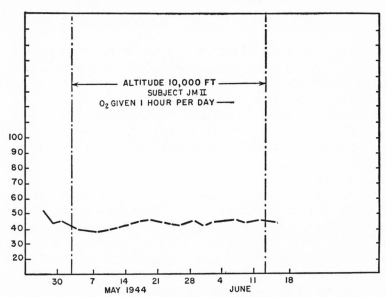

FIG. 9.—The relation of number of errors in the dynamic visual field test for a subject under low oxygen pressure for several hours per day when given pure oxygen 1 hour per day during the same period. It will be noted that whereas in the previous figure intermittent subjection to low oxygen pressure produced an effect detectable by the dynamic visual field test, the use of oxygen for 1 hour a day obliterates this effect. (*Halstead, W. C.: Chronic Intermittent Anoxia and the Dynamic Visual Field, Am. J. Psychol., 20: 49–56, 1945.*)

in two of the subjects, a transient elevation of 17-ketosteroid excretion in one, and a moderate drop in glucose tolerance in two. In contrast to the scant and nonuniform biochemical findings, performance on the dynamic visual field test deteriorated in the altitude ranges from 11,500 to 18,000 ft.

Subjective symptoms included mild headaches, slight blurring of vision, drowsiness, prickling of the skin, slight motor weakness, mild euphoria, depression, restlessness, etc. Lassitude was reported, but Halstead saw

[31] Bryan, A. H., and H. T. Ricketts: Effect in Man of Chronic Intermittent Anoxia on Glucose Tolerance and Urinary Excretion of Sodium, Potassium, Chloride, Phosphorous, Nitrogen, and 17-ketosteroids, *J. Clin. Endocrinol., 4:* 450–464, 1944.

nothing to indicate the presence of fatigue to a degree accounting for the impoverishment of test results.

While the dynamic field test does not measure impairment directly, it is reasonable to assume that tissue impairment has been induced by the intermittent exposure to scant oxygen supply.

IMPAIRMENT, FATIGUE, AND ANOXIA

There can be no question that *impairment* increases as anoxia becomes more severe. Signs of impairment vary from individual to individual with the same deprivation, but when the oxygen lack is severe enough, they are never absent. Cyanosis, tremor, muscular rigidity, and decreased muscular control are nearly always observed preceding collapse. In general, impairment clearly increases as oxygen lack becomes greater.

The relation of *fatigue* and anoxia is more complicated. Even in severe cases of anoxia, fatigue may be marked in one individual, present to a mild degree in another, and totally absent in a third. Little is known about fatigue specifically because it has so often been thought of as synonymous with impairment.

It is often reported that various reactions become more difficult as oxygen lack sets in. When this occurs, the individual is likely to put forth increased effort to achieve the tasks at hand. This is called "compensation." Compensation was noted by McFarland[32] in studying pilots by the use of rebreathing apparatus. Oxygen was decreased from 21 to 7 per cent (an altitude equivalent of 28,000 ft.) in 20 to 30 minutes. The tasks consisted of tests pertaining to turning off lights, maintaining the pointer of a meter at a constant setting, and foot regulation of the speed of a motor from auditory cues. At an altitude equivalent of about 14,000 ft., signs of anoxia were noted in nearly all the subjects. At higher oxygen concentrations, the overt measures did not indicate the deterioration that was setting in, although considerable added effort was required. Only when compensation failed did the overt effects appear. While compensation in some subjects began to fail at an equivalent of 15,000 ft., it persisted in others until near collapse.

Compensation in behavior, especially in relation to continuing a task over extended periods of time, is a factor stressed by Johnson[33] for performances such as automobile driving. Johnson's work brings up some points of complexity in relation to methodology in studying fatigue and impair-

[32] McFarland, R. A.: The Psychological Effects of Oxygen Deprivation (Anoxemia) on Human Behavior, *Arch. Psychol.,* No. 145, 1932.

[33] Johnson, H. M.: Rival Notions of the Nature of Physiological Impairment, a paper read at the Symposium of Visual Fatigue (organized by the Committee on Visual Fatigue) , Washington, D. C., May 20-21, 1939.

Johnson, H. M.: The Real Meaning of Fatigue, *Harper's, 158:* 186-193, 1929.

ment which are rarely taken into account. Since there is no measure of effort, the factor of effort cannot be abstracted from the total situation, and measures of deterioration in performance are not so significant as they are often imputed to be.

The published protocols from McFarland's studies indicated that the general attitudes of the subjects varied considerably from person to person. Some could be best characterized by irritation, others by amusement and exhilaration. Subjection to severe conditions seemed rather to emphasize personality differences. Fatigue could scarcely be attributed to the subjects who reported feeling particularly fit.

Barcroft[34] makes the analogies of alcoholic intoxication and acute anoxia and of fatigue and chronic anoxia. Just how far the analogies go, or what they are, is not made fully clear in Barcroft's discussion.

In the case of the acute anoxia and drunkenness comparison, it is apparently the signs and symptoms of the two which are taken to be similar.

In experiments in which oxygen deprivation is brief and severe, one might expect symptoms similar to those of drunkenness. These symptoms vary considerably from person to person. Some individuals become light-hearted, happy, and gay, whereas others become morose, irritable, and belligerent. Another similarity between the two states is the loss of motor coordination, accompanied by little concern on the part of the individual. His extreme awkwardness, even to falling down stairs, may strike him as highly amusing. The anoxic or drunken individual experiences little embarrassment in any situation. He may be totally oblivious of the significance of his social position, for example.

In the alleged analogy between chronic anoxia and fatigue, Barcroft seems to be referring only to what he calls "mental fatigue." From the effects of a series of mental tests given under moderately high-altitude conditions, he concludes that concentrated thought is "more fatiguing to the mind" under conditions of slight oxygen lack than it is otherwise. Nevertheless he also states that there is no clear evidence that mental fatigue is caused by oxygen lack. Although the accuracy of performance was little affected, an increased "effort of mind" was needed to do the tests. The subjects were said to show "mental apathy" amounting, according to him, to mere carelessness or even to a distortion of values. He says that, in both fatigue and chronic anoxia, emotional self-control is decreased.

Although Barcroft makes this analogy and proceeds to discuss it, the statements he makes are so varied, loose, and contradictory that, although they undoubtedly involve assailable concepts, they defy specific criticism.

[34] Barcroft, J.: "The Respiratory Function of the Blood." Part I. Lessons from High Altitudes, Cambridge University Press, London, 1925. Pp. 207.

Barcroft neglects even to make clear what he takes to be the common denominator for fatigue, impairment, and chronic anoxia.

The analogy between fatigue and chronic anoxia, although a poor one, requires inspection, since fatigue, impairment, and anoxia do have certain relations. Impairment is a tissue affair. Impairment, variously induced, may have somewhat similar features. If fatigue in the analogy refers to impairment, it is merely implied that two kinds of impairment are alike. The analogy implies that one kind (fatigue), induced by activity, is similar to the other, induced by oxygen lack. Whether or not impairment in two cases is alike can be determined only biochemically. If fatigue is taken to include experiential factors, as is often the case, certainly no analogy between it and anoxia can be entertained, whether anoxia refers to a kind of impairment or is also taken to include experiential factors (discomfort, etc.). If the analogy between fatigue and anoxia pertains only to the experiential factors in both cases, the analogy is rather ridiculous, owing to the fact that even here fatigue and anoxia are not comparable. Fatigue is a well-known experience, whereas the subjective state of anoxia is a variable complex of identifiable experiences, one of which may be fatigue, itself.

Chapter VI

LACK OF SUGAR IN THE BODY AS A LIMITING CONDITION

IN THE previous chapter the effects of oxygen lack were discussed. The organism may develop other deficiencies, especially in connection with food intake. One of these is the lack of sugar in the blood (hypoglycemia) and other tissues. The present chapter is concerned with a description of the consequences of this lack.

In sufficient sugar lack, as in oxygen lack, impairment is inevitable. Whether fatigue arises during sugar lack is determined not by the degree of the lack, but by the way in which the resulting impairment is involved in the individual's activity and in his attitude toward his activity. Since fatigue depends upon the individual's feeling of inadequacy for activity, the reader is not to consider that the impairment from sugar lack, even when extreme, is synonymous with fatigue.

Control of blood sugar. The maintenance of a blood-sugar concentration within certain limits of constancy is one of the many homeostatic manifestations of the organism. The sugar concentration seldom rests at a level above 110 mg. per cent for very long, though after a meal it may ascend to 180 mg. per cent for a short time. In the other direction, the level seldom descends below 60 mg. per cent, to which it drops for a short time a few hours after a meal. Symptoms are to be expected when the level rises above or falls below critical limits which, although suggested by the figures given, vary considerably from person to person.

The liver has the function of changing ingested carbohydrates into liver starch or glycogen and even changing some amino acids and fats into carbohydrate form for storage. This transformation also occurs in the case of other important intermediary metabolites such as lactic acid and pyruvic acid. Between meals, glycogen is transformed and released as glucose for distribution.

Blood-sugar-concentration limits are controlled by several factors, one of which tends to prevent it from rising too high, and several to preclude too great a fall. The sole neural mechanism engaged in preventing too great a rise is the parasympathetic-insulin system, whereby a rise in blood sugar excites the secretion of insulin as a reflex through hypothalamic and medullary centers. The vagus nerve is the agent for effecting the changes instituted in these centers, and its branches innervate the islands of Langerhans in the pancreas which secrete insulin. Since rise in blood-sugar concentration also excites the manufacture of insulin by direct action on the islands of Langerhans, the nervous mechanism does not reach the significance that it would if it were the exclusive agency. However, the nervous mechanism may act as an amplifying, moderating, or otherwise refining influence.

Acting against blood-sugar fall is the sympathetic-adrenal system, functioning by way of the hypothalamus, medulla, and pons, the innervation being carried via the splanchnic nerves to the medulla of the adrenal glands which secrete adrenalin. Adrenalin secures the release of liver glycogen to augment the low amount of sugar in the blood. It has been found that, unlike the islands of Langerhans, the adrenal medulla is not directly sensitive to blood-sugar levels.

The adrenals are not alone in preventing blood-sugar fall. Synergistically with them are the posterior pituitary and the thyroid glands. Participating also in the relief of hypoglycemia are the anterior pituitary glands and the adrenal cortex through their ability to reduce oxidation of carbohydrates. Hence not only the availability of new stores of carbohydrate, but also conservation is effected by the agencies mentioned. In women, the group of influences that combat hypoglycemia include the ovary through its ability to stimulate the activities of the anterior pituitary and the adrenal cortex.[1] Diabetes develops when the latter two glands become excessively active and raise blood sugar too high.

Defects in functioning.   The failure to maintain the proper range in blood-sugar concentration arises in three ways. The *first* of these is through liver failure. Liver tissue may be damaged through infection or through certain kinds of drug poisoning.

The *second* is the dysfunctioning of the islands of Langerhans which in some cases is organic, as in carcinoma. Curiously enough, in many instances, despite the disease of the cells, they continue to secrete but without the usual regulation. Hence in such states the normal limitation and delicate regulation of the cells' activity does not exist and an excess of insulin is produced. This is known as hyperinsulinism and results in an abnormally low blood-sugar level.

The *third* way in which blood sugar is kept too low is through the dysfunctioning of the neuroendocrine mechanism already described. Hence blood sugar becomes too low because it is not stored, because it is not

[1] Ingle, D. J.: The Production of Glycosuria in the Normal Rat by Means of Stilbestrol, *Am. J. M. Sc., 201:* 153–154, 1941.

released as needed, or because oxidation is not regulated in keeping with the supply released into the blood.

Blood sugar may also be lowered by artificial means, such as insulin injection. Insulin hypoglycemia, or insulin shock, may result.

Autonomic regulations in hypoglycemia.[2] The autonomic activities in hypoglycemia are vasomotor and respiratory excitement, enhanced secretion of adrenalin, diminished resistance in peripheral circulation, with increased blood flow and greater cardiac output. Curiously, the adjustments involve either no change or else a diminution of circulation in the brain.

There is an increased minute volume in respiration and a slight fall in alveolar carbon dioxide tension as a quite direct contribution to adjustment. This is evidenced by increased oxygen tension in inhaled air, offsetting recorded effects in the electro-encephalogram. Diastolic blood pressure usually falls, although pressure effects are somewhat variable.

When the sympathetic-adrenal system is stimulated, liberation of adrenalin antagonizes the effect of insulin on the blood sugar. This adjustment is apparently due to direct action of hypoglycemia on the sympathetic medullary center, since neither the pressure receptors nor the chemoreceptors in the carotid sinus are sensitive to variations in blood sugar.

Hypoglycemia contributes to a reduction in the oxidation rate in the central nervous system. It is calculated that the oxidative metabolism of the brain may be reduced to one-fourth of that in normal controls. In anoxia the same result accrues from diminishing the oxygen that is needed for the consumption of this fuel. And it is from this that the autonomic adjustment reactions arise. The essentially similar action of anoxia and hypoglycemia on the central nervous system is brought out by studies on the effect of anoxia on the vasomotor center under hypoglycemia. These studies contribute to understanding autonomic adjustments to hypoglycemia through demonstration of changes in sympathetic excitability.

For example, if an oxygen-nitrogen mixture is inhaled before and during various depths of insulin hypoglycemia, the pressor response increases with diminishing blood sugar. This increase is even greater than that obtained on inhalation of nitrogen at normal blood-sugar levels. The effects first become evident when the blood-sugar level falls below 50 mg. per cent.

This enhanced blood-pressure reaction may arise from sympathetic vascular action, from secretion of adrenalin, or from both. Ingraham and Gellhorn[3] showed that the reaction was similar in both adrenalectomized

[2] Gellhorn, E.: "Autonomic Regulations," Interscience Publishers, New York, 1943. Pp. 373.

[3] Ingraham, R. C., and E. Gellhorn: Role of Adrenals in Blood Pressure Reaction to Anoxia during Insulin Hypoglycemia, *Proc. Soc. Exper. Biol. & Med., 40:* 315–319, 1939.

and in normal control animals. It was established that a much greater sympathetic response is induced by anoxia in the hypoglycemic state than when blood sugar is normal in level.

Gellhorn[4] points out that sympathetic-adrenal stimulation in hypoglycemia serving to increase blood sugar and thus availability to tissues, including the brain, is comparable to the several adjustment processes in anoxia which tend to improve the transport of oxygen to the tissues.

One might expect from these resemblances between anoxia and hypoglycemia that the temperature effect in the two cases might be similar. It will be recalled that a diminution in metabolic demands in anoxia was effected by a reduction in body temperature. In the human, insulin hypoglycemia is consistently accompanied by temperature reduction. This similarity seems to indicate that this mode of regulation has the same economy in both cases.

Overt symptoms at various stages of hypoglycemia. Five arbitrary stages in the depth of hypoglycemia have been described by Himwich[5] and colleagues, paralleling the grosser levels of nervous organization that are affected in turn, beginning with the most vulnerable and ending with the least. These stages may be named roughly according to the anatomical structures involved. Stage 1 may be called cerebral and cerebellar; 2, subcortical or diencephalic; 3, midbrain with intact red nucleus; 4, midbrain sectioned to exclude red nucleus; and 5, medullary. The sequence of events as these stages are traversed is one of the most dramatic in all physiology and in clarity equals the behavioral demonstrations of the classical transections of the brain stem at various levels. While the description of the autonomic regulations in hypoglycemia have dealt with the vital adjustments, the behavioral events in stages of hypoglycemic involvement show the overt end results. The effects from lesser degrees of hypoglycemia will be made still more obvious when the description of the *personality effects* of sugar lack is made. The fact to be emphasized in anticipation of these two descriptions is that the three series of events (autonomic, motor, and psychological) go hand in hand and that the combined descriptions are necessary in order to give an adequate conception of what is happening to the individual.

About $\frac{1}{2}$ hour after the administration of a shock-producing dose of insulin, the typical case shows sweating, salivation, and muscular relaxation with tremor. Reduction in clarity of consciousness, slowing up of

---

[4] Gellhorn, *op. cit.*

[5] Himwich, H. E.: A Review of Hypoglycemia, Its Physiology and Pathology, Symptomatology and Treatment, *Am. J. Digest. Dis. & Nutrition, 11:* 1–8, 1944.

Himwich, H. E., J. P. Frostig, J. F. Fazekas, and Z. Hadidian: The Mechanism of the Symptoms of Insulin Hypoglycemia, *Am. J. Psychiat., 96:* 371–385, 1939.

mental processes, and disturbances of orientation may appear. These symptoms, which are the main ones involved in stage 1, are mainly cerebral and cerebellar. At the end of the first stage, loss of intellectual connection with the physical world and increased motor activity are characteristic. The loss of contact is the transition between the first and second stages.

In stage 2, stereotyped movements set in, and sucking, grasping, kissing, snarling, etc., are easily elicited. The spontaneous movements have been spoken of as "ceaseless" and "aimless" and described as "motor restlessness." As time passes, myotonic twitches appear and become more widespread and more intense, till definite clonic spasms develop, which in some cases become extremely violent.

This stage represents the liberation of the hypothalamus and a dominance of sympathetic nervous activity, which is shown periodically in increased heart rate. The pupils become dilated though still somewhat sensitive to light, and exophthalmos is manifested. The excessive sweat is of a viscid character. After a time, marked sympathetic dominance diminishes.

In stage 3, the midbrain is left in control. The "primitive movements" and restlessness characteristic of the second stage vanish. The trunk and limbs are arched. Apparently, for a time, a more nearly equal balance between the parasympathetic and sympathetic systems develops. The Babinski reflex, which was a whole-limb response in the previous stage, is now totally absent. Clonic activity shifts into tonic, in which paired muscle groups contract concomitantly. This tonic pattern emphasizes flexor tensions in the upper extremities and extensor in the lower. Torsion spasms may develop.

When the tonic spasm of this stage changes character enough to be called an extensor spasm, stage 4 is reached. The eyes, whose extrinsic muscles are regulated by centers in the midbrain, no longer act in a coordinated manner. There is a shift in the arm position from flexion to an extended position above and back of the head. During this time, the reflexes of Magnus and DeKleyn are obtainable. Turning of the individual's head spontaneously or passively is associated with extensor spasms of the side to which the face points and with flexor spasms of the other. The character of the response picture is reminiscent of decerebrate rigidity when midbrain section excludes the red nucleus.

In stage 5, the pupils are greatly constricted and insensitive to variations in light. The skin is pale. Breathing is superficial. Perspiration has changed to a watery consistency, and body temperature reaches a minimum. These symptoms indicate that all levels above the medullary have been excluded.

Personality symptoms in hypoglycemia. In medical practice, perhaps the most frequently observed symptoms of hypoglycemia are neuropsychiatric. Besides the behavior already discussed, which may be imputed to autonomic function, many of the symptoms observed can be better described in terms of personality itself.

A classification of hypoglycemic symptoms in terms of personality is particularly appropriate if not essential to a discussion of fatigue, which is itself a personality expression. The complexity of the factors influencing personality make the relating of any of its deviations to specific items such as, in this case, fuel lack extremely difficult. An infinite number of factors may lie behind "intellectual cloudiness," for example. If hypoglycemia is one of these, and yet has not become so severe as to show up in definite autonomic or other bodily symptoms, it may often be ignored as a contributing "cause" of the dullness.

Sigwald[6] classifies hypoglycemic attacks into three stages, which he calls *minor, medium,* and *major.* A division of this sort has apparently proved fruitful for clinical purposes, since it has been adopted by others.

Wilder[7] classifies the symptoms that appear in hypoglycemia into *autonomic, cerebrospinal,* and *mental.* In describing these neuropsychiatric symptoms, he uses the Sigwald classification of stages as a base.

Much of the material that appears in the following description of personality symptoms has been taken from Wilder's clinical descriptions of the behavior of hypoglycemic patients. His symptom classification, however, is not followed, since in dealing with personality factors an arbitrary separation of this sort would be most inappropriate. On the other hand, Sigwald's separation of stages into minor, medium, and major will be followed. It should be kept in mind, however, that this is also an arbitrary classification devised for practical purposes and that its various boundaries are anything but rigid. Since these categories apply to individuals whom the physician sees, a certain degree of difficulty must arise before an attack is classed as *minor.*

The *minor attack* is characterized by marked changes in the three commonly abstracted aspects of personality, *viz.,* thinking, volition, and mood. There is a weakness of concentration, and thinking becomes hampered. Attention cannot be held very long on any objective. There is extreme difficulty in making decisions, at times amounting to abulia. Acts that formerly were spontaneous lose that quality and come to require volitional effort. The patient is likely to feel somewhat depressed and anxious. The general impression of the onlooker is a dulling of the whole personality. The individual dislikes to move, and movement is difficult. Talking becomes labor, and speech is slow and dragging. Repeated attempts are often necessary to pronounce a word. Curiously, in combination with the dull-

---

[6] Sigwald, J.: "L'hypoglycemie," G. Dain and Co., Paris, 1932. Pp. 320.

[7] Wilder, J.: Psychological Problems in Hypoglycemia, *Am. J. Digest. Dis. & Nutrition, 10:* 428–435, 1943.

ness there is apt to be heightened irritability. This is shown in various vasomotor reactions. The individual inclines toward negativism and may show intense annoyance with what appears to be little or no provocation.

Many of the personality symptoms characteristic of the *medium attack* are an exaggeration of those found in the minor. Intellectual disturbances become more serious. The patient is somewhat disoriented in space and time and may complain of feelings of depersonalization. Disturbances of perception are often reported and form another facet in the widening disconnectedness of the person and his surroundings. Thinking, especially grouping, abstracting, etc., is almost impossible at this stage. The individual may suffer from aphasia. Decisions are not made, probably because there is little recognition of the significance of the situation's demands. The mood tends to be one of apathy and indifference. The patient is not consistently apathetic, however, and "emotional imbalance" is also characteristic of the medium stage. If the patient is asked to do anything, he is likely to become very uncooperative, and occasionally force is required to administer treatment. Paranoid reactions are common. Psychotic episodes, usually followed by amnesia, have been reported. Judging from the overt behavior, irritability is greatly increased. There may be various motor disturbances. The individual is likely to be overactive, showing all kinds of mannerisms and gesticulating wildly. Alternating with this sort of behavior, or even appearing at the same time, there seems to be an increased desire for sleep. The individual may act as if he were "drugged."

In the *major attack,* personality symptoms are at a minimum. The patient is quite unable to report events either during the attack or following recovery. He is stuporous and has lost contact with the physical world. The report upon the subject becomes simply a record of overt performance. It is true, however, that the onlooker is likely to make inferences about personality from the overt behavior, particularly if the behavior seems to consist of a series of continuous acts. Various clownlike antics and occasional acts of violence are reported at the beginning of the major attack. However, this stage is better characterized by an even greater lack of coordination and lack of contract with the physical world than can be imputed to behavior of this sort. Chorea and epileptiform convulsions are frequent. At the height of the major attack, the patient is comatose.

A parallel may be drawn between the minor, medium, and major stages of the clinical classification and the five stages based on nervous organization described by Himwich. In the latter, stage 1, the cerebral and cerebellar, might be said to include all the symptoms in the minor attack, all or nearly all those in the medium, and possibly a few of those often attributed to the major. Stage 2 in the Himwich classification, the subcortical or diencephalic, may conceivably be involved in some attacks called medium.

However, generally, when stage 2 is reached, the clinical classification would be that of a major attack. Stages 3 (midbrain with intact red nucleus), 4 (midbrain sectioned to exclude red nucleus), and 5 (medullary) would always appear clinically as stages in a major attack.

The looseness of both of these classifications, perhaps particularly of the clinical one, is brought out by this comparison. None of the categories involved have rigidly set limits, and diagnoses are bound to vary. Individual cases of hypoglycemia are likely to contain elements of more than a single stage or degree of attack.

Certain personality changes have sometimes been attributed to mild hypoglycemia. The petulance, impatience, and easy annoyance that many individuals experience and manifest before breakfast are among these. In fact, it is generally recognized that a good meal is almost certain to alter the moods and improve the dispositions of the partakers, and this may be in part due to the elevation of blood sugar.

As a hypoglycemic attack grows from minor to medium to major proportions, impairment increases. Many clinicians, confusing fatigue with impairment, might deduce that fatigue is also augmented in a progressive manner. However, fatigue as we have defined it would be expected to decrease when the individual begins to lose contact with his surroundings.

The minor stages of hypoglycemia, then, have particular bearing on the problem of fatigue. The individual dislikes to think, to talk, or to move. He has great difficulty in making required decisions, and his mood varies between apathy and irritation. Even if fatigue is not specifically reported, it may easily be suspected.

If activity requires great effort, full-fledged fatigue is likely to result very quickly. Beyond a certain point, fatigue decreases as hypoglycemia becomes more severe. In the minor stage, fatigue might be expected to wax and wane in keeping with the activity demands made upon the organism.

Chapter VII

TEMPERATURE EXTREMES AND WATER AND SALT LACKS

DEMANDS AND EFFECTS OF TEMPERATURE EXTREMES

SINCE human beings are homoiothermic, continuous active adjustment is necessary to maintain the required constancy of temperature. During active exercise and when external temperature extremes exist, the demands become difficult to meet. In the course of maintenance of temperature constancy, discomfort and fatigue often develop. It is necessary, however, to distinguish between the impairment resulting from the limiting conditions discussed in this chapter and the fatigue that is sometimes described as developing. Here, as in other types of situations, impairment and fatigue are obviously not identical, and may not even be correlated.

Even with minimum overt activity the organism evolves heat as a product of metabolism. When external temperature is lower than body temperature, the organism tends to compensate, but when the external temperature is higher, body heat, in tending to be added to the heat received from the surroundings, is unfavorable to the organism. This is one reason why hot surroundings, within the ranges usually encountered, impose even more severe difficulties than cold ones.

Insofar as tasks involve muscular movement, they and the physiological adjustments work in the same direction, *i.e.*, to maintain body heat against losses encountered in cool surroundings. Contradiction between work and physiological demands may, however, develop even in cold temperatures. The muscular activity needed in the task performed may be much less than that required to move about and keep warm; hence the task is constantly interfered with by the urge to greater muscular activity, and this provides a potential source of constant distraction. When physical surroundings are already quite warm, muscular activity adds to the demand upon the adjustment processes. Thus throughout all ranges, clash between work interests and physiological interests of the organism may develop.

At temperatures that require marked bodily adjustments, various kinds of experiential concomitants emerge in the individual. Long before there are outright physiological difficulties, discomfort may develop and work

99

may be interfered with. Although extreme temperatures are generally recognized as physiological limiters, less extreme conditions induce concomitant features in the organism which tend to be passed off by experimenters as simply subjective. These features nonetheless exhibit the limiting nature of physical influences.

Studies on the effect of temperature upon work or activity found in the literature have not dealt with the problem from what we have defined as the personalistic standpoint. Generally, the concern in such studies has been with work output or with efficiency.[1] On this account, we possess little information on the relation of temperature to fatigue. On the basis of everyday experience, however, it seems safe to believe that temperature is a sizable factor in fatigue. It remains for appropriately conceived studies to provide an analysis of the matter.

The experimental material is also limited in studies of water lack and of humidity and, in a lesser degree, of salt lack. The studies cited for each of these conditions will necessarily pertain more especially to physical and physiological details in a variety of situations. Our interest lies in the fact that the basic physiological adjustments that the organism must perform to maintain temperature balance may interfere with the overt activities demanded in everyday life.

Regulation, generation, and dissipation of heat. It has already been emphasized that the organism is not passive to its thermal demands. Certain operations must be constantly performed by the organism to maintain its own approximately constant temperature. Three processes may be distinguished: (1) regulation, (2) generation, and (3) dissipation. Regulation is the over-all activity of the organism as it pertains to the maintenance of body temperature. Thus regulation is personal. Generation has to do with the production of heat. When we deal with production in the narrow and specific sense, we are dealing with chemistry. When viewed more broadly, generation is also personal. Dissipation is the elimination of heat from the organism. In the narrow sense, dissipation is physical, since the organism dissipates heat as if it were an inert body. But again in a broader sense, dissipation is personal, since it may be retarded or promoted by certain operations of the organism. Although it is more common to consider generation and dissipation primarily from the chemical and physical

---

[1] Efficiency has three aspects: (1) the ratio of the energy turned into mechanical movement to the total energy released by the metabolic processes in the muscles, (2) the smoothness of reciprocity between opposing muscles and the way the movements succeed in accomplishing the task set for them, and (3) the extent to which muscles originally extraneous to the task are involved in a localized set of movements. The first factor is *in part* a matter of metabolism. The second is a matter of reciprocal innervation under guidance of a goal to be achieved. The third pertains to irradiation. It is, of course, the first of these aspects we refer to here.

standpoints, respectively, they must ultimately be seen and dealt with as personal.

In the analysis of what happens in this thermal milieu, the factors are so numerous and varied that any conventional ordering of them is precluded. For example, Bazett,[2] in his review of "physiological responses to heat," pointed out that "response to heat" is a phrase that has to be "interpreted liberally." He noted that it is not yet possible to distinguish among the results of (1) direct physical effects from change in temperature, (2) changes in chemical activity secondary to the physiological changes, and (3) modifications in glandular, muscular, or nervous processes secondary to these. Although this difficulty is seen to arise in part out of the complexity of the situation, there is also failure to view the situation as a whole.

The mode of actual heat loss is through evaporation from the lungs and skin, radiation from the body by conduction to its surroundings, and through convection by air movement. The range of evaporation from cool to warm surroundings varies from less than a liter per day to ten times that amount. In hot surroundings, body heat dissipation cannot easily keep pace with its production. This may give rise to dangerous body temperatures. In cold surroundings, the reverse is of course true. Heat production must keep pace with its dissipation. To aid this, body economy provides that the blood be shifted inward to retain its heat. In warm surroundings, the blood is circulated through the skin and subcutaneous tissues, bringing it near the surfaces that are being cooled by evaporation.

Air movement and humidity are sizable factors in the physical impact upon the individual. Dry air heated some degrees above body temperature does not necessarily induce rise in deep body temperature. Even surface temperature may not tend to be elevated by such conditions, for loss of heat through evaporation often balances heat gained by radiation, as well as intrinsic heat developed in metabolism. Saturated air leads to a different result. Even though such air is much below body temperature, it may not be able to remove as much heat through the avenues of conduction and convection as is developed in the body in the course of metabolism. A rise in temperature results. Such a rise in temperature tends in itself to increase metabolic rate and add to heat. There is, therefore, a tendency for rise in body temperature to be progressive. Air movement, since it increases the heat-carrying capacities of air, may be used to aid in such situations.

Neural mechanism for temperature regulation.   It has been customary for investigators to search for specific anatomical regions in the central nervous system which appear to be critically connected with physiological functions. Temperature regulation of the body is no exception in this re-

[2] Bazett, H. C.: Physiological Responses to Heat, *Physiol. Rev.,* 7: 531–599, 1927.

spect. Centers for temperature regulation have been located in the hypothalamus, as evidenced by the fact that after destruction of much of the hypothalamus, or after severing the major descending pathways at the mammillary level, mammals become poikilothermic.

The neural mechanisms which act to preclude overheating and those which act against chilling are not fully identical. Following destruction of the caudal region of the hypothalamus, exposures to low temperatures are not accompanied by somatic changes that prevent fall in bodily temperature. Muscle tensing, shivering, etc., which are innervated through the cerebrospinal channels, are absent, as well as the signs of sympathetic activity, such as vasoconstriction, piloerection, and medullari-adrenal secretion. When a less caudal region is inactivated, exposure to high temperatures is not followed by reactions providing for the organism's loss of heat, such as vasodilatation, sweating, and, in certain animals, panting and salivation. The region for the prevention of overheating is above and in front of the optic chiasma, while the region acting against chilling is in the more caudal part of the hypothalamus. Some lesions, however, may be so placed as to damage both kinds of reaction.

Of the cooling reactions, only the characteristic salivation of the carnivores is parasympathetic. Cutaneous vasodilatation is attributed to the inhibition of the normal tonic sympathetic discharge, rather than to direct parasympathetic action, since there is no known parasympathetic supply to cutaneous blood vessels. The innervation of the sweat glands is sympathetic although it is cholinergic.

Human temperature regulation as compared with physical heat-regulating devices.   Burton[3] states that the question of initial interest in the consideration of any thermoregulator is the nature of the *controlled variable*. In the case of the organism, the answer is obtained only after more than casual inspection. The human body is not an object that is maintained at an equal temperature throughout, but instead, varies several degrees from surface to interior and is not even uniformly warm at all surface points. Since the temperature gradient involves a depth of an inch or more, about one-half of the body tissue is within this depth. Although deep tissues do not usually vary more than 1°C., the skin may vary 10°. From this picture of variation, it is to be concluded that deep body temperature is the controlled variable.

One would expect to find the device sensitive to temperature at a place that partakes of the controlled temperature. In the body this seems to be

[3] This section follows the discussion by A. C. Burton, The Operating Characteristics of the Human Thermoregulatory Mechanism, in "Temperature, Its Measurement and Control in Science and Industry," Reinhold Publishing Corporation, New York, 1941. Pp. 1362.

the case, for it has been found that the heat-regulating center is in the hypothalamus and that it is sensitive to the temperature of the blood circulating through it. What Burton calls the main *primary elements* of the regulatory mechanism are the temperature receptors in the skin.

The controlled temperature bears no fixed relation to that of the skin receptors. The receptors are sensitive not only to the level of temperature, but to the rate of change and possibly to the skin-internal gradient in temperature. Burton defines the *control agent* by which the nervous system accomplishes regulation of body temperature as the adjustment of the blood flow in the peripheral tissues. This may, at times, vary[4] over a range of 1 to 100. The adjustment of blood flow is brought about by sympathetic action on the walls of the blood vessels. This range between full vasoconstriction and vasodilatation represents a factor of 5 or 6.

Despite constancy of surrounding physical conditions maintained in the laboratory, blood flow in the fingers is not found to rest at any single value. The variation in flow oscillates between high and low values quite rhythmically. As external temperatures increase, the vasodilatation is more complete between successive vasoconstrictions. The interval between constrictions becomes larger until nearly continuous dilatation develops. Thermal demand manipulates both the amplitude and the period of the fluctuations in flow. Although this points toward an "on-off" type of thermocontrol, Burton and Taylor's[5] experiments indicate that the control is of the continuously variable type.

The human organism manifests a *response characteristic*[6] quite opposite to the usual type of physical thermoregulator. The curve picturing this response shows that when the demand is heightened, instead of a momentary drop of the controlled temperature, as is usually the case in the physical regulator, there is nearly always a rise in deep body temperature.[7] This is a result of the particular mode of control.

The human organism manifests what is known as a *load error* or *droop*. There is an alteration of the level of controlled temperature following a change in thermal demand from the surroundings.

[4] Burton, A. C.: The Range and Variability of the Blood Flow in the Human Fingers and the Vasomotor Regulations of Body Temperatures, *Am. J. Physiol.*, *127*: 437–453, 1939.

[5] Burton, A. C., and R. M. Taylor: A Study of the Adjustment of Peripheral Vascular Tone to the Requirements of the Regulation of Body Temperature, *Am. J. Physiol.*, *129*: 565–577, 1940.

[6] Response characteristic is the type of disturbance shown when the thermal demand abruptly changes.

[7] Burton, A. C., and H. C. Bazett: A Study of the Average Temperature of the Tissues, of the Exchange of Heat and Vasomotor Responses in Man by Means of a Bath Calorimeter, *Am. J. Physiol.*, *117*: 36–54, 1936.

To complete the comparison between the organism and the ordinary thermoregulatory systems, Burton points out that the organism possesses what might be looked upon as a *reset mechanism*. In inanimate systems, thermoregulators are supplied with automatic reset devices, to make load errors as small as possible. The physiological characteristics that have been taken as comparable to this are represented in the fact that the thermoregulatory center in the brain is directly sensitive to the temperature of the blood flowing through it. Load errors may be made minimal by the employment of this direct sensitivity in conjunction with the peripheral receptors, rather than by the employment of receptors exclusively.

In this comparison between "physical" thermoregulators and the organism, there is no recognition of other factors that may operate on the organism concurrently with temperature changes. In order to acquire an adequate picture of organismic temperature regulation, the whole organism and all its activities at any one time must be considered together. Such a broad scheme is necessary, since much the same tissue operation in temperature regulation is reacting to other influences at the same time. Since the character of the temperature regulation varies greatly under the influence of nonthermal conditions, these should be systematically taken into account in fully defining temperature regulation.

Vascular reactions.   Exposure to low temperature slows the pulse and enhances the volume of the stroke. The minute volume remains the same until the conditions become extreme and shivering occurs. Both the output and the pulse rate then increase. Exposure to high temperature is commonly accompanied by a markedly increased cardiac output with an increased pulse rate but a slightly decreased stroke volume.[8] Prolonged exposure to high temperatures leading to dehydration is accompanied by a resumption of basal cardiac output in the face of high oxygen consumption and rapid pulse rate. Venous return is then insufficient.

When the surroundings are very warm, the superficial vessels are called upon to dilate to increase heat loss. It would seem that central vessels would have to constrict, or the volume of blood increase, or both. Actually, central constriction is the predominant reaction. This probably takes the form of constriction of large veins and centrally located arterioles, which in turn increases the arterial pressure via the concurrent increase in effective peripheral resistance. Some increase in blood volume may also occur, but this is limited and produces a reduction in plasma-protein concentration. Continuous demand for added blood volume seems to be followed by increase in the quantity of plasma protein to restore a balance while allowing for the added volume.

[8] Bard, Philip, in "MacLeod's Physiology in Modern Medicine," 9th ed., C. V. Mosby Company, Medical Publishers, St. Louis, 1941. Pp. 1256.

Cutaneous temperature is dependent upon blood flow, but flow is not directly related to the number and caliber of the vessels. A warm, pale skin is the concomitant of a relatively rapid circulation with capillary and venule constriction. On the other hand, a cold, pale skin represents a state in which the arterioles are also constricted. A ruddy, cold skin under exposure to low temperatures is concurrent with arteriole constriction and a sluggish blood flow through the dilated capillaries and venules. Dilated superficial vessels account for greater difficulty in the return of blood to the heart in standing postures. Pulse rate increases, stroke volume decreases, and mean blood pressure may fall. When adaptation to higher temperatures has been accomplished, changes upon standing may diminish. This diminution seems to occur in connection with increased blood volume, in which case the pooling of blood in the limbs has less significance.

At high temperatures even without muscular exertion, the individual becomes uncomfortable. Postural tone is at a minimum. Lassitude predominates. With exertion, difficulties are bound to become more acute, and fatigue may arise. In some cases, however, collapse may intervene before any considerable fatigue has developed. Fatigue and proximity to collapse are not directly related.

The temperature of the surroundings may become such a critical condition that the main trend of physiological events is aimed at cooling the body, rather than providing the blood distribution that is most effective for muscular exertion.

Methods used in temperature studies. The study of the various effects of external temperature requires the understanding of the factors involved. In the precise study of these effects, certain arbitrarily limited ranges and combinations of conditions have been selected and diverse techniques used. Some investigators have compared nude and clothed subjects over limited temperature ranges. Some have investigated the effects of air motion and relative humidity. Some have been interested in conditions of extreme heat and dryness.

Adolph[9] studied the effects of producing negative heat loads. Winslow, Herrington, and Gagge, using the method of partitional calorimetry,[10] placed subjects in a booth in a reclining position. The setup provided for the maintenance of wide differences between radiation and convection. Temperature and humidity were precisely manipulated by an air-conditioning system. Winslow, Herrington, and Gagge were able to make a com-

[9] Adolph, E. F.: "Physiological Regulations," The Jaques Cattell Press, Lancaster, Pa., 1943. Pp. 502.

[10] Winslow, C.-E. A., L. P. Herrington, and A. P. Gagge: A New Method of Partitional Calorimetry, *Am. J. Physiol., 116:* 641–655, 1936, and following papers.

plete partition of thermal exchange between the body and its surroundings.

They showed that it is possible to combine transfer by radiation and convection into a single term. The temperature derived from combining the radiation and convection constants was called the "operative temperature." It represents the net physical effect of the ambient air temperature and that of the surrounding walls.

Sweat secretion was dealt with by these authors in the following way. The amount of moisture evaporated from the body was ascertained by manipulation of air temperatures and relative humidities and converted to evaporative heat loss per unit skin area. The kilogram-calories per square meter per hour of evaporative heat loss per centimeter of mercury pressure difference between cutaneous and air moistures was calculated. The values arrived at are known as the "wetted area" and are taken as a measure of the quantity of moisture on the skin if sweat were evenly distributed. The maximum cooling effect from evaporation would be expected when the skin of the whole body is completely and uniformly covered with a thin layer of water. Since sweat is unevenly secreted, the limiting evaporative value is not reached. The minimum value of 3 kcal. was found at low temperatures. This is the evaporation occurring from the skin without sweating. (Water lost this way is known as the "insensible water loss.")

Heat exchange. Pinson and Adolph[11] measured heat exchanges in subjects who sat unclothed in air at 31°C., the relative humidity of which was 25 per cent. When 1½ l. of ice water was ingested, body heat was reduced by 0.72 Cal. per kg. In 3⅓ hours, 85 per cent of the original heat debt was paid off. One-half of this came by way of reduction in the loss by evaporation, the other half by reduction in loss by radiation and convection which accompanied diminished body surface temperatures. During this time, heat production by oxidation was not increased, and no shivering was induced. In some cases, water diuresis was delayed. Average production of heat of the four subjects varied as much as 16 per cent, but this was not consistently related in time to the drinking of the cold water.

The data of Winslow, Herrington, and Gagge[12] also showed that alteration in heat production was not induced even under conditions of distinct deficit. They found no material alteration over a range of 16 to 42°C., even with deficits of 1.0 to 1.5 Cal. per kg.

11 Pinson, E. A., and E. F. Adolph: Heat Exchanges during Recovery from Experimental Deficit of Body Heat, *Am. J. Physiol., 136:* 105–114, 1942.

12 Winslow, C.-E. A., L. P. Herrington, and A. P. Gagge: Physiological Reactions of the Human Body to Varying Environmental Temperatures, *Am. J. Physiol., 120:* 1–22, 1937.

Still earlier findings[13] showed that heat production was increased only when shivering took place or during muscular activity. Cannon and co-workers[14] found that their clothed subjects, without shivering, increased heat production as much as 10 per cent at a room temperature of 20°C. after developing a heat debt of about .45 Cal. per kg. With shivering, as much as a 90 per cent increase in production was found. Heat conservation is clearly more marked than added heat production when exercise does not occur.

Shivering and voluntary exercise have similar effects on radiation, convection, evaporation, and on skin and rectal temperatures.[15] When the naked individual lies still at a temperature of 22 to 25°C., rectal temperature drops 0.2 to 0.5°C. in 120 to 180 minutes, while the skin temperature drops about 3°. Shivering usually occurs, accompanied by a slight rise in average skin temperature. The individual is thereby warmed enough not to shiver again for about an hour. At comfortable temperatures (about 27°C.) exercise results in a definite increase in the percentage of heat loss by evaporation. Below this temperature level, exercise results in slight or no such change. By convection increased by limb movement in shivering and exercise, the body may lose more heat through a cool skin than through a warm one.

With violent exertion, the rectal temperature may rise and the skin temperature fall. Hardy and coworkers cite the rise of rectal temperature to 39°C. at the end of 36 minutes of playing squash, with a fall in skin temperature of 3°C. After a 40-minute rest, the two temperatures converge to their former levels. Exercise does not always induce the same rise in body temperature, owing to a shift in the behavior of the "heat-loss regulator." This regulator is different in malaria, for instance, than in normal states.

Functional zones in the temperature range. The findings of Hardy and Soderstrom[16] and those of Gagge, Herrington, and Winslow[17] will serve as indications of bodily reactions at various temperature levels. Both groups made their measurements on resting unclothed subjects. Both

[13] Loewy, A.: Über den Einfluss der Abkühlung auf den Gaswechsel des Menschen, *Pflüger's Arch. f. d. ges. Physiol., 46:* 189–244, 1890.

[14] Cannon, W. B., A. Querido, S. W. Britton, and E. M. Bright: Studies on the Conditions of Activity in Endocrine Glands, *Am. J. Physiol., 79:* 466–507, 1926.

[15] Hardy, J. D., A. T. Milhorst, and E. F. DuBois: The Effects of Exercise and Chills on Heat Loss from the Nude Body, *J. Nutrition, 16:* 477–492, 1938.

[16] Hardy, J. D., and C. F. Soderstrom: Heat Loss from the Nude Body and Peripheral Blood Flow at Temperatures of 22°C. to 35°C., *J. Nutrition, 16:* 493–510, 1938.

[17] Gagge, A. P., L. P. Herrington, and C.-E. A. Winslow: Thermal Interchanges between the Human Body and Its Atmospheric Environment, *Am. J. Hygiene, 26:* 84–103, 1937.

found three general ranges of temperature each of which was characterized quite definitely with respect to how the individual behaved physiologically. These are shown in Fig. 10.

Hardy and Soderstrom designate the range lying between 28 and 30 or 31°C. (82 to 88°F.) as the *neutral zone*. In this range, they say, heat loss is adjusted by shifts in peripheral blood circulation, and the resting individual does not sweat. Comfort is at its greatest, and heat loss is at its low-

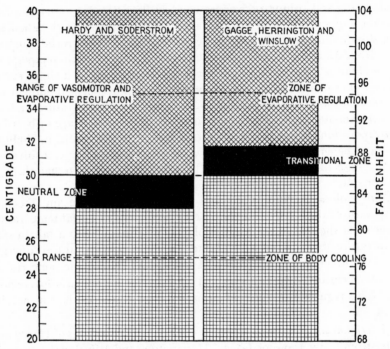

Fig. 10.—The functional zones of temperature, as specified by Hardy and Soderstrom and by Gagge, Herrington and Winslow.

est. Gagge, Herrington, and Winslow specify a zone lying between 86 and 89°F. as a transitional zone or a "zone of thermal neutrality." In this range, they report, the heat losses by radiation and convection and by evaporation are initially equal, each being about 20 to 25 kcal. per sq. m. per hr. and just compensating the heat produced by metabolism. Hardy and Soderstrom specify a *cold range* (below 28°C., or 82°F.) in which they say no regulation of heat loss occurs. The body loses heat simply as a physical object. Drop in skin temperature as surroundings cool is simply a physical cooling unmodified by additional vasoconstriction. Thermal conductivity of tissues near the surface is constant at 0.0005 gm.-cal. per sq. m. per °C.

per cm. Blood flow is constant to the skin at a rate of 0.015 cc. per min. per sq. cm.

Gagge, Herrington, and Winslow also designate a cold range, or "zone of body cooling," beginning at about 86°F. In it, evaporative heat loss drops but slightly with fall of "operative temperature," mainly owing to diminishing vapor pressure of the moisture in the atmosphere. The evaporative heat loss in this zone is about 15 kcal. per sq. m. per hr. Heat loss from radiation and convection does not diminish with decreasing operative temperatures as rapidly as in the warmer zones, because of a gradual fall in skin temperature which lessens the difference between it and the temperature of the surroundings.

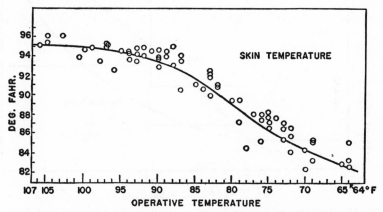

FIG. 11.—The relation of skin temperature to operative temperature. (*Gagge, Herrington and Winslow: Am. J. Hyg.*)

The adjustment is found to be imperfect, and throughout this "cooling-off zone," "positive storage" is occurring at a rate increasing directly with increase in heat loss by radiation plus convection. Evaporate heat loss drops only slightly between 31 and 25.5°C. Below this range in which the heat demand of the surroundings balances the sum of metabolism and minimal evaporative heat, while no further drop occurs, skin temperature begins to fall, and this provides protection. In the operative range from 31 to 20°C., skin temperature falls from about 34.5 to 29°C. In a drop of skin temperature from 35 to 32°, conductance[18] is said to be reduced to about one-half (see Fig. 11).

The third zone lies above 30°C. (86°F.) in the Hardy-Soderstrom study.

[18] Conductance is an index of fluctuations in peripheral blood flow, used by Winslow *et al.* The heat flux per unit skin area is the sum of metabolism and "storage" divided by body-surface area. If this heat flux is divided by the difference between skin and rectal temperature, the result is the heat flux per unit gradient drop in temperature.

It is called the *range of vasomotor and evaporative regulation*. In this range, blood flow to the periphery rises with temperature. Evaporation is said to rise, but not strictly in proportion to temperature. Skin temperature rises only slightly, and heat loss increases but slowly. Even though cooling is sufficient, comfort diminishes.

Gagge, Herrington, and Winslow call the high range the *zone of evaporative regulation*. In its storage remains virtually at zero—the body is not heating up. As operative temperatures rise beyond 89°F., heat loss by radia-

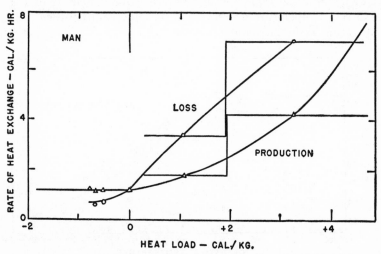

FIG. 12.—The rate of heat exchange in relation to heat load. Total heat equilibrium diagram. Heat storage estimated from rectal temperatures alone. Heat output was the sum of vaporization (from weight loss), radiation (from radiometric sampling) and convection (estimated) during period of 0.32 hour. Heat production was estimated from output plus storage. (*Adolph: "Physiological Regulations," Jaques Cattell Press.*)

tion plus convection diminishes, and above 95°F. radiation and convection become positive, producing a net gain in body heat from the walls and air. This gain and the heat produced by metabolism are perfectly offset by a concomitant increase in vaporization.

Adolph[19] gives curves to indicate the relations of exchange to heat load.[20] His equilibrium diagram (Fig. 12) shows that gains and losses are equal at only one point, *viz.*, when there is zero heat load. Balance may exist when the heat content of the body is unusual, but whatever it is, the rates

19 Adolph, *op. cit.*

20 Load is defined as any departure from the control content. It may thus be negative or positive. Heat load is the difference in degrees centigrade per kilogram from the control (B_0) multiplied by 0.83, the mean specific heat capacity of human tissues.

of both exchanges (loss and gain) are greater than basal ones. Usual balances are defined by Adolph as those in which the oral or rectal temperatures are the average found in a random population. Over-all gain is greater than over-all loss in deficit states, and is less than over-all loss in states of excess.

In Fig. 13 the rate of total heat loss in relation to heat load during recovery is shown. The diagram shows also the partitions or avenues by which the loss occurs. The curves indicate that up to a certain point, as

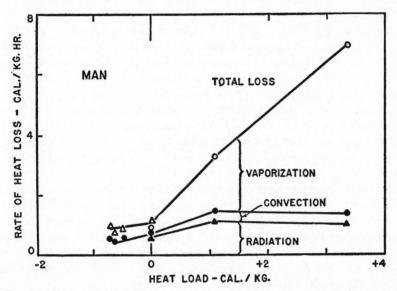

Fig. 13.—The rate of total heat loss and its partition in relation to heat loading during recovery. Vaporization is latent heat loss; convection plus radiation is sensible heat loss. The positive heat load in this case was created by physical exertion indoors. (*Adolph: "Physiological Regulations," Jaques Cattell Press.*)

load increases, all three factors, vaporization, convection, and radiation, increase, but beyond this vaporization alone increases. At all loads, vaporization is greater than either of the other two factors.

Gosselin[21] measured the heat absorbed from desert surroundings by acclimatized soldiers wearing full uniform during "standard" activity. These subjects were exposed to early afternoon sun at dry-bulb temperatures of 90 to 110°F., with air-movement velocities about 8 miles per hour. Under such conditions, all sweat evaporated. The individual of average size absorbed about 200 Cal. per hr. In this temperature range, the gain was about

[21] Gosselin, R. E.: Heat Gains by Man in the Desert, *Proc. Fed. Am. Soc. Exper. Biol.,* *4:* 25, 1945.

11 Cal. per hr. for each degree rise in air temperature. Apparently this gain was not noticeably affected by rate of activity so long as the individual remained clothed and in the sun. The readings were the same when the subject walked, stood, or remained seated. With only shoes and under-shorts as clothing, the gain was 100 to 140 Cal. greater per hour. Clothed men in the shade gained variable amounts of thermal protection by the shading ranging from 50 to 100 Cal. per hr. At night, with the same air temperature (100°F.), heat gains were 100 Cal. per hr. less than during afternoon sunlight, this being equivalent to a reduction of 9°F. in air temperature.

Sweating as a method of heat regulation and dissipation. The high specific heat of water enables considerable amounts of heat to be carried by the blood stream to cooling surfaces, where the high heat of vaporiza-tion permits the dissipation of heat at skin surfaces. The organism's chief means of heat dissipation is sweating, or the evaporation of water from the body surfaces. About 580 kcal. is involved in the evaporation of 1 l. of water at a skin temperature of 33°C.[22] This is approximately the amount of heat produced by the body processes in 1 hour of fairly hard work. Hard work in hot dry surroundings may evaporate one and one-half or more liters.

Sweating is not passively controlled by the mere combination of physical conditions, but is dependent upon active nervous regulation. The human body surface has two different types of sweat glands, the large apocrine glands occurring mainly in the auxiliary and pubic regions, and the small eccrine glands distributed over the rest of the body surface. The latter secrete mainly a dilute solution of sodium chloride and urea. The former secrete other substances as well.

Sweating pertains not only to temperature regulation. It is a reflex eli-cited by several sets of conditions. Besides (1) the thermoregulatory form, there are (2) "emotional" sweating, (3) gustatory sweating, and (4) spinal-reflex sweating.[23] Thermoregulatory sweating is general in its dis-tribution, while the other forms are more or less localized.

Gustatory sweating is confined to the face. Spinal-reflex sweating is a pathological form occurring in the cutaneous area supplied by the severed part of the spinal cord in cases of transverse syndrome. This reaction is a spinal reflex automatism.

The sweat glands activated by temperature conditions are innervated sympathetically and are not directly excitable by the physical conditions

[22] Dill, D. B.: "Life, Heat and Altitude," Harvard University Press, Cambridge, Mass., 1938. Pp. 211.

[23] List, C. F.: Sweat Secretion in Man: I. Sweating Responses in Normal Persons, *Arch. Neurol. & Psychiat., 39:* 1228-1237, 1938.

of the surroundings. Whenever sweat glands in a given skin area are deprived of their innervation, sweating ceases.[24] Cutaneous blood supply ordinarily contributes to sweating, but it may occur in the absence of circulation, as when amputated limbs are made to sweat by nervous stimulation. Vasoconstrictor action also seems to have a relation to sweating, for adrenine, which produces vasoconstriction, reduces sweating, just as does cooling of the skin.

The usual condition for profuse sweating is high external temperature or muscular activity, which tends to increase *body* temperature. But high temperature at the site of the glands alone neither activates them nor the efferent nerve fibers that supply them. It is the sensory cutaneous nerves, those through which we experience environmental temperature, that are activated. The sweat glands are then activated reflexly, through their supply from the sympathetic nervous system.

Body-surface exposure to high temperatures elevates the temperature of the blood, resulting in excitation of the autonomic sweat centers in the medulla or in the diencephalon. This elicits general perspiration acting to maintain the usual body temperature. Spinal centers involved in the innervation of the sweat glands also respond to increased blood temperature. The sweat centers also respond to shifts in the acid-base balance of the blood.

Dill and colleagues,[25] who made studies on sweating at Boulder City, Nev., made the following conclusions:

1. The character of sweat differs, depending upon rate of production, degree of acclimation, personal idiosyncrasy, environmental temperature, amount of exertion, and amount of exposure to the sun. In hot weather, salt loss is great, both on account of the amount of sweat and its high concentration of salt.

2. Although lactic acid is secreted in sweat, it seems to be of little significance in muscular exertion, since the only kind of exertion that raises the lactic acid level in the blood induces exhaustion before the sweat glands have opportunity to dissipate much of it.

3. The rate of sweating is not accurately adjusted to organic needs; some individuals undergo uncomfortable increases in body temperature from lag in sweating.

4. Adaptation to high temperatures includes an enhanced production of sweat, an increased sensitivity of the temperature regulation mechanism, and an economy in losing salt.

[24] Kuntz, A.: "The Autonomic Nervous System," Lea & Febiger, Philadelphia, 1929. Pp. 576.
[25] Dill, D. B., B. F. Jones, H. T. Edwards, and S. S. Oberg: Salt Economy in Extreme Dry Heat, *J. Biol. Chem.*, 100: 755–767, 1933.

5. Chronic effects of heat are not solely concerned with sweat reactions and temperature regulation. Untoward symptoms may appear even when these mechanisms seem to operate adequately.

Adolph and Dill[26] studied water exchange under conditions of a mean shade temperature of 96°F. with maximums of 109.4°F. The mean humidity was 12 per cent, and the range covered percentages from 6 to 30. They found more than an eightfold increase in sweat output, along with decrease in sweat concentration. The urine became chloride-free at evaporation rates of about 1,600 cc. per hr. and also when urine excretion was reduced to 10 cc. per hr. Water intake rose from three to six times the usual amount and was quite precisely adjusted to antecedent water losses. While the burro under the same conditions would drink rapidly enough to restore previous losses in a few minutes, restoration in man was much slower. Water content was found to be quite uniform from one 24-hour interval to another. During this time the daily water turnover ranged between ten and thirty times the daily fluctuation in body weight.

Perspiration occurring during periods of exertion in cold surroundings is only partly effective in inducing immediate cooling of the skin. A very large fraction is recondensed in the clothing usually worn. This recontributes some heat to the body. To offset this, the total amount of sweating is augmented. During rest which follows this perod of exertion, the moisture existing in the clothing tends to be reevaporated, this in turn taking heat from the body. Since it is then that maximum conservation of heat is necessary, the evaporation is particularly unfavorable. Belding, Folk, Forbes, and Darling[27] studied an electrically heated dummy "man" dressed in an Arctic outfit, at 0°F., to ascertain the influence of reevaporation of moisture from clothing upon heat loss. With 1,300 gm. of water put into the underclothing and socks each day for 10 days, about 18 Cal. per sq. m. per hr. were taken from the body by evaporation. This amount is three times the heat lost through insensible perspiration. It is a 50 per cent addition over the dry-clothing requirement of the sitting individual. Sweating was reduced from a rate of 350 to 400 gm. per hr. to as little as 50 gm. By reducing the clothing from an Arctic outfit to underwear, socks, and shoes, men worked hard enough at 0°F. to raise metabolism to six or seven times the basal rate. This shows the practicality of reducing clothing considerably during exertion in cold surroundings.

Insensible water loss. Along with water loss by perspiration via the sweat glands, a certain amount passes through the skin itself. According

[26] Adolph, E. F., and D. B. Dill: Observations on Water Metabolism in the Desert, *Am. J. Physiol., 123:* 369–378, 1938.

[27] Belding, H. S., G. E. Folk, W. H. Forbes, and R. C. Darling: Secretion and Evaporation of Sweat in Cold Weather, *Proc. Fed. Am. Soc. Exper. Biol., 4:* 7, 1945.

to Kuno,[28] this is quite uniform in amount over the entire body, aside from the palms of the hands and the soles of the feet. The rate of loss by this avenue varies but little and is not dependent upon sweat-gland activity.

The rest of the insensible water loss occurs from the lungs and respiratory passages. Its amount depends upon the exertion rate and outside conditions. The *expired* air is relatively uniform in composition, saturated at about 33°C., although *inspired* air may vary greatly in saturation, in temperature, and in volume. Ordinarily, water loss through respiration is about one-third of the insensible loss total.

Heat limits, humidity, and clothing. Humidity limits the more free exchange of heat when the exchange is from body to surroundings and accelerates the exchange when it is in the opposite direction. Dampness reduces vaporization, thus hindering the first type of exchange; damp air tends to dampen clothing, thereby increasing its conductivity of heat in the second type of exchange. It thus retards exchange when it ought to be accelerated and accelerates it when it ought to be minimized. Humidity plays an important role in limiting conditions for comfort, activity, and even for survival.

The studies of the effects of high humidity made by the armed forces furnish us with the most recent material. Shelley, Eichna, and Horvath[29] claim that the wet-bulb temperature is the limiting factor for activity. Their first study was made on nude subjects. Their second study was made on men clothed in a two-piece herringbone twill coverall. Twelve young men acclimatized to hot surroundings performed a daily work task of 4 hours of marching at 3 miles per hour, carrying 20-lb. packs. For this an energy expenditure of about 250 to 300 Cal. per hr. was required. Hourly heart rates, rectal temperatures, sweat losses, and skin temperatures at the outset and termination of task were recorded. They found that the single layer of herringbone twill imposed a heat load equivalent to an elevation of 2 to 4°F. Thus the unclothed men could work at wet-bulb temperatures 2 to 4°F. higher than could men clothed as described. They state that when the dry-bulb temperature is 120°F. the men were able to work nude at a wet-bulb temperature of 92°F. (relative humidity, 34 per cent). With the same dry-bulb temperature they would be able to work clothed only if the wet-bulb temperature did not rise beyond 88 to 90°F.

[28] Kuno, Yas: "The Physiology of Human Perspiration," J. and A. Churchill, London, 1934. Pp. 268.

[29] Shelley, W. B., L. W. Eichna, and S. M. Horvath: Effect of Clothing on the Ability of Acclimatized Men to Work at the Upper Limits of Environmental Heat, *Proc. Fed. Am. Soc. Exper. Biol.,* 4: 64, 1945.

At the end of the experiment the rectal temperature for the nude sub-jects was 99.7°F., and for the clothed it was 1° higher. The final heart rate for the nude was 115 per minute, whereas it was 135 for the clothed. The final skin temperature of the former was 97.0°F. and of the latter, 97.9°F. The clothed subjects manifested a larger sweat loss. They lost 1,419 gm. per hr. whereas the nude subjects lost only 1,125 gm.

Winslow[30] states that if the temperature of the environment is above the optimum, but below 95°F., the nude human body can adjust to a

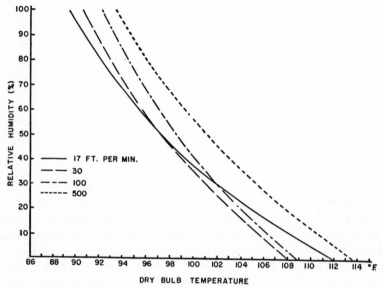

FIG. 14.—The upper limits ("wetted area" = 100 per cent) of the zone of evaporative regulation for various air velocities. (*Gagge, Herrington and Wins-low: Am. J. Hyg.*)

higher relative humidity than the clothed. But he suggests that clothing may provide advantage at environmental temperatures higher than this. In such circumstances, the body is absorbing heat from the air by convec-tion. Clothing limits this and at the same time increases evaporative loss by increase of evaporation surface. This accounts for the protection cloth-ing offers against the dry intense heat of the desert.

Upper limits of evaporative heat loss. There is a point at which sweat is produced in such abundance as to run off without evaporating, and thus

[30] Winslow, C.-E. A.: "Man's Heat Exchange with His Thermal Environment," in "Temperature, Its Measurement and Control in Science and Industry," Reinhold Pub-lishing Corporation, New York, 1941. Pp. 1362.

the excess cannot be used for evaporative cooling. Winslow[31] states that this point corresponds to about 30 kcal. of heat loss per square meter per hour per centimeter of mercury vapor pressure difference between skin and air.

For example, from his findings, Winslow calculates that, for a certain arbitrary metabolism at 45°C. (110.3°F.), the relative humidity can be taken advantage of by the nude subject until it becomes as low as 1 per cent and by the clothed subject, only as low as 18 per cent. At lower sur-

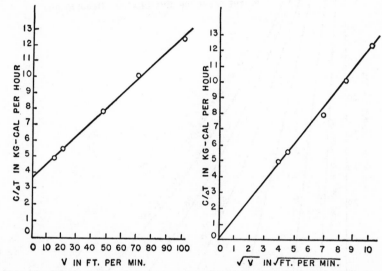

FIG. 15.—The relation between convection loss (C) and difference between skin temperature and air temperature (Δ T) plotted against air velocity and against the square root of air velocity. (Gagge, Herrington and Winslow: Am. J. Hyg.)

rounding temperatures, the relative conditions for nude and clothed subjects are reversed. For instance, at 32.5°C. (90+°F.), the air can be saturated before the limit is reached by the nude subject, while the relative humidity need only be 89 per cent for the same metabolism in the clothed subject.

The influence of air movement on the upper limits of evaporative heat loss has been calculated by Gagge, Herrington, and Winslow.[32] Figure 14 shows that with high relative humidities and comparatively low external

[31] Ibid.
[32] Gagge, A. P., L. P. Herrington, and C.-E. A. Winslow: Thermal Interchanges between the Human Body and Its Atmospheric Environment, Am. J. Hygiene, 26: 84–102, 1937.

temperatures the cooling effect on the nude body varies quite uniformly with external temperature. With high external temperatures and low relative humidities this is not the case. With air above skin temperature, the effect of increased air velocity is to augment both heat *gain* by convection, as well as evaporative heat *loss* (see also Fig. 15 and 16).

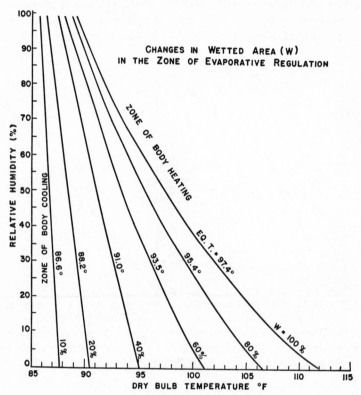

FIG. 16.—The variations in biothermally equivalent temperature and "wetted area" in relation to air temperature and relative humidity in the zone of evaporative regulation. (*Gagge, Herrington and Winslow: Am. J. Hyg.*)

Discomfort and physical conditions. Winslow, Herrington, and Gagge[33] have studied the relations of thermal balance and sensation. Correlations between physical conditions, physiological reactions, and reports of pleasantness ("comfort votes") turned out to be much higher than they had expected.

33 Winslow, C.-E. A., L. P. Herrington, and A. P. Gagge: Relations between Atmospheric Conditions, Physiological Reactions, and Sensations of Pleasantness, *Am. J. Hygiene, 26:* 103-115, 1937.

In this experiment, using the partitional calorimetry setup already mentioned, the subjects were asked to rate the atmospheric conditions, using the following five-point scale: (1) very pleasant, (2) pleasant, (3) indifferent, (4) unpleasant, and (5) very unpleasant. These ratings were found

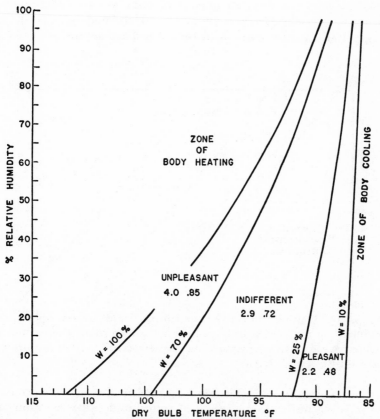

FIG. 17.—The limiting "wetted areas" associated with certain experiences of pleasantness (in the zone of evaporative regulation) in relation to air temperature and relative humidity. (*Winslow, Herrington and Gagge: Am. J. Hyg.*)

to be quite self-consistent. Skin temperature could be predicted from the subjective reports of discomfort. In hot surroundings, the subjective reports were closely related to secretion of sweat.

For the unclothed semireclining subject there is a middle zone, at which mean skin temperature lies between 88 and 92° F., in which conditions are reported pleasant. In this range, cooling of the body and measures of sweat secretion ("wetted area") are both low. Below this range, skin temperature falls, heat loss increases (storage), and discomfort rapidly increases. Above the middle range, when skin temperature exceeds 92°F. and evaporation increases, the experience of unpleasantness also becomes intense. This results despite the fact that thermal balance is well maintained by accentuated sweating. This is pictured in Figs. 17, 18, and 19.

Reactions of the clothed individual. Whereas most of the information given in the preceding sections has to do with the nude subject, the following pertains to the results with the clothed subject under analogous

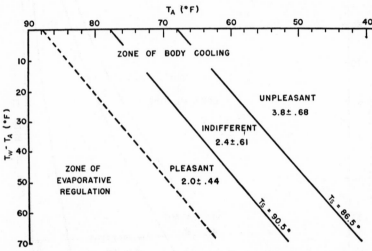

Fig. 18.—The limiting skin temperature associated with certain experiences of pleasantness (in the zone of body cooling) in relation to air temperature and difference between wall temperature and air temperature. (*Winslow, Herrington and Gagge: Am. J. Hyg.*)

experimental conditions.[34] The clothing used in the experiments about to be reported was a two-piece suit of cotton underwear, a cotton shirt minus necktie, socks, low leather shoes, and a dark-gray suit with three-quarter lining and a fully lined vest.

Some of the points used for measuring body-surface temperature were on the head and hands, which were exposed, whereas others were protected by clothing. The standard air velocity was 5 m. per min., and except in the specific studies on humidity, humidity was kept between 40 and 50 per cent.

In the clothed subject, thermal equilibrium is maintained when the

[34] Gagge, A. P., C.-E. A. Winslow, and L. P. Herrington: The Influence of Clothing on the Physiological Reactions of the Human Body to Varying Environmental Temperatures, *Am. J. Physiol., 124:* 30–50, 1938.

surface temperature[35] is between 25 and 29°C. Above this, evaporative regulation begins. The comparable level for the nude subject is 29°C.

Under the conditions studied, it was found that loss of heat by evaporation takes place at the skin surface rather than in the folds of the clothing. The thermal demand of the surroundings accordingly acts ultimately on

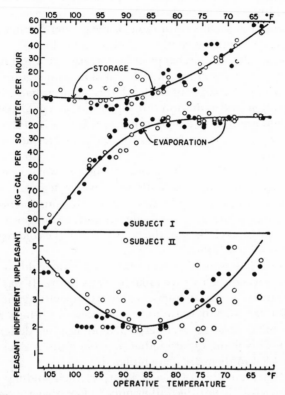

Fig. 19.—The relations of storage, evaporation and experience of pleasantness to operative temperature in subject I (pyknic) and subject II (leptosomic). (*Winslow, Herrington and Gagge: Am. J. Hyg.*)

the skin in both the clothed and unclothed subjects. In relating the various physiological factors to thermal demands, the physiological reactions were found to be broadly similar in both the nude and clothed subjects.

In the temperature zone of body cooling, for thermal demands exceeding 30 kcal. per sq. m. per hr., the mean skin temperature for both clothed and unclothed subjects is the same. But considering the various portions

[35] Surface temperature is the temperature measured on the surface whether this be on the clothing or on the skin.

of the body separately, this is not true. The head temperatures are identical. For both upper and lower limbs, the skin temperatures of the clothed subjects are lower than for the unclothed. The skin temperature of the trunk is higher in the clothed subject.

In the temperature range of evaporative regulation, for thermal demands below 25 kcal. per sq. m. per hr., the loss by evaporation increases in both the clothed and unclothed subjects in the same way. The difference in reaction in this temperature zone is the greater rise in skin temperature and thermal conductance in the clothed individuals.

Thermal demands for interchange of heat as regulated by radiation and convection are somewhat different.[36] Mean skin temperatures are lower for cold-air warm-wall situations in the clothed subject than when the two factors, convection and radiation, are operating at equal temperatures. The chief difference in skin temperatures in this case is in the lower temperatures of the two extremities. Trunk temperatures are more nearly alike in the two cases.

Conductance of the skin is much less for the cold-air warm-wall conditions than when warm air and walls are alike in temperature. This is particularly true at upper temperature regions. In consequence of higher skin temperatures, heating of the body (negative storage) is greater at high temperatures and chilling of the body is less in the cold region for the cold-air warm-wall conditions.

"Wetted area" is less at high temperatures for the cold-air warm-wall conditions than when the two are alike in temperature. It was found that personal discomfort is less at high ranges of temperature and greater in cold ranges for the cold-air warm-wall conditions. Such facts as these are pertinent to understanding architectural and heating design in which heating systems involving diffuse radiation from walls or floors by piping systems embedded in them are contemplated.

Winslow, Herrington, and Gagge[37] interpret their findings to indicate that vasoconstriction is not the "all-or-none" affair that it has commonly been interpreted to be. They suspect that after vasoconstriction has set in the human body does not act simply like any other physical body, but that there are fundamental physiological adjustments still in operation in keeping with variations in demand in the very cold temperature zone.

Winslow, Herrington, and Gagge[38] also studied the influence of atmos-

[36] Winslow, C.-E. A., L. P. Herrington, and A. P. Gagge: The Relative Influence of Radiation and Convection upon the Temperature Regulation of the Clothed Body, *Am. J. Physiol., 124:* 51–61, 1938.

[37] *Ibid.*

[38] Winslow, C.-E. A., L. P. Herrington, and A. P. Gagge: The Reactions of the Clothed Human Body to Variations in Atmospheric Humidity, *Am. J. Physiol., 124:* 692–703, 1938.

pheric humidity upon the clothed subject. The range they covered lay between 12 and 18 per cent. Comparisons were made with findings on the nude subject.

In the temperature zone of body cooling (with external temperatures less than about 25°C.), sweating and "wetted area" are at their minimum. Relative humidity thus is a scarcely appreciable factor upon physiological adjustments. As the relative humidity rises from 20 or 25 per cent to 75 or 80 per cent, the evaporative heat loss is less by an amount equal to that produced by a rise in only about one-half degree centigrade.

"Wetted area" of the clothed subject increases as surrounding temperature rises above 25°C. The greater the relative humidity, the higher the rate of increase. Up to about 32°C., reasonable adjustment to decreases in caloric demand are made. The authors assign this to the greater numbers of sweat glands coming into action, rather than to physical processes understood in terms of increase in area of a uniform layer of water over the skin. Rises in deep body temperature rather than in skin temperature are thought to account for this change.

As was stated in a previous section, the upper limit of evaporative cooling occurs when about 30 kcal. per sq. m. per cm. of mercury pressure of difference in vapor pressure between skin and surroundings are lost. This holds true for the clothed as well as the nude body. With very low humidity this point is reached at just over 43°C. in the nude subject. In the clothed subject, it is reached at 52°C. with minimum relative humidity. When relative humidity is high, the reverse relations between nude and clothed subjects hold true.

Comfort and health conditions as considered by engineers. Heating and air-conditioning engineers have given the matters of temperature and humidity consideration from the standpoints of comfort and health. To picture the thermodynamics of air, they use a form of psychometric chart, the elements of which are indicated in Fig. 20.

Raber and Hutchinson[39] give a diagram of the comfort and health zones on the psychrometric chart derived from the results of experimental work of the American Society of Heating and Ventilating Engineers. This diagram is reproduced in Fig. 21 and applies to conditions within buildings.

It is stated by Raber and Hutchinson that, at relative humidities outside the ranges indicated, the individual is likely to find the surroundings uncomfortable even though the cooling power of the air is sufficient. Radiation from floors, ceilings, and walls is a factor to be considered in conjunction with air conditions.

The amount the winter comfort zone on the chart differs from the sum-

[39] Raber, B. F., and F. W. Hutchinson: "Refrigeration and Air Conditioning Engineering," John Wiley & Sons, Inc., New York, 1945. Pp. 291.

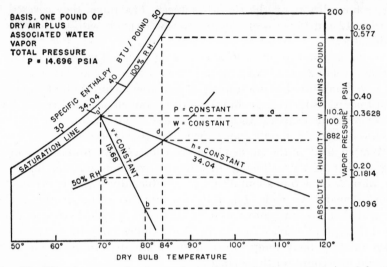

FIG. 20.—The elements of a form of psychrometric chart. (*Reprinted by permission from Raber and Hutchinson: "Refrigeration and Air Conditioning Engineering," John Wiley & Sons, Inc.*)

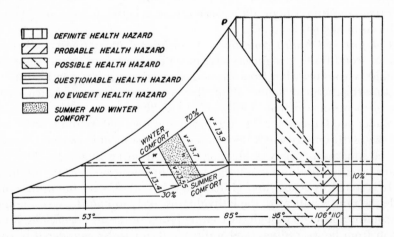

FIG. 21.—Raber and Hutchinson's abbreviated psychrometric chart showing regions of human comfort in summer and winter in terms of specific volume of air and relative humidity. (*Reprinted by permission from Raber and Hutchinson: "Refrigeration and Air Conditioning Engineering," John Wiley & Sons, Inc.*)

mer zone is imputed to be based on the difference in physiological adjustment of individuals to outdoor temperatures such as found in the eastern United States. Shifts in bounds of the areas indicated on the chart would be expected to result if tests were made using subjects in other climates.

Figure 21 also indicates air-property regions in which definite hazards or supposed hazards to human life exist.

Conditions in which radiation is the chief mode of heat exchange. It is perfectly familiar to everyone that even on a cold day the sun feels warm, when shining directly on either the clothed or unclothed parts of the body, especially if air movement is at a minimum. Although the familiar examples of the effect of solar radiation and the radiation from a hot stove in a cool room are understandable, it is less easy to accept the fact that the air temperature in a room may be held at a level greatly below those of the floor or walls, with consequent comfort.

Mills[40] tells of experiments in which radiation was virtually the exclusive source used for heating and cooling. In his own laboratories, he built four experimental rooms, two of which had the inner surfaces covered with aluminum foil so as to reflect heat rays. On the walls on two sides of one of the foil-covered rooms, steel plates were installed. These could be cooled by cold circulating fluid from an outside source. When the air in this room was kept at 93°F., and the relative humidity at 70 per cent, Mills found that an individual could be comfortable if the wall plates were sufficiently cold. In air temperatures of 110°F., individuals could remain comfortable if humidity were held down. Despite the tropical humid heat of this "hot" room, the inhabitant was cooled by losing the necessary body heat through radiation to the plates. In fact, with the cold plates in full operation, loss of heat from the body was so rapid that the net effect of 1 hour spent quietly reading in the room was discomfort. Shock from passing from this room to outside summer conditions was minimized or obviated if the air temperatures and humidities of the two were about the same.

In a second foil-covered room, the conditions were reversed. Radiant heat furnished what Mills calls "delightful shirt-sleeve" comfort while air temperatures were held down to nearly freezing temperatures. A particularly pleasing aspect of such a situation was breathing cold air during maintenance of body warmth. Mills also relates that, by making the radiant input sufficiently great while holding air temperatures low, free perspiration could be induced. Animals raised under these conditions manifested the same slow growth and low vitality common in tropical humid heat.

[40] Mills, C. A.: "Climate Makes the Man," Harper & Brothers, New York, 1942. Pp. 320.

Mills and Ogle,[41] using a set of experimental rooms including the ones already mentioned, found that an essential factor in the growth and well-being of laboratory animals was the ease of heat loss provided by the surroundings. This loss could as well occur through radiation exclusively as through the usual combinations of conduction, convection, and radiation.

Such laboratory arrangements would be particularly significant for studying limiting conditions in fatigue experiments.

WATER LACK

When the quantity of water eliminated from the body is greater than the quantity produced through metabolic oxidation plus the amount imbibed, desiccation sets in. This varies greatly from organ to organ. The muscles, skin, and blood lose the most water, whereas the brain, fatty tissues, heart, and skeleton lose the least. The skin seems not to be greatly damaged by water loss, and the loss of 10 to 20 per cent of the total water content is said not to impair muscle tissue. It is water loss from the blood which induces the greatest difficulties. Circulation becomes disturbed, and secondary disturbances then occur throughout the body. Metabolic processes are altered, and the heat-regulating mechanism becomes deranged. On this account the condition of the blood is often taken as the indication of the water balance of the body. Insufficient water in the blood is called "anhydremia." Water lack is a condition that is at times controlled by non-availability, and at others by conditions peculiar to the individual.

Water exchange. Conditions underlying water exchange are complicated by the fact that water intake is not directly regulated by physiological demand. The individual largely determines voluntarily the amount imbibed.

Water exchange plays an important role in body economy. (1) water exchange is a means of heat exchange. Evaporation of water from body surfaces, as has been said, is one of the chief means of accomplishing heat loss. (2) Urinary excretion, in eliminating various waste substances, incidentally involves water loss. The passing of 45 gm. of urea or 15 gm. of sodium chloride requires 1 l. of water.[42] With large salt intake or high protein metabolism, a large amount of water must be excreted. A mixed diet involves the excretion of 30 to 35 gm. of urea per day, or 650 to 800 gm. of water (about 0.69 to 0.84 qt.). In all, 1,000 to 2,000 cc. of water is ordinarily eliminated from the body per day.

Anhydremia may be produced by excessive elimination with insufficient intake. Excessive loss of water may occur by sweating and insensible water

[41] Mills, C. A., and C. Ogle: Ease of Body Heat Loss as a Basic Developmental and Functional Factor in Warm-blooded Animals, *Am. J. Physiol., 125:* 36–40, 1939.

[42] Marriott, W. M.: Anhydremia, *Physiol. Rev., 3:* 275–294, 1923.

loss. Excessive elimination of water may be produced by diuresis. Water may be lost in large quantities from the intestines in diarrhea. Vomiting also may produce dehydration.

Adolph,[43] from imposing both positive and negative water loads and studying intake and excretion over short periods such as an hour's time, presents diagrams to show certain relations between size of load and rate of exchange. One of these equilibrium diagrams for the first hour of recovery in man is given in Fig. 22. Water load is expressed in percentage of

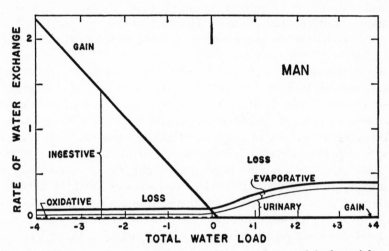

Fig. 22.—The rate of water exchange (per cent of control body weight per hour) in relation to water load (per cent of control body weight). This is an equilibrium diagram during the first hour of recovery. (*Adolph: "Physiological Regulations," Jaques Cattell Press.*)

control weight of the body, and exchange is expressed in rate of gain or loss in percentage of this body weight per hour. The diagram shows that water balance exists only at a single water content. Even small deviations from this content mean large changes in exchange. Actually, the body is under small positive or negative loads nearly all the time. When the apparent balance is considered uniform, the constancy of water content lies within a range of ±0.22 per cent of the control weight over a 24-hour period. For single-hour periods this is reduced to ±0.08 per cent.

Ingestion rather than oxidation within tissues provides most of the restoration, and urinary elimination rather than evaporation provides most of the usual loss. The velocities of exchange in gain and loss (during the initial 1-hour period) are equal only up to ±0.2 per cent of control body weight. With all greater loads, recovery by gain is faster than by loss. De-

[43] Adolph, *op. cit.*

spite the apparent slowness of gains by ingestion, they are faster at loads greater than ±0.2 per cent control body weight than the greatest rates of urinary losses.

Regulation of retention.   In regulating water balance, retention is one of the major factors. The neurohypophysis secretes a hormone with anti-diuretic functions. The anterior hypothalamus is believed to exert a tonic excitatory action on these hormone-secreting elements. Just what prompts the various degrees of action of this nervous center is not yet fully determined. The rest of the nervous system, no doubt, exerts various kinds of influence on the neurohypophysis. The unusual vascularity of this region of the hypothalamus strongly suggests that the composition of the blood has something to do with its activity.

Regulation of intake—thirst.   Another important feature in the regulation of water balance is the determination of intake. According to the views of some, devices to adjust intake to body needs must be presupposed. Examination of a dehydrated person reveals dryness of skin, shrinkage of subcutaneous tissue, loss of weight, reduction of urine flow, and dry mouth and throat. The individual is unaware, or only indirectly aware, of most of these signs. On the other hand, he probably experiences a desire for water, and this thirst, along with its allied sensations and the distraction from work it entails, represents the demands imposed by dehydration occupying all the person's attention when dehydration becomes extreme. In cases of extreme deprivation, thirst is often lacking although bodily discomfort is present to a high degree.

Although water output is regulated on the organic level and can be little influenced by the individual, water intake is partly a matter of whim, convenience, and convention. The individual can set out to force fluids or can hold water intake to a minimum. The individual is able by determination to drink several times his habitual amount. When, however, negative water loads are imposed by any set of conditions, water drinking seems to bear a rough relation to the deprivation. Adolph's[44] diagram is reproduced in Fig. 23. It suggests that the greater the negative load, the greater the rate of water ingestion.

There are two opposing views on the origin of thirst, one stressing its diffuseness, the other maintaining that it arises directly from a dry throat and mouth.[45] The former view is based on the fact that thirst is associated with conditions involving a general depletion of the body fluids and may be abolished by intravenous injections of water or salt solutions. Actually,

[44] Adolph, *op. cit.*

[45] Cannon, W. B.: "The Wisdom of the Body," W. W. Norton & Company, Inc., New York, 1932. Pp. 312.

thirst may be defined as a peculiar sensory experience, or as a desire for water.

If dehydration simply induced thirst as a sensory experience, and thirst until satisfied became a distraction from work, then fatigue might develop in the face of such a distraction. But dehydration bears on the problems

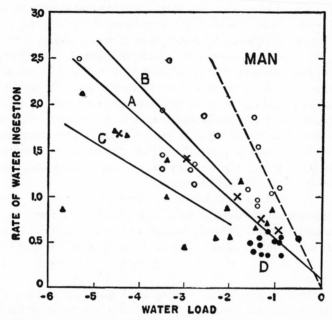

Fig. 23.—The relation of water ingestion to water load. The rate is measured in per cent of control live weight of the body per half hour, to water load or deficit measured in percentage of control live weight. A = regression line representing group means (x) of 44 tests on 10 individuals. B = 11 tests with water deficits greater than 2 (hot desert). C = 10 tests with water deficits greater than 2 in winter laboratory conditions. D = group of 12 tests following physical exercise. (*Adolph: "Physiological Regulations," Jaques Cattell Press.*)

of fatigue and impairment in a broader way. It represents a particular kind of unfitness. It may become thwarting in the individual's activity.

Water compartments. The body has been divided into three compartments: the *blood plasmal,* the *interstitial,* and the *intracellular.* Owing to the selective diffusibility of ions through the compartment membranes, the water balance in the three compartments varies. It is possible to identify certain behavioral limitations as dependent upon the absolute and relative balances among these compartments.

Kerpel-Fronius[46] differentiated clearly between two kinds of dehydration in rabbits: (1) water loss associated with a primary loss of salt, and (2) a deficit of water not accompanied by a proportionate loss of salt. The first involves circulatory disturbances, and the second is characterized by thirst.

Nadal, Pedersen, and Maddock[47] confirmed the findings of Kerpel-Fronius on human subjects. They found that simple water deprivation is characterized by thirst and oliguria. Circulation is not disturbed, and the condition is completely relieved by resumption of water intake. Dehydration arising from unusual salt loss results chiefly in a loss of extracellular fluid, a drop in plasma volume, and circulatory disturbance. Thirst is not characteristic, and intake of salt-free fluid does not relieve the condition. Intake of fluid containing sodium chloride, however, provides prompt relief. Kerpel-Fronius had previously stated that in dehydration with salt loss the chief loss of fluid was from the extracellular compartment and from the blood. In contrast to this, all the fluid compartments were involved in simple water loss. These findings seem to support the idea that thirst is a function of cellular dehydration.

Signs of dehydration. Nadal and coworkers[48] point out that the main signs of desiccation are those of peripheral circulatory failure. Extracellular loss results in reduced plasma volume, and various systemic effects arise. These authors refer to dehydration with salt loss as "electrolyte shock" and point out that it may be indistinguishable from shock arising from other origins.

A subtle fact in dehydration is that water ingestion and urine output may lie within normal limits.[49] For this reason, voluntary or involuntary water deprivation is in itself no indication of the existence of dehydration.

Black, McCance, and Young[50] report an exaggeration of their subjects' temperamental characteristics in experimental dehydration. Serious individuals became extremely somber, whereas cheerful ones developed what

[46] Kerpel-Fronius, E.: Über die Beziehungen zwischen Salz- und Wasserhaushalt bei experimentallen Wasserverlusten, *Ztschr. f. Kinderh., 57:* 489–504, 1935.

Kerpel-Fronius, E.: Durstexsikkose und Salzmangelexsikkose, *Acta pædiat., 22:* 143–145, 1937.

[47] Nadal, J. W., S. Pedersen, and W. G. Maddock: A Comparison between Dehydration from Salt Loss and from Water Deprivation, *J. Clin. Investigation, 20:* 691–703, 1941.

[48] *Ibid.*

[49] Darrow, D. C., and H. Yannet: Metabolic Studies of the Changes in Body Electrolyte and Distribution of Body Water Induced Experimentally by Deficit of Extracellular Electrolyte, *J. Clin. Investigation, 15:* 419–427, 1936.

[50] Black, D. A. K., R. A. McCance, and W. F. Young: A Study of Dehydration by Means of Balance Experiments, *J. Physiol., 102:* 406–414, 1944.

was described as a "hollow vivacity." Concentration in all the subjects was poor, although they were capable of performing certain mathematical calculations. The subjects reported that the days during the dehydration period seemed long, but that they were not especially uncomfortable. During this period, they were never intolerably thirsty. Their throats and mouths became dry by the third day. Their voices were husky, and swallowing was difficult. By the fourth day their faces appeared pinched, and a trace of cyanosis was observable about their lips.

Teitelman[51] points out that slight degrees of dehydration are hard to identify. Dryness of throat and mouth seems to be the best index. A loss of about 6 per cent of the body weight in water is said to be accompanied by characteristic symptoms, such as warm, dry, wrinkled, and inelastic skin. The tongue is also dry, and speech becomes thick. Acidosis develops, and the perceptions of the individual are dulled. With or following these symptoms, a loss of appetite, nausea, muscle cramps, and tetany may occur.

SALT LACK

The role and fate of sodium chloride. Sodium chloride, or table salt, besides being our chief condiment, is the major electrolytic constituent of most of the body tissues and is essential for the functioning of most cells. Sodium chloride provides the body with sodium and chloride ions, each playing a particular role in organic functioning. Concentrations of both sodium and chloride vary from tissue to tissue.[52] The total amount of salt in the body might be estimated at about $\frac{1}{2}$ lb., although it varies over a considerable range. The daily turnover is about one-twentieth of the total amount, but this too varies.[53] Regardless of whether the lack of sodium or of chloride is being considered, the study is referred to as having to do with salt lack.

Ordinarily, most of the elimination of chlorides from the body occurs in the urine, but in cases of profuse sweating, more chlorides may be lost through this channel than any other. The chloride content of the blood tends to be constant. This constancy is maintained by excretory regulation in the urine and by reabsorption by the kidney tubules, the hormone of the suprarenals supposedly playing a role. In some disease conditions, chloride is said to be retained. This is supposedly true of pneumonia and other fevers, of cancer, and in some cases, of nephritis.

[51] Teitelman, S. L.: Dehydration: An Analysis of the Methods Used in Diagnosis, *Internat. Abstr. Surg., 78:* 105–108, 194.

[52] Hastings, A. B., and L. Eichelberger: The Exchange of Salt and Water Between Muscle and Blood. I. The Effect of an Increase in Total Body Water Produced by the Intravenous Injection of Isotonic Salt Solutions, *J. Biol. Chem., 117:* 73–93, 1937.

[53] Ashe, B. I., and H. O. Mosenthal: Protein, Salt and Fluid Consumption of 1,000 Residents of New York, *J.A.M.A., 180:* 1160–1163, 1937.

Years ago, Claude Bernard originated the idea of "threshold" concentration with reference to blood sugar. Magnus later applied this idea to plasma chloride. In so doing he used rabbits as test animals and found that under some conditions their urine was almost chloride-free. From these findings it has been suggested that the kidneys are an overflow mechanism, excreting chloride into the urine only when its level in the blood plasma exceeds a certain point. It must be kept in mind, however, that rabbits and man are not alike. The urine of the former may become chloride-free, but the urine of the latter, except in cases of excessive sweating, apparently does not.[54]

Aitken,[55] having found that the relation between urine-chloride excretion and plasma-chloride concentration follows a smooth but inflected curve, showed that the concept of a strict threshold is untenable. With low plasma-chloride concentrations, urine-chloride excretion fails to diminish appreciably after a certain point. Thus, no matter how low the plasma concentration falls, the urine does not become chloride-free in man. If one follows the curve upward, the inflection indicates the rapid onset of an increase in urine-chloride excretion for slight rises in blood-plasma concentrations. Aitken found the curve to straighten out at about 0.585 gm. per 100 cc. Wolf[56] assumes what he calls the *threshold of retention* to be at 6 mg. per cc., or roughly at the same concentration as that found by Aitken. This author uses the terms *threshold of appearance* and threshold of retention to deal with the two aspects of chloride level. The hypothetical threshold presumed by Magnus is Wolf's threshold of appearance, while the more tangible threshold is that of retention. It was this threshold of retention that Aitken indicated to be uncritical.

Wolf[57] determined what happened when water was given continuously for a number of hours at rates of 6 to 10 cc. per min. He found that a steady state was reached at about the third hour. Under these conditions, the fluid output was larger than the intake and represented a progressive dehydration—the development of a "negative water load." The ratio of the rate of chloride excretion to rate of extra water excretion was equal to normal plasma concentration in the steady state. This means that plasma will remain at the same concentration only when a solution whose concentration is equal to that of the blood is removed. After the third hour of

[54] Adolph, E. F., and D. B. Dill: Observations on Water Metabolism in the Desert, *Am. J. Physiol., 123:* 369–378, 1938.

[55] Aitken, R. S.: On the Renal Threshold for Chloride in Man, *J. Physiol., 67:* 199–210, 1929.

[56] Wolf, A. V.: The Dehydration Effect of Continuously Administered Water, *Am. J. Physiol., 143:* 567–571, 1945.

[57] *Ibid.*

continuous water intake, the theoretical values predicted by Wolf's equation and the actual values corrected for insensible water loss were found to be in remarkable agreement. Wolf points out that steady state does not indicate an equilibrium. When the input is steady, the output may or may not be. He indicates that the water output may drop below the intake when the rates of the latter are very high, thus quickly increasing the water load. As far as kidney function is concerned, the concentration of blood chloride tends to be more stable than the volume of water in the body.

Wolf[58] performed other experiments in which salt-solution intake was maintained at a steady state for 3 hours. At 10-minute intervals, 100 cc. of fluid was ingested. This was considered to be at a rate of 10 cc. per min. Urine samples were collected at half-hour intervals. From these experiments, Wolf found three critical concentrations at which neither water nor chloride was retained relative to the other. The lowest, called the *minimal isorrheic*[59] concentration, was 1.4 mg. per cc. The central concentration was 6 mg. per cc., or the so-called *threshold of retention*. The highest concentration, called the *limiting isorrheic* concentration, was 17 mg. per cc.

The initial effect of administration of isotonic and slightly stronger saline solutions is the retention of the water. With steady water intake, the "leakage" concentration into the urine may be about one-fifth of the normal plasma concentration. The threshold of retention may fluctuate. Wolf states that saline solutions in the isotonic range are the most edema-forming, since they have the lowest initial excretion rates of water per unit load of fluid. Much less concentrated solutions can often relieve dehydration with little risk of overtaxing the body fluid compartments, assuming normal kidney action.

Diets vary considerably in their salt content. Animal substances contain enough salt for dietary purposes, whereas plant foods do not. Fasting does not produce symptoms referable to salt lack. Rosemann[60] found that in a 10-day fast the salt capital was diminished by only 2 per cent and that the chloride percentage was above normal owing to the wasting of tissue more rapidly than the disappearance of chloride.

When excessive salt depletion occurs, it leads promptly to extreme and

[58] Wolf, A. V.: The Retention and Excretion of Continuously Administered Salt Solutions, *Am. J. Physiol.*, *143:* 572–588, 1945.

[59] By definition, the concentrations of fluid intake and urine output are said to be isorrheic when the intake induces no retention of chloride relative to water.

[60] Rosemann, R.: Über den Gesamtchlorgehalt der tierischen Körpers, *Pflüger's Arch. f. d. ges. Physiol.*, *135:* 177–195, 1910.

Rosemann, R.: Die Magensaftsekretionen bei Verminderung des Chlorvorrates des Körper's, *Pflüger's Arch. f. d. ges. Physiol.*, *142:* 208–234, 1911.

even fatal symptoms. The symptoms of excessive sodium chloride depletion induced by insufficient salt intake and copious water drinking are
similar to heat stroke and to Addison's disease and include cramps, fatigue,
depression, and cardiovascular distress upon exertion. Prior to the occurrence of severe symptoms, we could expect some inefficiency in the body
economy to develop. The discomfort induced by impairment resulting
from salt lack would be expected to contribute to fatigue.

Chapter VIII

METABOLISM AND NUTRITION

METABOLISM

To THE biochemist, the essential problem of muscle contraction is how chemical reactions are transformed into mechanical work. The question of whether the contraction processes are anaerobic or aerobic is of central importance. Although it has long been held that they are anaerobic, and that only the recovery processes require oxygen, certain more recent workers have found evidence to the contrary. They believe that aerobic processes occur under all conditions in which oxygen is available. The chemical possibilities are of such an extremely complex character that no one is certain of all that does occur. The subject is still open enough so that all description of the muscle metabolism must retain an element of conjecture.

The approach of those interested in tissue impairment is to examine the facts of metabolism for the factors that lessen or forestall the usual energy transformations. For those interested in fatigue, such information is a means to a still further end, *viz.*, to determine how mechanical incapacity operates in personal behavior. The question of whether the development of the difficulties in the individual in everyday life can be deduced from studies under laboratory conditions is also pertinent to the student of fatigue.

Although the details of muscle metabolism may appear only very remotely related to fatigue, they should not be ignored in a satisfactory understanding of it. The difficulties arising in the complex interrelations among physico-chemical processes lead not only to reduced efficiency, but also to pain, soreness, stiffness, and other forms of discomfort.

Muscle and nerve metabolism. Muscle is about four-fifths water; the other known components have been divided into 10 classes.[1]

The relation between oxygen consumption and the production of carbon dioxide varies in accordance with the particular fuel utilized by the

[1] Wiggers, C. J.: "Physiology in Health and Disease," 4th ed., Lea & Febiger, Philadelphia, 1944. Pp. 1174.

body. When only carbohydrates are being used, the respiratory quotient (R.Q.) is 1.00. When fats alone are being used, it is 0.703. Various combinations of fats, carbohydrates, and proteins give different quotients. The measurement of the carbon dioxide production during any short period may be complicated by a number of factors. For example, in periods of violent exertion the R.Q. of the individual may rise above the value of 1.00. Certain conditions, which must be adjusted following energy expenditure at this excessive rate, account for this.

In cases of violent exertion, a chemical imbalance, known as "oxygen debt," develops and must be paid off eventually.

The energy for muscle contraction has been presumed to be obtained anaerobically. Oxygen was thought to be required only for the process of chemical recovery from contraction. Hill[2] had supposed this to be the case when he found that the heat liberated in contraction when oxygen was absent was identical to that liberated in the presence of oxygen.

Within the last few years, three separate anerobic reaction system theories have been proffered to explain how energy for muscle contraction is provided. Meyerhof[3] believed the source of energy to lie in the breakdown of glycogen to lactic acid. Lundsgaard[4] asserted that the hydrolysis of phosphocreatine supplied the energy and that the formation of lactic acid provided for resynthesizing phosphocreatine and was thus a recovery reaction. Lohmann[5] looked upon the hydrolysis of adenosinetriphosphate as the immediate source of energy for contraction and claimed that the resynthesis of this substance by transfer of phosphate groups from phosphocreatine was the initial stage in recovery.

Sacks and Sacks[6] could not interpret their findings in terms of the hypotheses existing in 1933. They postulated that the fundamental reactions in contracting muscle are oxidative and not anaerobic and that anaerobic reactions occur only when the oxygen supply is insufficient to support a completely aerobic metabolism. They stated that the primary anaerobic reaction is the breakdown of glycogen to produce lactic acid by a route that does not involve the transfer of phosphate groups from either phos-

[2] Hill, A. V., and W. Hartree: The Four Phases of Heat Production of Muscle, *J. Physiol.*, *54:* 84–128, 1920.

[3] Meyerhof, O.: Die Energieumwandlungen im Muskel. III. Kohlenhydrat- und Milchsäurumsatz im Froschmuskel, *Pflüger's Arch. f. d. ges. Physiol.*, *185:* 11–32, 1920.

[4] Lundsgaard, E.: Untersuchungen über Muskelkontraktion ohne Milchsäurebildung, *Biochem. Ztschr.*, *217:* 162–177; *227:* 51, 1930.

[5] Lohmann, K.: Über die enzymatische Aufspaltung der Kreatinphosphosäure; zugleich ein Beitrag zum Chemismus der Muskelkontraktion, *Biochem. Ztschr.*, *217:* 264–277, 1934.

[6] Sacks, J., and W. C. Sacks: The Fundamental Changes in Contracting Mammalian Muscle, *Am. J. Physiol.*, *105:* 151–161, 1933.

phocreatine or adenosinetriphosphate. The formation of hexosemono-phosphate from glycogen and phosphocreatine is an auxiliary mechanism to the glycogen-to-lactic acid route. This makes it obvious that hexose-monophosphate is not an intermediate in the formation of lactic acid. Sacks and Sacks agree with Fiske and Subbarow[7] that the primary function of phosphocreatine hydrolysis is to supply a buffer for lactic acid formed in contraction under inadequate oxygen supply. It is a source of energy only in a supplementary role, and this is when it is used to form hexose-monophosphate under anaerobic conditions. Phosphocreatine hydrolysis is not supposed to take place until other sources of alkali are much reduced.

Sacks[8] points out that, since hexosemonophosphate can readily be reconverted to glycogen within muscle tissue, its formation is a means for conserving the muscle's glycogen. Reconversion into glycogen occurs both in the steady state and in the recovery period. Use of the steady state provides a means for differentiating between reactions that have been postulated to account for recovery. The steady state is the condition in which the supply of oxygen to the contracting muscles is great enough to prevent the accumulation of anaerobic metabolites. The rate of recovery must be great enough to account for the nonappearance of anaerobic metabolites in the steady state, if contraction is assumed to involve anaerobic reactions even in the presence of oxygen. Lactic acid, in contrast to hexosemono-phosphate, is lost from the muscle when the intensity of anaerobic work is maximum.

Caffeine, epinephrin, and dinitrophenol lead to augmented lactic acid formation. Epinephrin also induces hexosemonophosphate formation. Caffeine and epinephrin are additive in the production of lactic acid, but dinitrophenol is not, although when the three are used together, hexose-monophosphate formation is augmented.

Sacks examined the three anaerobic reactions that should first be considered as possible direct sources of energy for contraction in the presence of oxygen. These reactions are the production of lactic acid from glycogen, the hydrolysis of phosphocreatin, and the hydrolysis of adenosinetriphosphate. Sacks found it necessary to ascertain whether the oxidative reversals of these three reactions could occur at high enough rates to maintain the steady state. He points out that various workers have shown that the resynthesis of glycogen from lactic acid is very slow. In fact, to account for

[7] Fiske, C. H., and Y. Subbarow: Phosphocreatine, *J. Biol. Chem., 81:* 629–679, 1929.

[8] Sacks, J.: Changing Concepts of the Chemistry of Muscular Contraction, *Physiol. Rev., 21:* 217–241, 1941.

Sacks, J.: Recovery from Muscular Activity and Its Bearing on the Chemistry of Contraction, *Am. J. Physiol., 122:* 215–223, 1938.

the steady state, its re-formation during muscle activity would have to occur many times faster than it is known to occur during recovery. The phosphocreatine cycle was also found to be too slow for this purpose. For example, if phosphocreatine were the source of energy (as asserted by Lundsgaard), all the substance formed during 5 minutes of recovery would be required to maintain the steady state only ½ minute. Furthermore, it is not lack of oxygen that limits this reaction. Millikan has shown that oxygen tension rises to resting level in the muscle within a few seconds after the termination of tetanus. Sacks shows that the adenosinetriphosphate hydrolysis is an even more unlikely source of contraction energy under conditions of ample oxygen supply. It is also far too slow.

The following is the sequence of events as put forth by Wiggers[9] in his "Physiology in Health and Disease."

Hydrolysis of adenosinetriphosphate is the initial event in muscle contraction. Phosphocreatine breakdown also occurs, its onset slightly antedating full contraction, and may furnish part of the energy used in contraction. The resynthesis of adenosinetriphosphate begins also slightly prior to the peak of contraction and is buffered by the phosphocreatine breakdown. This breakdown continues into the initial part of muscle relaxation, afterward beginning to undergo resynthesis, the energy for which is supplied by breakdown of glycogen to lactic acid or by oxidations not involving intermediary glycolysis.

The energy for the molecular reorganization of myosin chains, finally responsible for contraction, is supplied by the splitting of phosphate from adenyl compounds under the influence of adenosinetriphosphate. Myosin is to be regarded as the "contractile enzyme." Wiggers believes that the preponderance of experimental evidence denies the view that oxidation reactions underlie the initiation of contraction.

Nerve metabolism also involves phosphorus participation. Nerve discharge involves the breakdown of phosphocreatine with its resynthesis during the refractory period, but the energy source of the resynthesis is unknown. Adenosinetriphosphate is apparently broken down in the early refractory period, possible with the production of lactic acid. It is interesting to note that the energy needed by the salivary glands, kidney, and liver, for secretion, is derived from the breakdown of organic phosphorus compounds.[10]

Obviously with the present stage of incompleteness in knowledge of muscle metabolism, little can be ascertained about the relation of difficul-

9 Wiggers, *op. cit.*

10 Ferrari, R., and R. Höber: Untersuchungen über den der Sekretions-arbeit Zugrunde liegenden Stoffwechsel von Leber, Niere und Speicheldrüse, *Pflüger's Arch. f. d. ges. Physiol.*, 232: 299–321, 1933.

ties arising in particular stages of the metabolic cycle to loss in mechanical output of the muscles. The same pertains to the relation between products formed and the kinesthetic discomfort. Neither can the existence of the frequently alluded-to "fatigue toxins" be presumed, nor the character of the possible effects of such substances on the action of the nervous system be conceived.

The prescribing of supplementary amounts of certain compounds known to participate in muscle metabolism for fatigue is one example of how little practical knowledge has been gained about it from studies of metabolism. For example, sodium phosphate was tried in Germany during the First World War with the unconfirmed assertion that it reduced fatigue in troops. The idea was probably based on the relative prominence of phosphate in muscular contraction. The experimenters failed to recognize that phosphate is not used up in such processes, and it is therefore hardly necessary to furnish additional supplies from special sources. Were the usual sources of phosphate supply deficient, it is likely that bone rather than muscle would suffer first.

Modification of acetylcholine synthesis. Some of the possible metabolic events that occur during muscle activity are becoming clearer through studies such as those conducted by Torda and Wolff.[11] Their investigations center around the differences between results obtainable on normal and myasthenic subjects, individuals who manifest chronic muscle weakness and easy exhaustibility.

Using a slightly modified method of Quastel, Tennenbaum, and Wheatley,[12] they determined the relative amounts of acetylcholine synthesis induced in the presence of sera (1) taken from normal resting control arms, (2) from normal exercised arms, (3) from myasthenic resting control arms, and (4) from myasthenic exercised arms. With serum from the healthy individuals, about 40 per cent less acetylcholine was synthesized after exercise to the point of inability to move the fingers in the task assigned. Acetylcholine synthesis in the presence of the serum from the myasthenic control arms was less than that from the normal controls. Exercise to exhaustion reduced the efficacy of the serum obtained from the myasthenic patients 15 to 26 per cent. Since the control serum from myasthenics reduced acetylcholine synthesis by 22 to 36 per cent as compared with the effect from healthy serum, the total reduction was on the average about 42 per cent. From this it is deduced that, when blood changes during muscle

[11] Torda, C., and H. G. Wolff: Depression of Acetylcholine Synthesis by Serum from Working Muscles. Healthy Subjects and Myasthenia Gravis Patients, *Proc. Soc. Exper. Biol. & Med., 59:* 13-16, 1945.

[12] Quastel, J. H., M. Tennenbaum, and A. H. M. Wheatley: Choline Ester Formation in, and Choline Esterase Activities of, Tissues in Vitro, *Biochem. J., 30:* 1668-1681, 1936.

activity decrease acetylcholine synthesis by about 40 per cent tested in vitro, voluntary muscle activity can be considered exceedingly difficult in any subject.

If these results obtained during occlusion can be transferred to activity with free blood supply, muscle impairment ("fatigue") is partly attributed to decreased local production of an acetylcholine-like substance. Torda and Wolff point out certain facts that tend to make this seem likely. It is known that, in continued activity, cholinergic systems synthesize locally an acetylcholine-like substance.[13] They point out that local production of acetylcholine is conceivable, since intermediate anaerobic metabolism of carbohydrate and fat, which possibly produces acetylphosphate, may provide it as one of the precursors of acetylcholine.

The method they used indicates that many intermediate products of carbohydrate metabolism increase the synthesis of acetylcholine. Products of adenosinetriphosphate decomposition decrease acetylcholine production. All this would tend to indicate that, during prolonged muscular exercise, the balance in metabolic organization shifts toward the lessened local production of acetylcholine. This would contribute to the lessened ability of muscle to contract. The authors stated that they were unable to say whether the drop in acetylcholine synthesis arose from the action of a depressor substance released from muscle during activity, or from the exhaustion of some potentiator substance usually present in the blood but used in muscle contraction. The existence of potentiator substances can be supposed from the findings of these authors. They found that the amount of acetylcholine produced in vivo in the presence of serum from the motionless arm of healthy persons was twice as much as that produced during absence of the serum.

It is both interesting and significant to reflect that working muscle may somehow induce changes that have to do with the neuromuscular juncture rather than only with contractile processes in muscle itself. In this way, it may be said that muscle, after a period of activity, produces or is instrumental in producing conditions that reduce or even preclude its further stimulation through its motor nerve. This is the conclusion to be drawn from the decreased production in acetylcholine, which is the substance enabling nerve impulses to pass certain types of synapse.

It has been suggested that less acetylcholine is produced in myasthenic patients than in healthy subjects. This result may be due to lack of the supposed potentiator substances in the blood serum or the presence of a

[13] Brown, G. L., and W. Feldburg: The Acetylcholine Metabolism of a Sympathetic Ganglion, *J. Physiol., 88:* 265–283, 1936.

Kahlsen, G., and F. C. MacIntosh: Acetylcholine Synthesis in a Sympathetic Ganglion, *J. Physiol., 96:* 277–292, 1939.

depressor substance, which in turn may be a foreign substance, an intermediate product of metabolism, or an imperfectly metabolized substance released during contraction.

The methods employed give promise toward solving some of the basic problems involved in metabolism as concerns muscle contraction and the neuromuscular juncture. They form an additional link between the electrophysiological studies and the purely biochemical ones.

More recently, Torda and Wolff[14] have reported further results in their studies on processes that seem to be vital to metabolism. They investigated the possible modifying effect on the synthesis of acetylcholine of certain isocyclic and aromatic hydrocarbons and heterocyclic compounds. They chose these substances because some of them occur naturally as intermediate or end products of metabolism, and because some are commonly used in therapy, and still others are known to influence the activity of certain enzymes.

The isocyclic and aromatic hydrocarbons either failed to modify the synthesis of acetylcholine or diminished it only in high concentrations. The substances used were cyclohexane, inositol, benzol, toluol, benzoic acid, and naphthalene. Hydroxyl derivatives, aldehydes, and ketones diminished synthesis in concentrations beginning at 10^{-5} mole. The substances used were (1) phenol, p-aminophenol, hydroquinone, salicylic acid, α-naphthol, β-naphthol; (2) benzaldehyde; and (3) camphor and penicillin. Conjugated substances, such as potassium phenol sulfonate, phenactine, diphenylamine, benzedrine, acetylsalicyclic acid, and the sulfonamides, either did not influence or else decreased synthesis slightly. The heterocyclic compound indol decreased the synthesis in concentrations of 10^{-5} mole upward. Skatol was not so active as indol, and indol-3-acetic acid was almost inactive. *Dl*-tryptophane was inactive, and *l* (−) tryptophane *increased* acetylcholine synthesis. The remaining two substances mentioned by Torda and Wolff, quinoline and carbazole, both decreased it, the latter being less effective.

These findings were based on in vitro experiments. As yet no direct corroborative experiments have been made in the living animal.

NUTRITION

In considering metabolism in relation to muscle activity and impairment ("fatigue"), we are not only concerned with the actual chemical processes involved in contraction and recovery from it, but also with the way the body provides materials for these processes. Questions regarding

[14] Torda, C., and H. G. Wolff: Effect of Some Isocyclic, Aromatic, and Heterocyclic Compounds on Acetylcholine Synthesis, *Proc. Soc. Exper. Biol. & Med., 59:* 183–184, 1945.

the possible critical nature of the energy-yielding substances are of basic importance. In nutrition, not only amount and kinds of food, but also timing of the food intake is important. We shall introduce the latter problem first.

Temporal distribution of food intake. In America, the most customary eating schedule involves three meals per day. Food taken at other times is considered "eating between meals." There are some commonly given reasons for the employment of the three-meal schedule. One of these is that the long intervals between meals give the stomach time to rest. The assumptions are made that two or more hours are required for completion of gastric digestion and that the stomach rests when empty of food. The latter idea is fallacious, since the stomach is far from inactive when empty. On the contrary, "hunger" contractions are likely to be set up. Variously spaced groups of contractions occur which tend, within limits, to increase in vigor, the longer eating is delayed. There is not even chemical "rest" while the stomach is empty of food. Excess acid is likely to develop, the untoward results of which may be obviated by food intake.

The problem of timing of food intake is one of considerable importance. In the work of Haggard and Greenberg,[15] from which we draw, the question of the number and distribution of meals per day is given systematic attention. Haggard and Greenberg set out to discover a dietary regimen that would minimize what they call lasssitude, fatigue, irritability, and muscular inefficiency. They attempted, by the manipulations of the eating practices of workers, to accomplish results similar to those obtained by other investigators who manipulated hours of work.

Given a total daily intake, it is, generally speaking, the quantity taken at any one time that puts the burden on bodily functions, or as we generally say, upon digestion. Not only are large loads mechanically less easy for the stomach to handle, but they also call for a great over-all blood redistribution in the body. Removal of blood from the brain and muscles leads to lassitude and decided disinclination for thought and mechanical exertion. It is obvious that this factor may become a source of personal inefficiency and discomfort and a potential source of fatigue. It should be pointed out that the temporal redistribution of daily food intake into four, five, or six meals, instead of the customary three, may be accomplished without changing the total quantity or upsetting the dietary balance. Haggard and Greenberg in their study, however, did not control either quantity or quality of food intake.

Multiplying the number of meals per day so as to provide shorter intervals between times of food intake is based upon what is now known about

[15] Haggard, H. W., and L. A. Greenberg: "Diet and Physical Efficiency," Yale University Press, New Haven, 1935. Pp. 180.

the sugar utilization in the body. Food that can be used ultimately for energy is of three kinds: carbohydrates, fats, and proteins. Some of the carbohydrates actually need undergo no process of digestion, whereas others vary in the amount of breakdown necessary. Glucose is the only sugar that can be used to any appreciable extent by the muscles as a source of energy. Some glycogen formed from glucose is stored by the muscles, but none can be formed from the other sugars or from protein by the muscles. The liver, however, is able not only to convert the simple sugars into its own form of carbohydrate (glycogen) for storage, but it is also able to convert certain products of protein digestion into glycogen.

The muscles obtain glucose for storage or for immediate use from the blood stream. If the concentration is too low, insufficient opportunity is given for muscle uptake. At mealtime and shortly afterward, during the active uptake of carbohydrate from the digestive tract, the blood accumulates sugar at a rate beyond which it can be used by the muscles. Part of this excess is removed by the liver and stored. When the storage process continues beyond the period during which the blood is receiving sugar from the digestive tract, the sugar concentration in the blood is lowered. Under normal conditions, a reversal sets in, and the liver begins to yield up sugar. Normally there is considerable persistence in the maintenance of the concentration of blood sugar within certain limits, first by the use of liver glycogen and later, if no additional food is consumed, by the use of the proteins of body tissue.

Diabetes arises in part from insufficient insulin formation. When sugar utilization is impossible, fat forms the main source of energy. In an opposite condition, hyperinsulinism, too much insulin is formed, keeping the blood-sugar concentration unusually low. The symptoms of this condition, now recognized as more common than formerly thought, are similar to those in diabetes. Weakness, irritability, and fatigue are said to occur 2 to 4 hours after meals. Harris[16] found the blood sugar to be at 0.06 or 0.07 per cent when the symptoms occurred, or at the same level at which muscular weakness is manifested after the administration of a large dose of insulin. Haggard and Greenberg point out that even lower concentrations may occur in individuals during prolonged fasts, without the occurrence of severe symptoms. Blood-sugar level is not an absolute measure of sugar utilization in the body. Under steady conditions such as fasting, the blood-sugar level is likely to be higher than the effective concentrations in the tissues themselves. In such cases, the tissues are deprived of sugar more than is indicated by the blood-sugar level. It might be said that oftentimes in a fast less work is attempted; hence there is less need for sugar.

16 Harris, S.: Hyperinsulinism, a Definite Disease Entity, *J.A.M.A.*, *101:* 1958–1965, 1933.

The extreme situations in blood-sugar deficiency (hypoglycemia) have already been dealt with as a limiting condition for action in another chapter. It was suggested that not only are extreme sugar deficiencies accom-

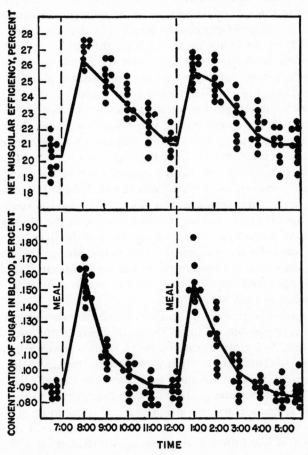

FIG. 24.—The muscular efficiency and blood sugar level for individuals eating three meals a day. (*Haggard and Greenberg:* "*Diet and Physical Efficiency,*" *Yale University Press.*)

panied by marked symptoms, but that lesser degrees of sugar deficiency tend also to be conducive to inefficiency and unpleasant symptoms.

Figures 24 to 29 are taken from the work of Haggard and Greenberg on determining the relation of muscular efficiency[17] to the number and

[17] Muscular efficiency is the relation between total energy liberated and the work output. Gross efficiency is the value obtained by dividing the thermal equivalent of

distribution of meals. Figure 24 shows the result for three meals a day, beginning with the level of efficiency at about 6 A.M. and ending with that at 6 P.M. It will be noted that net efficiency is highest about an hour after mealtime and descends to its minimum just before the next meal. Before

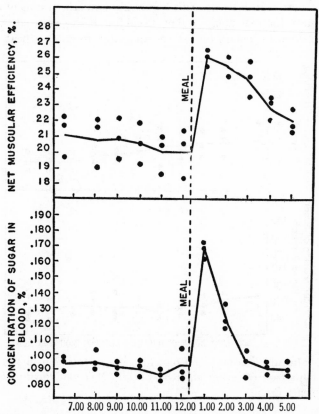

FIG. 25.—The relation of net muscular efficiency and concentration of sugar in the blood to food intake in three subjects omitting breakfast. It will be noted that both muscular efficiency and blood-sugar level are considerably lower during the fast of the morning than at most of the time following the noon meal. Both blood sugar and muscular efficiency probably reach their peak about 1 hour after the meal. Efficiency does not drop in the same manner as blood-sugar level, which has reached the morning level in 2 hours. (*Haggard and Greenberg: "Diet and Physical Efficiency," Yale University Press.*)

the mechanical work by the total energy expended in the task. Net efficiency is the value obtained by dividing the heat equivalent of the work by the *increase* in energy spent while performing the task. This increase is the remainder when the energy consumption at rest is subtracted from the total energy spent during the task. In their studies, Haggard and Greenberg use net efficiency.

lunch, it is almost as low as it was prior to breakfast. Concentration of sugar in the blood is indicated in the bottom section of the same figure. It, too, is greatest about an hour after meals and falls to a minimum just before the next meal. Blood sugar, however, first drops at a somewhat greater rate and then tapers in its later descent. Figure 25 shows the results of the same kind of study for two meals a day, breakfast being omitted. Muscular efficiency is seen to remain low all morning and to reach a peak an hour

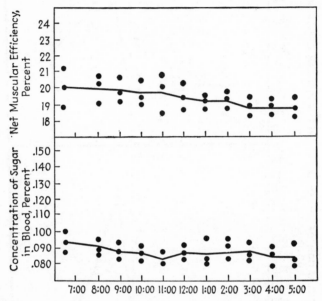

FIG. 26.—Muscular efficiency and blood sugar concentration in three subjects during a day's fast. (*Haggard and Greenberg: "Diet and Physical Efficiency," Yale University Press.*)

after the noon meal. Blood-sugar concentration does likewise. Figure 26 indicates the results from omitting both breakfast and lunch, in which case neither the level of muscular efficiency nor the blood sugar rises during the day to the peaks previously indicated under the other conditions.

When the R.Q. is measured in subjects eating three meals per day, its level from hour to hour forms a pattern much like those of muscular efficiency and blood-sugar level. This would strongly suggest that one could use the R.Q. as an indication of muscular efficiency (see Fig. 27).

Figure 28 shows the course of the R.Q. throughout the day for individuals eating four meals. When three meals per day were eaten, the R.Q. fell almost to 0.80 by noon. Before an extra morning meal was added, the R.Q. fell to between 0.85 and 0.84. After the meal, it rose almost to early-

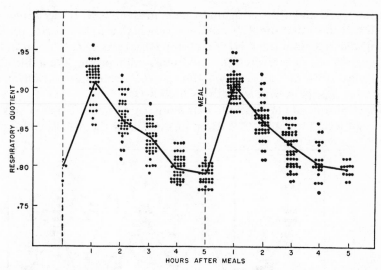

FIG. 27.—The respiratory quotient in three subjects eating 3 meals per day (ages 21–30). (*Haggard and Greenberg: "Diet and Physical Efficiency," Yale University Press.*)

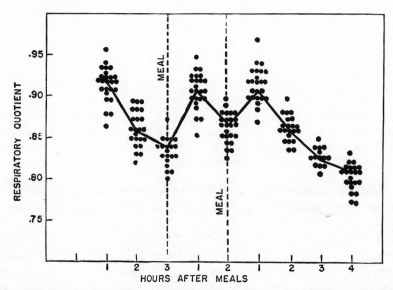

FIG. 28.—The course of the respiratory quotient in subjects eating 4 meals a day. The first meal (breakfast) and the fourth meal (dinner) are not indicated by perpendicular lines as are the mid-morning and noon meals. The location of breakfast is obvious from the abscissa. The fourth meal was taken some time after the point represented by the end of the curve. (*Haggard and Greenberg: "Diet and Physical Efficiency," Yale University Press.*)

morning peak, and dropped again by noon to above 0.87. Inspection of the graph will show that the R.Q. was relatively high a much greater proportion of the time than when no midmorning meal was eaten.

Figure 29 indicates the results with both a midmorning and a midafternoon meal (five meals per day). Here a still greater proportion of the active day was spent with a relatively high R.Q.

It is probably safe to conclude that muscular efficiency tends to be kept at a high level for a greater fraction of the day by the distributed intake

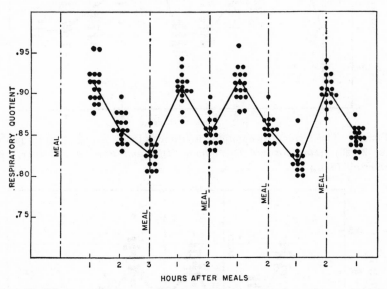

FIG. 29.—The respiratory quotient in subjects eating 5 meals per day. Each meal raises the respiratory quotient with the net effect of keeping it at a higher average level during the working day. (*Haggard and Greenberg: "Diet and Physical Efficiency," Yale University Press.*)

of food (five or six meals), as contrasted with the usual three meals. Although Haggard and Greenberg's study was motivated by knowledge of the relation of food intake to blood-sugar level, and of food intake to the relief of symptoms of weakness and irritability, no systematic study of the subjective symptoms in connection with the added meals per day was made. From their definitions of fatigue and the discussion of its sources, it is certain that to them fatigue is of physiological origin. For this reason, the demonstration that muscular efficiency (economical use of body fuel) is improved by redistribution of food intake would naturally constitute virtually the entire problem for them.

For those who understand fatigue to be a personal affair, attention to the question of the subjective effects from redistribution of food intake could not have been avoided. Although this question was not investigated, we should expect to find improvement in general personal outlook from the changed efficiency in metabolism. An investigation of the personal factors included as a part of a controlled study on muscular efficiency might well be a good demonstration of how even slight hypoglycemia is conducive to an unfavorable subjective outcome. In such a study, the task situation would have to have been varied considerably, for a relatively idle or untaxed individual could not be expected to experience any inadequacy.

Nutritional components in diet. Thorn, Quinby, and Clinton[18] find that a high carbohydrate meal given in the morning leads to hypoglycemia in 2 or 3 hours. Their investigation consisted in the comparison of the effects of three types of meals: one with high carbohydrate content (82 gm.) with negligible amounts of fat and protein, another with 32 gm. of fat and small amounts of carbohydrate and protein, and another with 55 gm. of protein, 20 gm. of carbohydrate, and 8 gm. of fat.

Following the high-carbohydrate meal, blood-sugar, after an initial rise, dropped in 2 hours to 69 mg. per cent, and hypoglycemic symptoms appeared. After about another hour, blood sugar rose and the symptoms disappeared (see Fig. 30). With the high-fat meal the blood-sugar drop was less and occurred more gradually. The lowest point (71 mg. per cent) was reached in about 5 hours. The high-protein meal did not result in a significant lowering of blood sugar at all, and a feeling of well-being was maintained throughout the 6-hour experimental period.

Shifts in metabolic rates, ascertained at hourly intervals, indicated a rapid ascent and subsequent drop after a high-carbohydrate meal, only a slight change after a high-fat meal, and an extended gradual rise after a high-protein meal. This is pictured in Fig. 31.

The differential measurements of caloric utilization manifested fluctuations in the energy furnished by the high-carbohydrate meal (60 per cent, first hour, 15 per cent, the fifth and sixth hours). The utilization of the fat calories in the high-fat meal rose gradually to 71 per cent during the observation period. Combustion in the high-protein meal changed very little throughout the observation period.

These findings were obtained on a single subject. It is possible, however, that a group of subjects would have given virtually the same results. The subject used was kept in bed, and thus nearly basal rather than work conditions were used.

18 Thorn, G. W., J. T. Quinby, and M. Clinton: A Comparison of the Metabolic Effects of Isocaloric Meals of Varying Composition, with Special Reference to the Prevention of Postprandial Hypoglycemic Symptoms, *Ann. Int. Med.*, *18:* 915–919, 1943.

In a more recent study, Haldi and Wynn[19] compared the blood-sugar levels of 59 male subjects following low- and high-carbohydrate meals. These subjects were engaged in their usual activities during the 2½- to 3-hour interval between the meal and the determination of blood-sugar levels. The investigators found no appreciable difference in the level after

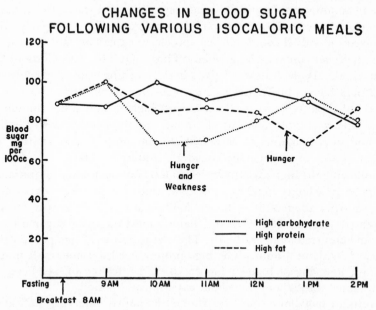

CHANGES IN BLOOD SUGAR
FOLLOWING VARIOUS ISOCALORIC MEALS

Fig. 30.—The relation of blood-sugar level and time elapsing following 3 different kinds of isocaloric meals. It will be noted that blood sugar rises following a high-carbohydrate meal, but drops markedly some time later. A meal with higher fat content tends to induce a rise following eating, but this is not followed by so marked a drop in blood-sugar level. The low point is reached much later. A high-protein meal does not tend to induce so rapid a rise in blood-sugar level, nor is this rise followed by a marked drop as with the other two kinds of meal. (*Thorn, Quinby and Clinton: Ann. Internal Med.*)

the two types of meals. They also state that no relation was discovered between blood-sugar level and the "sense of hunger and weakness." Some of the subjects complained of feeling tired and hungry, although their blood-sugar levels remained within normal limits. There was no consistency, however, in these results, even in the case of a single subject.

[19] Haldi, J., and W. Wynn: The Effect of Low and High Carbohydrate Meals on the Blood Sugar Level and on Work Performance in Strenuous Exercise of Short Duration, *Am. J. Physiol., 145:* 402–410, 1946.

The same procedure was then followed with 12 swimmers serving as subjects. Determinations of blood-sugar level were made just after the subjects had swum 100 yd. (2½ to 3 hours after the meal). The blood-sugar level showed about the same rise after swimming, following the two types of meals. There was no change detected in swimming performance.

Whereas the authors concluded that in healthy individuals high-carbo-hydrate meals are "not conducive to hypoglycemia and its usual symptoms

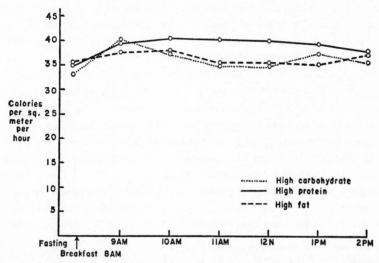

CHANGES IN METABOLIC RATE
FOLLOWING VARIOUS ISOCALORIC MEALS

FIG. 31.—The relation of metabolic rate and elapsed time following various isocaloric meals. Distinctions between high-carbohydrate, high-fat, and high-protein meals are also apparent, as they were in the previous figure. (*Thorn, Quinby and Clinton: Ann. Internal Med.*)

of hunger, weakness and fatigue," from their experiments they could make conclusions justifiably only regarding the relation of the meals to blood-sugar levels. Since the high-carbohydrate meals did not induce hypogly-cemia, the authors were not in a position to generalize regarding the rela-tionship of hypoglycemia to hunger, weakness, and fatigue. Their inciden-tal observations did, however, show that, in the course of everyday activity, hunger, weakness, and fatigue may emerge without hypoglycemia.

An exclusive meat diet has been shown to maintain individuals in a state of well-being in an experiment performed on two subjects.[20] Such a diet has also been found not to alter physiological function in harmful ways. The blood picture is little affected except for the manifestation of lipemia and hypercholesteremia, which return to "normal" when a conventional diet is resumed.[21] In these experiments, uric acid content rose and then fell after some time on the meat diet. The carbon dioxide combining power remained within normal limits even in light of daily ketonuria throughout the entire experiment. There was no blood change that was considered suggestive of kidney damage. In both the experimental subjects, glucose tolerance diminished,[22] and glycosuria appeared in one subject. The explanation for the reduced tolerance was that the normal carbohydrate mechanism requires daily stimulation in order to function properly. It has been found, however, that such groups of people as the Polar and Baffin Bay Eskimos manifest a high carbohydrate tolerance, in spite of their high-protein diet.[23] The use of an all-meat diet did not diminish the efficiency of the intestinal tract in absorbing foodstuffs.[24]

Dietary supplements—vitamins, gelatin.   Investigations regarding diet constituents have not been confined to the question of the partitioning of the three basic fuel essentials, but have included the question of supplementing the diet with specific components such as vitamins.

The question has often been raised as to whether vitamin supplements to a well-balanced diet would retard the development of fatigue. Answers vary. Keys and Henschel[25] reported no manifest effects produced by vitamin additions to the diet under a variety of conditions. Vitamin supplementation had no effect upon muscular strength, endurance, or resistance

[20] Stefansson, V.: Adventures in Diet, *Harper's, 171:* 668–675, 1935; *172:* 46–54, 178–189, 1936.

Lieb, C. W.: The Effects of an Exclusive Long Continued Meat Diet, Based on the History and Clinical Survey of Vilhjalmar Stefansson, Arctic Explorer, *J.A.M.A., 87:* 25–26, 1926.

Lieb, C. W.: The Effects on Human Beings of a Twelve Months' Exclusive Meat Diet, *J.A.M.A., 93:* 20–22, 1929.

[21] Tolstoi, E.: The Effect of an Exlusive Meat Diet on the Chemical Constituents of and Blood, *J. Biol. Chem., 83:* 753–758, 1929.

[22] Tolstoi, E.: The Effects of an Exclusive Meat Diet Lasting One Year on the Carbohydrate Tolerance of Two Normal Men, *J. Biol. Chem., 83:* 747–752, 1929.

[23] Heinbecker, P.: Studies on the Metabolism of Eskimos, *J. Biol. Chem., 80:* 461–475, 1928.

[24] McClellan, W. S., V. R. Rupp, and V. Toscani: Prolonged Meat Diets with a Study of the Metabolism of Nitrogen, Calcium, and Phosphorus, *J. Biol. Chem., 87:* 669–680, 1930.

[25] Keys, A., and A. F. Henschel: Vitamin Supplementation of U. S. Rations in Regard to Fatigue, *J. Nutrition, 23:* 259–269, 1942.

to fatigue. The tests ran 4 to 6 weeks, a period that they believed was long enough to produce any possible effect. The vitamins studied were thiamin chloride, riboflavin, nicotinic acid, pyridoxine, pantothenic acid, and ascorbic acid. Henschel[26] in another paper makes essentially the same conclusion. Other authors[27] do likewise.

Gelatin, a partly hydrolyzed protein, has been suggested as a source of amino-acid for treatment in muscle diseases such as myasthenia gravis and has been advertised to prevent fatigue. Investigators have obtained conflicting results, some finding a beneficial influence in preventing or relieving fatigue, and others making opposite claims. Hellebrandt, Rork, and Brogdon[28] found gelatin to have no effect upon the ability of women to perform maximum anaerobic work. Ray, Johnson, and Taylor,[29] using both men and women as subjects, reported that, with adequate amounts of gelatin, men were able to increase work output from 37 to 240 per cent above the "training level." The work output of the women was unchanged. The first-mentioned authors suggest that the enhancement of work output may have been due to training rather than to the gelatin. Knowlton[30] was unable to find any change as the result of feeding gelatin supplements to normal adult male rats. Induction shocks at 60 per second were employed as stimuli to the gastrocnemius muscle. No additional creatine was found in the test muscles.

Whether or not the addition of special substances to the diet has any beneficial effect on work output might well depend upon the diet of the subject previous to the experiment. Only if the diet was lacking in these substances would improvement be expected. Failure to take this into account may explain some of the diversity of results. Obviously, a continued poor diet will result in impairment, or a tendency to become easily impaired with activity. Nevertheless fatigue need not follow, unless the impairment presents a sufficient thwart to the individual.

[26] Henschel, A. F.: Diet and Fatigue, *Minnesota Med., 25:* 974–976, 1942.

[27] Foltz, E. F., A. C. Ivy, and C. J. Barborka: Influence of Components of Vitamin B Complex on Recovery from Fatigue, *J. Lab. & Clin. Med., 27:* 1396–1399, 1936.

[28] Hellebrandt, R. A., R. Rork, and E. Brogdon: Effect of Gelatin on Power of Women to Perform Maximal Anaerobic Work, *Proc. Soc. Exper. Biol. & Med., 43:* 629–634, 1940.

[29] Ray, G. B., J. B. Johnson, and M. M. Taylor: The Effect of Gelatin on Muscular Fatigue, *Proc. Soc. Exper. Biol. & Med., 40:* 157–161, 1939.

[30] Knowlton, C. C.: Effect of Gelatin Feeding upon the Strength and Fatigability of Rats' Skeletal Muscles, *Am. J. Physiol., 131:* 426–427, 1940.

Chapter IX

CONVENTIONAL VISUAL-FATIGUE STUDIES

THAT ANY chapter in the present volume should be labeled *visual fatigue* arises from two facts: (1) it has been customary to speak of certain phenomena as those of visual fatigue; and (2) although fatigue is actually not a localized phenomenon, individuals do become tired while attempting to see.

Vision involves processes that are variable in their characteristics. Both the sensory and motor aspects of visual performance are subject to changes in the course of activity. The changes may be marked, rapid, and readily reversible.

Perceptual changes may arise from variations within unitary structures, sense cells, and also from shifts in the interrelations among functional elements in a complex system, the nervous system. Variations of the first type (certain tissue changes) are called *impairment* and are analyzable on the chemical level. Changes of the second type may occur independently of impairment. These changes in organization may be viewed as *disorganization* when appropriate reference points are used. Organizational changes, for our purposes, are analyzable on the personal level, or, in other words, in terms of the individual as a whole.

It is customary to interpret the evidences of both kinds of changes as indicative of fatigue. In some cases, the "fatigue" that is deduced is impairment, in other cases it refers merely to a functional diminution, and in still others it is true fatigue. Oftentimes it is a confused combination of the three.

We may now proceed directly to a description of methods and to the specific studies of phenomena labeled visual fatigue and reserve for a succeeding chapter the discussion of visual fatigue itself.

Approaches to studying so-called visual fatigue. The ways problems in connection with alterations in visual function have been studied may be divided into five classes: (1) sensory, (2) ergographic, (3) symptomatic, (4) ease of seeing, (5) conflict.

1. *Sensory methods.* The four kinds of sensory methods utilize the following phenomena: (*a*) sensory thresholds, (*b*) fixation disappearance,

(c) adaptation, (d) flicker. Discrimination thresholds are measured repeatedly, to determine a possible change in them. If a rise in threshold is discovered, sensitivity (the reciprocal of the threshold) is said to have become diminished and this is taken as an indication of fatigue of the physiological mechanism involved. In the second method, targets are fixated steadily to determine any possible change in their appearance. This has been done with both chromatic and achromatic targets. Blurring of edges, desaturation, other qualitative alterations, or disappearance of the target are taken as fatigue, possibly of the retina. In a third method, levels of

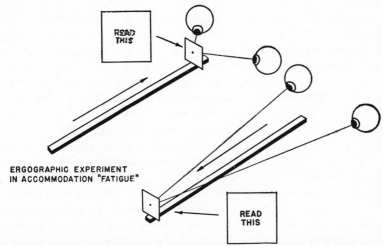

READ
THIS

ERGOGRAPHIC EXPERIMENT
IN ACCOMMODATION "FATIGUE"

READ
THIS

Fig. 32.—The essentials of the ergographic technique for studying accommodative fatigue. The card, on which small print is used, is the target and is moved back and forth along the bar. When too near, the printing naturally becomes blurred to the observer. The essentials of the experiment are discussed in the text.

photic adaptation are studied. The effects of certain amounts of preexposure to light are used to determine either monocular or binocular effects. The study of critical flicker frequency is a fourth way of studying "fatigue."

2. *Ergographic methods.* Certain investigators interested in the motor-adjustment component of the visual apparatus have subjected the ciliary and the extrinsic ocular muscles to ergographic tests. These essentially are tests in which the muscles of accommodation and convergence relax under systematic variations in stimulus conditions. The observer's eyes may have to follow a target moving to and from him or a target moving toward him till blur occurs and then look suddenly at distant target (see Fig. 32). In the case of convergence, variable prisms are used to test limits of activity. Regardless of how the demands are made in each case, they consist in hav-

ing the eye muscles contract and relax alternately as the arm or finger muscles are called upon to do in the classical Mosso ergograph. Any diminution in the amplitude between contraction and relaxation as the test proceeds is taken as ocular fatigue.

3. *Symptomatic studies.* Individuals who present ocular or visual complaints are used as subjects in these studies. The complaints after using the eyes in visual tasks may range from feeling generally tired to headache, gastrointestinal disturbances, nystagmus, blurring, and to eye discomfort itself. The complaints may be summarized as those of discomfort, inability, and fatigue.

Such individuals are given standard tasks such as reading for ½ hour. Both before and after the test period, they are given standard accommodation and convergence tests. Occasionally, their eye movements in reading are photographed by such instruments as the ophthalmograph.

4. *Ease-of-seeing methods.* Experiments of this kind are based on the presumption that external conditions have considerable influence on the ease and efficiency of visual function. In such studies, it has been customary to use some physiological (nonsubjective) indicator of the facility with which seeing occurs, the presumption being that the greater the ease, the less the fatigue, or the slower its onset. Two factors are of primary importance: the nature of the target, and the illumination used. With the elapse of time at the task, the performance that was originally relatively easy becomes less so. Presumably the easier the task, the less the measured performance aspects manifest a change with elapse of time. Those tasks which induce the greatest changes, such as increases in number of eye blinks, reductions in speed of reading, and pupillary dilatation, are considered the most fatiguing.

5. *Conflict methods.* In these methods, the visiomotor apparatus is subjected to various conditions (including extremes) to determine how the ocular muscles perform. These methods can be called conflict methods, since it has been discovered that certain situations demand action from the apparatus which it is not organized to execute. In attempting to meet this demand, certain incompatibilities develop in the timing of contraction and relaxation, so that reciprocal activity in paired muscles shifts into partly overlapped or even simultaneous contraction. This method could be expanded to include vision in a study of personal conflict, and thus go beyond certain limitations that are implied when conflict is seen only in muscular or other organic functions.

SENSORY METHODS

Sensitivity manifests some form of diminution with passage of time. This holds true for three conditions to be discussed: *viz.* (1) gross exposure of the whole or considerable parts of the retina to imaged light, (2) exposure of small areas of the retina by maintained fixation, and (3) in repeated discriminations, as in a series of observations to obtain thresholds. If the diminution is of one character, it is conventionally thought to be receptor adaptation, if of another, fatigue.

In condition 1, a kind of diminution called "adaptation" occurs regardless of alertness, stance, posture, steadiness of gaze, etc. Photochemical processes underlie much of this diminution, but in the over-all behavior outcome which is used as the indication of "adaptation," the nervous system or metabolism underlying nervous activity as a concrete physiological datum must not be neglected. In condition 2, diminution of function takes on the form of blurring and ultimate disappearance.

In condition 3, the result may accrue from unavoidable diminutions of general alertness as well as events specifically ocular. It is not certain how alertness should be defined, but it is observed that muscle tone, etc., are concomitants of what is usually taken to be alertness. Alertness flags under some conditions more than others, as was shown in McFarland, Holway, and Hurvich's[1] experiment on maintained posture.

Sensory thresholds. Threshold observations are the most common kind of measurement made in studying sensory function, and it is presumed that, within limits, threshold readings show no systematic decline during the course of an hour's time. McFarland, Holway, and Hurvich investigated the possible decline in sensitivity (reciprocal of threshold) during a 30-minute period. To do this, they limited the observers to steady posture during this test period. Ten-minute intervals were injected between successive test periods. Some of these intervals were spent in maintained constant posture, others in moving about. Following the maintained-posture intervals, the subjects made no recovery in sensitivity lost during the test period, whereas following the intervals spent in motion and postural adjustment, sensitivity improved regardless of whether a light source equal in intensity to the one used in the sensitivity measurements was fixated or whether the subject remained in the dark. The decline in alertness incident to retaining a fixed posture was assigned as the reason for decline in sensitivity, along with the apparently inevitable decrease in cerebral circulation which goes hand in hand with quiescence. Although the individuals may have become tired of their task, the relation of this fatigue and sensitivity was not worked out.

Fixation-disappearance methods. Under some conditions a small area steadily fixated blurs and finally disappears. This occurs incidentally in

[1] McFarland, R. A., A. H. Holway, and L. M. Hurvich: "Studies of Visual Fatigue," Graduate School of Business Administration, Harvard University, Cambridge, Mass., 1942. Pp. 255.

certain laboratory setups and has been the object of study. One significance of this phenomenon was brought into Lancaster and Williams'[2] experiment on accommodation fatigue, which will be mentioned later.

The effect of steady fixation was involved in Geldard's study of retinal fatigue. Geldard[3] photometrically matched two halves of a disk after exposure of the one-half to the eye for various lengths of time. In one set of experiments the second half of the disk was imaged on the adjacent area of the same retina, and in another set of experiments it was presented to the other eye. After 20 seconds' exposure of the first half disk, only 55 per cent of the physical intensity was required in the second half disk for the two to match in brightness, if the binocular procedure was used. If the images of the two half disks fell on adjacent areas of the same retina, only 28 per cent of the intensity of the first, or exposed, half disk was required for the second half disk in the matching procedure. This was taken to mean that during exposure of the one half disk, not only the retinal area imaging the disk, but also the adjacent areas underwent change in sensitivity. The retinal area receiving the stimulation was affected alike in all cases. Since to provide for brightness equality the adjacent area required less intense stimulation than an equal area in the opposite eye, it must have become particularly sensitive. Thus while the stimulated area became less sensitive (adapted, fatigued), the adjacent area was affected in the opposite direction.

Geldard found that the opposite changes in sensitivity in the two areas ceased at the same time. Although Geldard imputed these effects to the retina, the conditions of experimentation do not rule out the possibility of crucial participation of higher centers.

So-called color fatigue, a diminution phenomenon, has long been the object of study. Cogan and Cogan[4] point out that there are three ways in which color may diminish and vanish. (1) A colored object may desaturate and become part of the background. This, they say, is perhaps best observed with red, which changes rapidly at first and then more gradually. They find the course of change in a target at 10 degrees from the fovea to be an initial darkening followed by a progressive graying and ultimate vanishing. This may happen as quickly as in 15 seconds. The graying is not uniform, but develops as waves of grayness sweeping across the color field. When the color has completely vanished, the achromatic quality of the

[2] Lancaster, W. B., and E. R. Williams: New Light on the Theory of Accommodation, with Practical Applications, *Tr. Am. Acad. Ophth.*, pp. 170–195, 1914.

[3] Geldard, F. A.: The Measurement of Retinal Fatigue to Achromatic Stimulation. I and II, *J. Gen. Psychol., 1:* 123–135, 578–590, 1928.

[4] Cogan, D. G., and F. C. Cogan: Color Fatigue in the Peripheral Field, *Ophthalmologica, 96:* 137–154, 1938.

area persists until eye movements occur. (2) The second manner of disappearance is less common but not rare. It is a sudden disappearance not only of the colored area, but also of the immediate background to be substituted by a granular form of blackness. The authors report never finding this kind of result with binocular fixation, but almost uniformly after one eye has been blindfolded for about 15 minutes. Dark adaptation of the nonexperimental eye and light adaptation of the test eye are most favorable for the phenomenon. This type of disappearance is both more sudden and more irregular than the first kind. (3) A rarer type involves the disappearance of the immediate background prior to that of the colored area.

The following are the results from Cogan and Cogan's experiments: (1) A progressive decrease in disappearance-time from fovea to periphery; (2) the longest time required for disappearance of objects at a given distance from center was in the lower temporal quadrant; and (3) the shortest was in the upper vertical field; (4) the disappearance-times for green were generally the shortest, red the longest, and other colors inconsistently between; (5) generally the larger the colored area, the longer the time required for disappearance; (6) the times for disappearance of blue and red were shortened upon dark adaptation; (7) the time for color disappearance increased with stimulus intensity; and finally (8) binocular disappearance-time was about equal to monocular.

Recovery of color perception was measured by the same authors.[5] A large screen with a square hole cut in it and fixation points 10 and 30 degrees from the opening were used. Behind the screen a magenta-red stimulus and substitute secondary stimuli were suddenly alternated in accordance with the plan of experimentation. The observer first looked at the magenta area, and after a constant time (time usually required for disappearance) the red surface was removed from behind the opening, leaving a gray surface exposed. This gray square was observed for various periods of 1 to 150 seconds. At the end of the designated time, the red surface was lowered into view behind the opening and observed till it lost its color. This time measured the amount of recovery that had taken place. All readings were made binocularly. This procedure was then repeated with a green (complementary to the red) square in place of the gray one.

The results of the study were as follows: (1) A *light*-gray secondary square preceding the second exposure of red caused the red to take longer to disappear than did a *dark*-gray one, but recovery in both cases required about 40 seconds. (2) Use of a green secondary square involved no materially different recovery time than did gray of an equal brightness.

[5] Cogan, F. C., and D. G. Cogan: Recovery Time from Color Fatigue in the Peripheral Vision Field, *Ophthalmologica, 96:* 267–276, 1939.

(3) Recovery was shorter at 30 degrees from the fovea than at 10 degrees.

(4) Eye movements seemed to have no appreciable effect on recovery time.

Adaptation methods.   McFarland, Holway, and Hurvich classify light and dark adaptation as a kind of visual fatigue in their monograph.[6] Troland[7] wished to consider phenomena in this field in neutral terms and to avoid commitment with regard to fatigue, adaptation, recovery, etc. He suggested the terms *minuthesis* and *auxesis* as names for decrease and increase of sensitivity.

Dark adaptation is an increase in sensitivity to small amounts of light and is produced by withdrawing stimulation. Recovery from previous stimulation is allowed to take place during this adaptation period. Light adaptation is reduced sensitivity to light, making possible a differential response to large amounts of light. The first effect of exposure to light after dark adaptation is a peculiar floor of undifferentiated subjective brightness which may be strong enough to produce pain. This extreme sensitivity diminishes rapidly, soon reaching a degree allowing orderly and highly differentiated activity. Intensity relations can best be discriminated at this point. Shortly following this, diminution of sensitivity occurs, and the individual is less well able to distinguish gradations in intensity.

Undoubtedly, photochemical changes in the retina are involved in "adaptation," but neurophysiological processes also play an important role.

Certain experiments in photic adaptation have led to the surmise that the perceptual result is not patterned by the retinal contribution alone. For example, Elsberg and Spotnitz[8] assert that *the effect of binocular pre-adaptation on uniocular vision last longer than it does on binocular vision, and not so long as uniocular preadaptation on uniocular vision.* If this kind of complication exists, there are important factors beyond the photochemistry of the eyes to be taken into account.

The problems pertaining to the separate contributions of the two eyes have customarily been dealt with under the title of "binocular summation." Binocular summation or interaction has been shown to exist, but it so happens that adaptation has conventionally come to be thought of solely in terms of ocular photochemistry.

[6] McFarland, Holway, and Hurvich: *op. cit.*

[7] Troland, L. T.: The Laws of Visual Minuthesis: The Threshold Pre-exposure Time and the Equilibrium Time for a Projected Negative After-image, *J. Franklin Inst., 181:* 579–581, 1916.

   Troland, L. T.: The Laws of Visual Minuthesis: The Influence of Intensity on the Equality Time-function, *J. Franklin Inst., 181:* 855–856, 1916.

[8] Elsberg, C. A., and H. Spotnitz: Factors Which Influence Dark Adaptation. *Am. J. Physiol., 120:* 689–695, 1937.

McFarland, Holway, and Hurvich[9] attempt to dispose of Elsberg and Spotnitz's results by stating that the experiments were inadequately designed and that more evidence is necessary before accepting the attribution of binocular effects in dark adaptation. More evidence is to be desired, but the direction of Elsberg and Spotnitz's conclusions is consistent with their findings.

McFarland, Holway, and Hurvich used a setup in which no contralateral preadaptation was employed. Thresholds for a foveally fixated patch slightly over 3 degrees were obtained, alternating uniocular and binocular observations. The result of using two eyes was about equivalent to using the more sensitive one of the pair. It is not certain that the alleged contradiction between the two sets of findings precludes taking them both at face value.

Flicker methods. The experience resulting from intermittent stimulation at high rates is the same as though stimulation were continuous and uniform. Flashing lights are seen as steady illumination at rates dependent upon the intensity of flash, flash duration in relation to the intervening dark intervals, and the area of the flashing surface, etc. This "fusion" property of the visual mechanism has been used in experimentation to test physiological state or function, the presumption being that a neural system that can respond to the high rates of intermittency by an intermittency of its own (sensation, etc.) is functionally better than one that responds by continuity. The flash rate at which full subjective uniformity just occurs is called the critical flicker frequency (c.f.f.), and its value is taken as an indication of functional state. The higher the c.f.f., the better the functional state usually is assumed to be.

Various workers have attempted to use c.f.f. as an index of fatigue, or as we would say, impairment. Certain workers[10] have obtained indication that c.f.f. changes with lack of sleep, with the time of day, etc. Other workers have had much less success in revealing consistent and significant difference. Some of the latter[11] were, however, able to say that following loss of sleep a higher intensity of light was necessary to induce fatigue at a fixed frequency, but no systematic distinctions between morning and afternoon readings were found. A higher average intensity for a given

[9] McFarland, Holway, and Hurvich, *op. cit.*

[10] Lee, R. H.: IV. Critical Fusion Frequency of Flicker. In Fatigue and Hours of Service of Interstate Truck Drivers, *U. S. Pub. Health Service Bull.* 265, 1941.

Simonson, E., and N. Enzer: Flicker and Fatigue, *J. Indust. Hyg. & Toxicol.*, *23:* 83–89, 1941.

Simonson, E., N. Enzer, and S. S. Blankenstein: The Influence of Age on the Fusion Frequency of Flicker, *J. Exper. Psychol.*, *29:* 252–255, 1941.

[11] McFarland, Holway, and Hurvich, *op. cit.*

c.f.f. was found to be required in older persons throughout the whole range of intensities tested. The differences between ages were greater at the higher illuminations. This might be expected, for it is at high levels (high c.f.f.'s) that the greatest demands in temporal terms are made on the nervous system.

ERGOGRAPHIC METHODS

The ergographic method consists in (1) measuring amplitude of accommodation when in a series of trials the subject tries to prevent blurring as a target is brought close to the eye, or (2) measuring fusional reserve of convergence when in a series of trials prevention of diplopia is attempted as increasingly strong prism power is interposed.

The ergographic method is the outgrowth of the assumption that visual fatigue is a condition either of the muscles, or some other part of the organism, which becomes manifest in deficiencies of muscle behavior, especially diminution of contraction.

Ergographic studies of fatigue of accommodation.   Lancaster and Williams[12] in 1914 studied accommodation. Their experiments consisted in prolonged reading of fine print, prolonged focusing on objects at the point of greatest accommodation, serial attempts to eliminate blur of objects nearer than the near point, and processional and recessional pursuit of a test object. Occasionally during experimentation, near point was measured. At the end of the experiments, the same was done for the far point. They found that both near and far points were usually brought closer to the eyes with practice, this procession continuing even after an hour of repeated trials. Other subjects, however, demonstrated a recession after a half hour, but this occurred only with strict fixation on a single part of the target. In the experiments, there were few reports of fatigue.

Howe,[13] using a self-recording ergograph, found diminution in the amplitude of accommodation which he termed fatigue. From the results, he was able to place his subjects in six different classes based on muscle characteristics.

Blatt[14] reported a ready recession of the near point and long periods required for recovery in patients showing various types of pathology. He

---

[12] Lancaster, W. B., and E. R. Williams: New Light on the Theory of Accommodation, with Practical Applications, *Tr. Am. Acad. Ophth.,* pp. 170–195, 1914.

[13] Howe, L.: The Fatigue of Accommodation, *J.A.M.A., 67:* 100–104, 1916.

Howe, L.: The Fatigue of Accommodation as Registered by the Ergograph, *Tr. Sect. Ophth., A.M.A.,* pp. 130–142, 1916.

Howe, L.: Registration of Fatigue of Accommodation, *Tr. Am. Ophth. Soc., 15:* 145–153, 1917.

[14] Blatt, N.: Weakness of Accommodation, *Arch. Ophth., 5:* 362–373, 1931.

suggested that recession was influenced by disease toxins acting on the accommodation center in the brain.

Berens and Stark[15] found in their study of 195 subjects a decrease in accommodative amplitude in 30.8 per cent of the cases, an increase in a similar percentage, and no change in the remainder. They used a card of small letters, and the range of excursion was only 20 cm. beyond the average near point.

Hofstetter[16] more recently used the ergographic technique in three types of experiments.

1. *Sustained effort.* The smallest letters the subject was able to see at the remotest distance provided by the ergograph were determined. The test target monocularly viewed was then brought slowly toward the observer who reported when blur occurred. The target was then slowly moved away till the letters cleared. This type of experiment required of the observer a continuous effort to keep the letters clear.

2. *Repeated efforts.* In this case the target was brought closer and closer till blur was reported, whereupon the target was quickly restored to its starting position. Both monocular and binocular tests were made.

3. *Alternation of far and near accommodation.* This procedure differed from the last in the following respect: while the target was being returned to its starting position, the observer was asked to fixate upon a chart of letters 5 m. away, requiring an almost complete relaxation of accommodation between trials. As an alternative for producing this relaxation, a $+3.00\,D$ lens was added to the observer's distance correction, bringing his far point within the range of the ergograph. By moving the target back and forth until the letters blurred at both ends of the excursion, alternate measures of far and near point were recorded.

The outcome of Hofstetter's experiments was as follows: (1) Amplitude diminution was elicited more readily by repeated effort than by the sustained effort.[17] Hofstetter entertained the opposite expectation, *viz.,* that the "sustained" effort would be greater, and uses his findings in this particular to support the idea that the basis of diminution of amplitude is not in the ciliary muscle itself. (2) There was definite lack of correlation between symptoms of discomfort and amplitudes of accommodation expected

[15] Berens, C., and E. K. Stark: Fatigue of Accommodation, *Am. J. Opth., 15:* 527–542, 1932.

[16] Hofstetter, H. W.: An Ergographic Analysis of Fatigue of Accommodation, *Am. J. Optom. Arch. Am. Acad. Optom., 20:* 115–135, 1943.

[17] This is not unexpected when it is recalled that ocular and other visual adjustments are usually continuous affairs made in order to follow the movement of objects, and not repeated alternate and rapid jumps between near and far points. Thus sustained effort, although calling for more or less continuous adjustment, is not so extreme in the acceleration and excursion demands upon the ciliary muscle.

to permit satisfactory vision for close work. There seemed to be no relation between the individual's reports of symptoms of fatigue and a ready recession of the near point disclosed by the ergograph. This applied to symptoms both in the subject's everyday life and during the tests themselves. (3) Diminution in amplitude was the exception rather than the typical result on the ergograph tests; it was unpredictable, often disappeared suddenly and "spontaneously" with added or renewed effort, a change in attitude, or following distraction. Both the procession and recession of the near point were so rapid as to be entirely out of line with the subject's normal visual requirements. (4) No diagnostic significance could be given to fatigue found by the ergograph technique. Hofstetter dismisses the idea that the fatigue occurs in the ciliary muscle. In fact, he cannot think of it occurring in the neuromuscular junction, the ciliary ganglion, or even in the nucleus of the third cranial nerve, but places it in the higher centers of the brain.

McFarland[18] studied the effect of conditions at high altitudes on accommodations and convergence, by the ergographic technique. The test object was moved toward the subject's eye till blur developed, whereupon the test card was reset to the original starting distance and a new trial made. Each test consisted in 10 minutes of repetitions at a rate of about 30 to 36 strokes per minute. Ergograms of the performance at sea level and at 9,200, 12,020, 15,440, and 17,500 ft. above sea level were presented. The profiles of diminishing amplitudes of successive excursions were called "fatigue curves." As altitude increased, the decrease in amplitude of accommodation developed progressively earlier, and the rate of diminution was more rapid. At high altitudes, a full 10 minutes of performance was not possible. Changes in performance were taken to be indications of fatigue. McFarland stated that deterioration of convergence was quite similar to that of accommodation.

SYMPTOMATIC METHODS

The implication of symptomatic methods is that exercising the eye muscles of individuals with ocular complaints will disclose ocular behavior not produced in "normal" individuals. This behavior, of course, is expected to manifest itself in the usual clinical tests for phorias, etc. Although those employing this method do not literally define visual fatigue, the subjects' complaints are interpreted as signs of it. The search for possible concrete physiological components proceeds from such a point. This method is similar to the preceding one inasmuch as it involves the expec-

[18] McFarland, R. A.: Psycho-physiological Studies at High Altitudes in the Andes. II. Sensory and Motor Responses during Acclimatization, *J. Comp. Psychol.*, 23: 227–258, 1937.

tation that static accommodation and convergence tests relate closely to behavior in reading and other practical situations. In "ergographic" concepts of visual fatigue, the presence of subjective symptoms is incidental, for the criterion was the actual behavior of ocular muscles.

Kurtz[19] had his subjects read for periods of 30 minutes, before and after which they were tested with an ophthalmograph, a camera by which the eye movements in reading are photographed. Common clinical tests, including one for accommodative amplitude, were also used.

Of his seven subjects, only one showed a considerable decrease in amplitude of accommodation. The other six showed practically no change, although they reported the conventional symptoms of fatigue: a tired feeling of the eyes, difficulty in keeping the eyes open, eye ache, "drawing" of the eyes, feeling as though nystagmus were present, itching of the eyes, periodic disappearance of print, difficulty in reading, and diplopia. In addition to these more or less ocular symptoms, some mentioned a general feeling of tiredness. The single subject showing decreased accommodative amplitude reported a tired feeling of the eyes, need of effort to keep the eyes open, occasional fading of the type, headache, and a general feeling of tiredness. This individual had to spend about $4\frac{1}{4}$ seconds longer in reading 150 words at the end of a 30-minute reading period than at the beginning. Twelve more fixations were made during the fatigue test than in the control.

The salient point in this study is the fact that the static test for amplitude of accommodation was negative in most of the cases despite the existence of annoying subjective symptoms and a definite loss in reading ability as shown by the ophthalmograph. Not only was there discomfort and poor performance, but definite fatigue was reported in some cases. This study demonstrated that, although amplitude of accommodation and fusional reserve remained in the normal range, unfavorable symptoms and fatigue developed.

EASE-OF-SEEING METHODS

Ease-of-seeing methods imply that the crucial factors in seeing lie in the physical conditions, exemplified in illumination, etc. (see Fig. 33). Ease-of-seeing methods also imply that there is a relation between performance and fatigue and that both fatigue and difficulty of performance increase in the course of a task. Frequently little distinction has been made between "difficulty" as a subjective state and decrement in performance. Various investigators have sought "physiological indices of difficulty" to use in preference to measuring performance in the task involved—work output.

[19] Kurtz, J. I.: The General and Ocular Fatigue Problem, *Am. J. Optom.*, *14:* 273-280; 308-317, 1937.

These indices are involuntary activity such as heart beat, blinking, skeletal muscle tension, and pupil area. These are thought to be influenced little if at all by the individual's attention to them and thus are believed to be "true" measures of the subject's state. These physiological measures are used in test situations in which size and form of a test object and level of illumination are varied. Reading prints varying in size, style, color, and

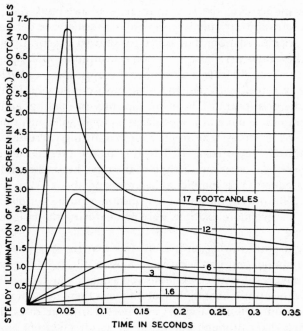

Fig. 33.—The temporal course of brightness sensation with stimuli of different intensities. The curves are from data of Broca and Sulzer. (*Luckiesh and Moss: "The Science of Seeing," D. Van Nostrand Company, Inc.*)

degree of "contrast" with page have been employed to reduce the test situation to practical terms.

Illumination and near point. It has been found that by raising illumination the near point for clear vision is made to proceed toward the eye. Since the pupil constricts as intensity of light is increased, the reduced aperture could be expected to contribute to sharpening the retinal image, other features of the optical system remaining constant. This in effect is equivalent to an added amount of accommodation; hence objects slightly beyond the near point would be expected to require less accommodation (see Fig. 34).

Ferree and Rand[20] found, in nonpresbyopic subjects ranging from 20 to 41 years, that the effect of change of intensity upon distance of near point was more marked above 30 years than below. Ferree and Rand considered the possible role of the pupillary aperture in the procession of near point. They measured the effect with three pupil diameters, 3.45, 2.76,

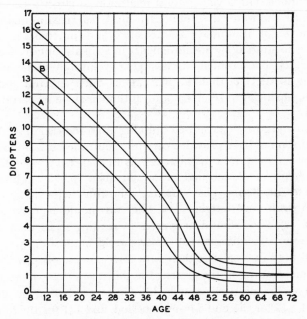

Fig. 34.—The decrease in amplitude of accommodation with increase in age. Curves *A, B,* and *C* indicate minimum, average, and maximum amplitudes respectively. (*Luckiesh and Moss: "The Science of Seeing," D. Van Nostrand Company, Inc.*)

and 2.56 mm., equating the light flux. About one-third of the effect could be attributed to focusing action of the reduced pupil over a range of 1 to 25 ft.-c. Over this intensity range as much as 4 diopters was added to the range of accommodation. Ease and possibly skill in using the eyes in close vision were increased.

Ocular muscle behavior. Luckiesh and Moss[21] report that "convergence reserve" with 1 hour's reading diminshes three times as much under 1 ft.-c. as under 100 ft.-c. Even more marked differences in convergence re-

[20] Ferree, C. E., and G. Rand: Intensity of Light in Relation to the Near Point and the Apparent Range of Accommodation, *Am. J. Ophth., 18:* 307–318, 1935.

[21] Luckiesh, M., and F. K. Moss: Fatigue of Convergence Induced by Reading as a Function of Illumination Intensity, *Am. J. Ophth., 18:* 319–323, 1935.

serve were found in a prolonged study[22] on key-punching operators working under illuminations of 10 and 60 ft.-c. measured daily for 6 weeks. The decrease in convergence reserve was four times as great under the low illumination.

Rate of involuntary blinking.   Blinking, with other eyelid movements, has been studied with a view toward relating it to larger aspects of physiology. Ponder and Kennedy[23] found that blink rate remains unaltered over a wide range of illumination intensities and in complete darkness. Blount,[24] who studied eyelid movements in animals, obtained essentially similar results. The problem of classifying eyelid movements is a crucial one, owing to the fact that the movements differ in kind and possible origin. Discrepancies in results among authors may be in part due to this complexity.

Luckiesh and Moss[25] have used blinking as an indication of the ease of seeing and seem to have provided carefully controlled conditions for their tests. They report quite consistent results in 81 persons possessing either normal or corrected-to-normal vision, in about 5,000 reading periods, totaling over 400 hours. They state the following "self-evident facts" pertaining to strain and fatigue: (1) The two should increase as reading continues. (2) They should be greater in reading small than large type under the same conditions. (3) They should be greater with incorrect refractions used in eyeglasses than with correct ones. (4) They should be greater while reading in the presence of glare than in its absence.

In an hour's reading, the average blink rate was 100 for the first 5-minute period, 146 for the mid 5-minute period, and 171 for the final period. When the blink rate of 12-point type was 100, the corresponding blink rate for 6-point was 148. When experimental errors of $\frac{1}{2}$ diopter were introduced, the blink rate rose from 100 to 144 blinks for a plus error, to 140 for a minus error. The effect of glare produced by a 50-watt frosted lamp 3 ft. from the eye and 20 degrees above the line of regard was indicated by a rise from 100 to 156 blinks per 5-minute period.

The relation of illumination and blink rate was found to be as follows. When reading at 100 ft.-c., the blink rate was 100; at 10 ft.-c. it was 115, and at 1 ft.-c., it was 154. The percentage increase in blinks during an

[22] Luckiesh, M., and Moss, F. K.: "The Science of Seeing," D. Van Nostrand Company, Inc., New York, 1938. Pp. 548.

[23] Ponder, E., and W. P. Kennedy: On the Act of Blinking, *Quart. J. Exper. Physiol.,* *18:* 89–110, 1927–1928.

[24] Blount, W. P.: Studies of the Movements of the Eyelids of Animals: Blinking, *Quart. J. Exper. Physiol., 18:* 111–125, 1927–1928.

[25] Luckiesh, M.: "Light, Vision and Seeing," D. Van Nostrand Company, Inc., New York, 1944. Pp. 323.

hour's reading was found to be 6 for 100 ft.-c., 31 for 10 ft.-c., and 72 for 1 ft.-c.

McFarland, Holway, and Hurvich[26] also investigated blink rate as a possible index of fatigue and were unable to obtain consistent results. Some subjects manifested an increase in blinking, others a decrease, and still others showed no change as the task proceeded. For this reason they concluded that blink rate is not a valid indication of fatigue and that it may serve as a preventive of fatigue. McFarland, Holway, and Hurvich also object to the use of blink rate as an indication of fatigue, since illumination is said to control blink rate and shifting illumination up and down reverses the rate quite rapidly. They claim that this reversal is too rapid to allow for recovery from fatigue.

Pupillary behavior and ease of seeing. A test on office workers[27] disclosed that over a period of 4 weeks the average increase of pupil area during the day's work was 15 per cent. Not only was there an increase during the day which was reversed each night, but as the work week passed the reversal was less and less complete. This is to say that at the end of the week the average pupil area was greater than at its beginning. Luckiesh and Moss deduce fatigue from this type of finding.

Tinker[28] conducted a number of tests both to determine the critical illumination for speed in reading and the critical illumination for fatigue in reading. He defined the critical level of illumination as the one beyond which no further increase in efficiency of performance was found. In the first case, this is the level above which no added speed in reading was found, and in the second, the level below which no added disturbance to clear seeing was found. Tinker's definition of fatigue uses failure (the failure to see clearly) as its criterion.

Beutell[29] found the following to be some of the levels of illumination for efficient performance: clerical work, 6 ft.-c.; surgical operations, 70 ft.-c.; tennis court, 24 ft.-c.; drafting room, 12 ft.-c.; corridors, 2 ft.-c. Six-point type setting was found to need 25 ft.-c., a figure comparable to that of Tinker.

Luckiesh[30] recommends much higher values than these. However, when we consider that stimulus values should be reckoned in logarithmic terms,

---

26 McFarland, Holway, and Hurvich: *op. cit.*

27 Luckiesh and Moss, *op. cit.*

28 Tinker, M. A.: Illumination Standards for Effective and Comfortable Vision, *J. Consult. Psychol., 3:* 11–20, 1939.

29 Beutell, A. W.: An Analytical Basis for a Lighting Code, *Illuminating Engineering (British), 27:* 5–11, 1927.

30 Luckiesh, *op. cit.*

doubling or trebling an absolute value is not so great a change as it otherwise appears to be. The following are Luckiesh's suggestions:

Foot-candles	
1-5	Insufficient for reading and similar critical seeing. Satisfactory for seeing large objects and for room lighting for conversation
5-10	Interrupted or casual visually controlled work
10-20	Ordinary reading and sewing on light material
20-50	Fairly critical and prolonged work
50-100	Proof reading, drafting, watch repairing, etc.
100 or more	Severe and prolonged fine tasks

In 1938, a school lighting code called "American Recommended Practice" suggested 15 ft.-c. as a minimum illumination for desks and tables. Still other recommendations have been made.[31]

Paterson and Tinker[32] found that type sizes between 9 and 12 points can be read equally fast and that beyond 12-point and below 9-point reading speed decreases. These authors not only noted speed, but also studied eye movements associated with the variant of type size, using the Minnesota eye-movement camera.

Use of the Luckiesh and Moss visibility meter indicates a 30 per cent greater visibility for the 10-point than for 6-point type.

Ten-point type was read more efficiently than 14-point, though the differences in eye movement were not the same as in the first comparison. The fixations were greatly increased for the 14-point type. Pause duration, however, became less for the 14-point than the 10-point, a reversal of the 6- and 10-point comparison. Again there is a difference in favor of the 10-point type for regressions, though it is slight and not reliable. The authors point out that one factor in the reduced efficiency in reading 14-point type is the increased printing area that must be covered per unit of text material.

Tinker and Paterson[33] in 1928 showed a more than 13 per cent advantage in reading speed for lower-case type. Later,[34] eye-movement photographs showed that this advantage is associated with increasing the num-

[31] Adams, S.: "The Effect of Lighting on Efficiency of Rough Work," His Majesty's Stationery Office, London, 1935.

Allphin, W.: Influence of School Lighting on Scholarship, *Tr. of the Illuminating Engineering Soc.* (*N. Y.*) , *31:* 735-754, 1936.

[32] Paterson, D. G., and M. A. Tinker: Influence of Size of Type on Eye Movements, *J. Appl. Psychol., 26:* 227-230, 1942.

[33] Tinker, M. A., and D. G. Paterson: Influence of Type Form on Speed of Reading, *J. Appl. Psychol., 12:* 359-368, 1928.

[34] Tinker, M. A., and D. G. Paterson: Influence of Type Form on Eye Movements, *J. Exper. Psychol., 25:* 528-531, 1939.

ber of fixations in reading the all-capital type and a corresponding decrease in the number of words per fixation. Total time required for perception is increased despite shorter pauses per fixation. Apparently the difficulties met with in reading all-capital printing do not upset the habitual pattern of fixation sequences, since regressions are equal in number in the lower-case and all-capital reading.

Atkins[35] performed an extensive study of visual performance under different conditions of illumination. The visual field was divided into two parts in terms of illumination level. The one was the work sheet with a reflectance of 66 per cent, and the other were the surroundings which in some cases were black, having a 3.9 per cent reflectance, and in others, white, having an 80 per cent reflectance. Three visual tests were applied. The first was a number cancellation test (Johns Hopkins Number Work Test). The second was a so-called coordination test, in which the subject was required to draw a pen line through a narrow path and to synchronize the strokes with a 72 per minute metronome beat. The third test was the Chain Association Test of Bates. A measure of pulse rate was also made.

CONFLICT METHODS

Conflict methods of studying visual fatigue emphasize the *organizational* aspect of the behavior of the individual. Attention is especially directed to the so-called "reflex acts" to show how even these are capable of disorganization. One significant form of this disorganization occurs as simultaneous contraction of muscles, which under other conditions reciprocally contract and relax. Such opposition is accompanied by discomfort as well as by ineffectual behavior.

A number of years ago, Dodge[36] made some observations that are pertinent here. He used horizontal eye movements to study the interrelations of the various extrinsic ocular muscle activities. As he said, the activity of 12 closely related and delicately adjusted final common paths involved in important biological behavior could be studied by this method.

The performance Dodge studied was a series of repeated ocular excursions back and forth in a horizontal direction. By use of a spot of light reflected from the cornea, these excursions were photographically recorded for determining amplitude and velocity. What he called the "angle of velocity of the movements" was maximum only when the relaxations of antagonistic muscles were perfectly coordinated with contractions of the others. Dodge partly recognized that movement was a product of organi-

35 Atkins, E. W.: The Efficiency of the Eye under Different Intensities of Illumination, *J. Comp. Psychol.*, 7: 1–37, 1927.
36 Dodge, R.: The Laws of Relative Fatigue, *Psychol. Rev.*, 24: 89–113, 1917.

zation; hence what he calls the "pseudo work decrement" is not purely muscular, but is in part a case of "defective coordination." The increasing errors were said to have the same origin. He showed that the over-all coordination of the contraction and relaxation of the several muscles involved becomes less exact in successive repetitions of the fixation act. As evidence that the excursions were not dependent upon the internal and external recti muscles alone, Dodge pointed out a vertical component in the movements. All records showed an elevation of the line of regard, varying from movement to movement. Since the deviations were homologous in the two eyes, they could not be purely muscular accidents, but rather were taken to be examples of central-nervous involvement.

Pupillary conflict. Certain experiments have revealed that disorganization can occur within oculomotor reflexes. This disorganization is demonstrated in pupil behavior. Owing to the oppositional arrangement of the two sets of muscle fibers, the pupil constricts as illumination is increased and dilates as illumination is decreased. The action of both groups of fibers is relatively slow, and one would expect that it could not keep pace with rapidly changing conditions from light to dark, and vice versa.

Although several workers have studied time factors in the contraction of the two sets of fibers, few have studied the outcome of serial flash stimulation directly. Bartley[37] believed that the pupil played a crucial part in the discomfort that arose in the course of brightness discrimination under stimulation with "subfusion flash frequencies." Halstead[38] showed that when the pupillary mechanism was immobilized by drugs, the usual discomfort was not elicited by slow flashes.

The flash-frequency range that Bartley used ran from about one flash in $4\frac{1}{4}$ seconds to four or five flashes per second. The slowest rates allowed enough time for the pupil to dilate almost fully, while the fastest rates went beyond the point just providing for a stationary pupil. As flash rate rose, the amplitude of excursion between constriction and dilatation diminished. (When the rate reached between three and four per second, the pupil became stationary.) He found that as flash rates rose the contraction of the one set of fibers began before proportionate relaxation of the other occurred. Contractions in the two opposing sets of muscles began to overlap, and a tug of war developed. The final stationary state of the pupil came about as a deadlock rather than as an easygoing reciprocity. The existence of a sizable degree of independence between the behavior of the two sets of muscle fibers as implied in Bartley's findings was further

37 Bartley, S. H.: A Factor in Visual Fatigue, *Psychosomatic Med., 4:* 369–375, 1942.

38 Halstead, W. C.: A Note on the Bartley Effect in the Estimation of Equivalent Brightness, *J. Exper. Psychol., 28:* 524–528, 1941.

shown by Lowenstein and Givner.[39] They found that there is a pupillary dark reflex which remains after the obliteration of the light reflex in certain cases of trauma. Bartley,[40] in a theoretical paper, placed this view of ocular discomfort in a larger framework in which conflict was related to the production of fatigue. More recently, further clarifications[41] were made in this general view of fatigue.

An example of functional disorganization that may arise within the oculomotor mechanism occurs when an observer is required to gaze steadily

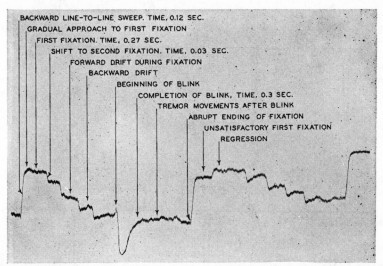

Fig. 35.—The eye movements made in reading two successive lines of print. The details are labeled in the figure. The record indicates mainly the gross over-all movements resulting from the combined action of the several extrinsic ocular muscles. A method of measuring contributions of the separate muscles so as to disclose any existing conflict in their operation is needed. (*Luckiesh: "Light, Vision, and Seeing," D. Van Nostrand Company, Inc.*)

into darkness midway between two lights for 5 minutes. In an experiment performed by Bartley,[42] two small bright lights were placed about 60 degrees apart in a dark visual field. No fixation point was provided. The eye movements of the observers were watched, and the observers were asked to report effort, discomfort, etc., at the end of each observation period.

[39] Lowenstein, O., and I. Givner: Pupillary Reflex to Darkness, *Arch. Ophth., 30:* 603–609, 1943.

[40] Bartley, S. H.: Conflict, Frustration and Fatigue, *Psychosomatic Med., 5:* 160–163, 1943.

[41] Bartley, S. H., and E. Chute: A Preliminary Clarification of the Concept of Fatigue, *Psychol. Rev., 52:* 169–174, 1945.

[42] Bartley, S. H.: A Factor in Visual Fatigue, *Psychosomatic Med., 4:* 369–375, 1942.

Bartley found not only that steady fixation was impossible, but also that the attempt to maintain it involved the observers in much difficulty and discomfort. Nystagmus sometimes occurred, and, at best, gaze varied within the area between the two lights. The observers, however, were not always aware of their eye movements, but sometimes only of the effort and dis-

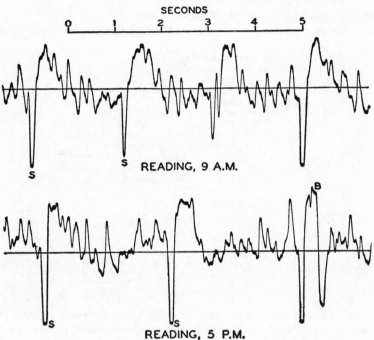

Fig. 36.—Reading records taken at two different portions of the day. It will be seen that the record taken later in the day is somewhat more irregular. This irregularity suggests that the eye muscles are not working smoothly but are exerting extra pull against each other in an incoordinated way. S = shift from the end of one line to the beginning of next. B = blink. Time taken for reading 3 lines varied from 0.100 minute to 0.137 minute. The frequency of fixational pauses increased from 7 to 11. (*Luckiesh and Moss: "The Science of Seeing," D. Van Nostrand Company, Inc.*)

comfort that they experienced. Observations of the eye movements indicated that momentary fixations were accomplished only by conflicting oculomotor adjustments.

Conflict in oculomotor behavior is also observable in reading records. Samples of reading records are given in Figs. 35 and 36 from Luckiesh and Moss. Further study with an aim toward analysis of intermuscle conflict would be profitable.

Chapter X

HOURS AND CONDITIONS OF WORK IN INDUSTRY

IN DEALING with fatigue in industry, the main concern has long been with matters of sheer exertion. These have been expressed in quantitative terms, such as number of body movements made during unit time, amount of lifting, number of pieces of goods processed as related to the length of work day, and rest periods. Tasks have been thought to be more fatiguing when more measurable energy was required of the worker. Despite the attempt to confine attention to energy concepts, it has also been found that fatigue is in some way related to monotony and that poorly motivated workers become tired before their better motivated fellows. In industry, fatigue has generally been defined in terms of productivity alone and has been classified on various utilitarian bases, with little regard to underlying psychophysiology.

Early studies. Until 1912,[1] there were only a few isolated industrial studies dealing with effects of hours of work on output. Beginning his observations in 1816, and continuing for a period of 12 years, Robert Owen found that a 10½-hour day was as productive as a 16-hour day in his cotton mills. In 1893–1894, Mather and Platt discovered the 48-hour week gave the same annual output as a 53- or 54-hour week in the Salford Iron Works.[2] From 1899 to 1901, Abbé found an 8-hour day gave 3 per cent greater total earnings than a 9-hour day at the Zeiss Optical Works.

Some major auspices for industrial studies. More elaborate studies of the effects of hours of work began in 1913 when the British Association for the Advancement of Science appointed a committee to study fatigue from the economic standpoint. This was followed in 1915 by the appointment of the Health of Munitions Workers Committee by the Ministry of Munitions. Following the war, this committee was renamed the Industrial Fatigue Research Board, and later the Industrial Health Research Board. In the United States, investigations have been carried on under the auspices

[1] Flinn, F. B., *et al.:* Industrial Fatigue, *Am. J. Pub. Health, 23:* 74–78 *(Yearbook Suppl.)* , 1933.

[2] Vernon, H. M.: "Industrial Fatigue and Efficiency," George Routledge & Sons, Ltd., and Kegan Paul, Trench, Trubner & Co., Ltd., London, 1921. Pp. 264.

of the United States Public Health Service[3] and state health departments. Private industry has also made some notable contributions. Many types of work have been studied, from heavy steel manufacture and mining, to light mechanical operations and clerical work.

Factors thought responsible for fatigue. Vernon[4] has classified the factors responsible for fatigue into three categories: (1) time spent at work, (2) character of the work, (3) conditions under which it is performed. Fisk[5] has added another category, *viz.*, the condition of the individual, referring specifically to state of nutrition and health. Both health and nutrition depend largely on industrial conditions, or viewed from another standpoint, they may represent a state of fatigue, either initial (brought to the job) or basic (produced in the long run by the job).

Although there has been no separation of fatigue and bodily impairment in industrial studies, it is occasionally recognized that the fatigue problem cannot be dealt with exclusively by measuring work output. It is also occasionally recognized that the study of fatigue cannot even be confined to physiological or biochemical activity. Investigations have failed to disclose any characteristic pattern in the physiological state which could be called fatigue. Certain authors who study the physiological effects of exertion admit that definitions of fatigue covering such things as depletion of energy reserves, accumulation of lactic acid, and insufficiency of oxygen have scarcely any connection with some fatigue states.[6] Among the bulletins of the last several years there appears to be an increasing recognition of the personality factor. The American Public Health Association's Committee on Industrial Fatigue[7] states that it has veered from the physiological aspects of the problem of fatigue toward the psychological and psychiatric.

The measurement of industrial fatigue has been attempted primarily in five ways: (1) variations in work output, (2) sickness and mortality, (3) frequency of accidents, (4) lost time and ruined work, and (5) labor turnover. Studies focused on factory conditions include a number of miscellaneous factors, such as excessive hours of work, split shift, abnormal atmospheric conditions, defective lighting, noise, monotony, and awkward posture and movements.

Measurement of output. Work output has been investigated in various

[3] Florence, P. S.: The 48-hour Week and Industrial Efficiency, *Internat. Labor Rev., 10:* 729–758, 1924.

[4] Vernon, H. M.: "Health in Relation to Occupation," Oxford University Press, London, 1939. Pp. 355.

[5] Fisk, E. L.: Industrial Fatigue, *Am. J. Pub. Health, 18:* 1465–1469, 1928.

[6] Dill, D. B., A. V. Bock, H. T. Edwards, and P. H. Kennedy: Industrial Fatigue, *J. Indust. Hyg. & Toxicol., 18:* 417–431, 1936.

[7] Flinn *et al., op. cit.*

ways. Curves have been plotted for output from hour to hour during the day and for successive days during the week. Output has also been noted in relation to changes in schedule, *i.e.,* before and after changes in the number of working hours, before and after the interspersion of rest periods, and before and after vacations and holidays.

The general principle that fatigue *decreases* output while alleviation of fatigue *increases* it is demonstrated by all the methods of investigation. The cumulative effects of hours of work on the efficiency of the worker are indicated in a gradual decrease in rate of production toward the end of the day and the week. A diminution in the total hours worked is generally found to increase the rate at which work is accomplished. When fatigue has been extreme, a reduction in hours may accelerate production more than enough to compensate for the loss in time.

Lipmann[8] points out that a reduction in hours may yield contradictory results in terms of output since other factors may also be operative. Efficiency of plant organization, wage incentives, distribution of reduced hours, and the worker's physical and emotional state may play a complex part in the net result. Differing relative amounts of machine and hand work in various industries may account for some disagreement in results. Lipmann states that the more precise the data on which a report is based, the more often increased output from a reduction in hours is represented, or its absence accounted for by nontemporal factors. On the other hand, reports based on mere estimates often indicate decreased output from reduction in hours of work.

Wyatt,[9] in studying efficiency in cotton weaving in relation to hour and day, found the following to be true. (1) A longer time was taken to attend to loom stoppages in the afternoon than in the morning. (2) Monday morning showed less efficiency than Tuesday morning, and from Tuesday on, each succeeding day showed measurably less efficiency. (3) The point of maximum efficiency for the day tended to move up from the end of the morning on Monday to its beginning on Friday. He concluded that the drop in efficiency was due not to a habitual relaxation of effort owing to approach of mealtime, but to fatigue or impairment becoming greater as the week progressed.

The typical work-output curve manifests a gradual rise during the first few hours of the working day followed by a steady decline after the third or fourth hour. Production increases after the lunch hour, although decline soon sets in again, the postlunch output never reaching that of the prelunch period. The chief factors influencing the work curve are *prac-*

[8] Lipmann, O.: Hours of Work and Output, *Internat. Labor Rev., 9:* 481–506, 1924.

[9] Variations in Efficiency in Cotton Weaving, *Great Britain Medical Research Council, Industrial Fatigue Research Board, London, Rep. 23,* pp. 35–39, 1923.

tice, impairment, neuromuscular disorganization, and *fatigue.* Practice and motivation increase the rate of production; impairment and neuromuscular disorganization decrease it; fatigue, while it may ultimately reduce or preclude productivity, has a less determinate relation to output. The work curve is also influenced by such factors as pacing and working against time.

The output pattern differs for various kinds of work. At two plants (8- and 10-hour day) studied by the U.S. Public Health Service,[10] several kinds of work were compared with respect to output. Where skill and manual dexterity were needed, output manifested a definite rise in the early part of the week and a less marked fall toward its end. This was true also for the work spell. In machine work, which is paced and less dependent upon the human factor, output was more nearly uniform through the day and hence relatively high in the afternoon. In work requiring heavy muscular exertion, less increase in output occurred, and an earlier and more definite decline ensued. Impairment would appear to be a large factor in output in heavy muscular work, where organic limitations figure more largely. An output curve for mental work would again differ somewhat in general character.

In some studies it has been found that the output on Monday morning is lower than that for any other morning, supposedly due to loss of practice efficiency over the week end. The output quickly rises and then before the week is over drops again almost to where it was on Monday.[11]

Length of working day and week. Studies of the relation of production and work output to length of the work day and week have been of two sorts: (1) questionnaires and interviews, and (2) objective measurements. As might be expected, the results of the former have been contradictory.

Vernon's summary[12] will serve as an example of the latter type of study.

Observations over a peroid of 13½ months upon the output of workers making fuses showed that a reduction of working hours was followed by a relative and absolute increase of production. The production rate increased gradually for 4 months and then remained constant for the rest of the period observed. The gradual change negates any suggestion that the

[10] Comparison of an Eight-hour Plant and a Ten-hour Plant, *U.S. Pub. Health Service Bull.* 106, 1920.

[11] Preliminary Notes on the Boot and Shoe Industry, *Great Britain Medical Research Council and Department of Scientific and Industrial Research, Industrial Fatigue Research Board, London, Rept. 10,* 1920.

[12] Further statistical information concerning output in relation to hours of work with special reference to the influence of Sunday labour, *Gr. Brit. Ministry of Munitions, Health of Munition Workers Committee, London, Mem.* 18, 1917.

effect was due merely to the workers' desire to maintain the same wages although the hours were reduced.

An opportunity to compare output under three conditions was given by a change from a 12-hour day to a 10-hour day, and then by the abolition of Sunday labor. A study was performed on a group of women engaged in turning aluminum fuse bodies. When the hourly rate and gross production for 66.2 hours per week was taken as a reference, it was found that for 54.8 hours per week the hourly production increased 34 per cent and the gross production, 11 per cent. When the work week was reduced to 45.6 hours, the hourly production increased 58 per cent and the gross production, 9 per cent.

Quantitative studies have also been made in cases where the number of hours of work per day was *increased*.[13] In an English munitions plant during the First World War the shift was changed from $8\frac{3}{4}$ to $10\frac{1}{2}$ hours. This increase of $1\frac{3}{4}$ hours per day resulted in the loss of 1 hour's output per day. Decrease in production resulted in an American war plant when the work day was extended by the addition of "overtime." When $2\frac{2}{3}$ hours was added to the normal 10-hour working day, two groups engaged in loading the powder ring of a fuse lost, respectively, 5.5 and 6.5 per cent in hourly rate of production. The two groups showed 4.9 and 3.9 per cent loss, respectively, on the normal day following overtime work. Although the amount of work done was greater on the day with overtime, the labor costs were augmented out of all proportion. The total productivity was 18.4 per cent greater with overtime, while labor costs were 40 per cent higher, owing in part to the combined effect of reduced output rate and time and one-half being paid for overtime work. Florence points out that if overtime were added to the normal work day on 2 days during the week, the enhanced output would amount to 5.48 per cent, with the wage cost increasing by 13.33 per cent. If a day with added overtime plus a normal day is compared with two normal days (not preceded by a day with overtime), the added output is 7.24 per cent, while the wage cost is increased by 20 per cent. This indicates that the real cost of overtime is not $1\frac{1}{2}$ but over $2\frac{3}{4}$ times the base rate.

A temporary reduction in output is sometimes the immediate result of a shift to shorter working hours. Following a transition period there appears to be recuperation from the effects of long hours, and output is increased.[14] This suggests that impairment as much as fatigue may be responsible for reduced output in prolonged working periods.

[13] Florence, P. S.: "Economics of Fatigue and Unrest and the Efficiency of Labor in English and American Industry," Henry Holt and Company, Inc., New York, 1924. Pp. 426.

[14] Bentinck, H. C.: 'Industrial Fatigue," P. S. King, London, 1918. Pp. 43.

The rates of production in the tinplate industry[15] were found to increase when working days were shorter than 8 hours. With a reduction from 8- to 6-hour shifts, the hourly production rose 10 per cent, and the total output was 8.3 per cent greater. When the shifts were reduced to 4 hours, the hourly production rate was 11.5 per cent greater than that of the 8-hour shift. But owing to the great time reduction in the shift, the increase in hourly rate could not maintain gross production.

It is recognized in an occasional industrial study that work output and fatigue are not necessarily parallel. May Smith,[16] in discussing the results of a study made on laundry workers, states the belief that fatigue is greater toward the end of the working day than the observed reduction in output would indicate. She points out that, even if there is no observable decrease in output as the day wears on, fatigue may well be present. Smith suggests that a certain customary standard of production is maintained, but at a greater exertional cost to the worker.

Such an analysis constitutes an important advance over the usual viewpoint, for it recognizes the individual as a system capable of compensating to reach a goal or maintain a level of activity.

Smith cites certain qualitative facts that substantiate her conclusions. Even though production may not diminish noticeably during the last hours of the work day, changes are known to exist in the workers. The workers are not only aware of these changes, but take them into account in planning their work. A case in point is that of one hand ironer of shirts who always attempted to do the ironing of overmeticulous customers early in the day for the expressed reason that she did not feel equal to the care it would entail toward the end of the day. According to Smith, this is a fatigue effect, and one not measured in quantitative studies of output.

Rest periods.   Rest periods may be of two general sorts, the voluntary and the formal. The former refers to incidental pauses the worker takes at irregular intervals on his own volition, the latter to those introduced by the management and spaced in a predetermined manner. The formal rest periods are intended for all workers in the plant or department simultaneously or in shifts. A weekly day of rest and periodic longer vacations have also received attention from those studying fatigue, and both have been deemed necessary.

Voluntary or spontaneous rest periods have been studied[17] as an at-

[15] The Influence of Hours of Work and of Ventilation on Output in Tin-plate Manufacture, *Great Britain Medical Research Council and Department of Scientific and Industrial Research, Industrial Fatigue Research Board, London*, Rept. 1, 1919.

[16] Some Studies in the Laundry Trade, *Great Britain Medical Research Council, Industrial Fatigue Research Board, London*, Rept. 22, 1922.

[17] Vernon, H. M., and T. Bedford: Rest Pauses in Heavy and Moderately Heavy Industrial Work, *Industrial Fatigue Research Board*, Rept. 4, 1927.

tempted measure of fatigue. Vernon believes that the use of rest pauses is the worker's form of self-protection in industries where management has not undertaken a formal study of the fatigue problem. Voluntary rest periods were found quite constant in occurrence, and fairly regular after the first hour of continuous work, both in the morning and the afternoon. Various industries were found to differ in the time used in pauses. In road building the average time was 10.9 minutes per hour; in dock labor, 11.2 minutes; in agriculture, 10.3 minutes; in boot and shoe making, 2.9 minutes; in tinplate rolling, 6.3 minutes. In general, pauses were fewer and shorter during the second hour of the morning and afternoon than in succeeding hours. Moore,[18] in commenting on the findings, states that except for this, the regularity with which pauses are taken gives no indication of accumulated fatigue.

The number, placement, and duration of rest periods should vary not only with the kind of work, but also with the individual working. Possibly no other single item illustrates so well the factor of individual differences. A recognition of individual differences would conflict with the current practice of thinking and planning in terms of statistical norms. In industry, individual differences are often completely ignored for administration purposes.

A wide variety of patterns of work and pause have been tried in several different kinds of work situations. Only one or two examples are necessary here. In a manufacturing concern, 40 minutes of work was followed by 20 minutes of pause. Although the pause required the hiring of one extra person for every two initially employed, the enhanced production rate and employee satisfaction more than compensated for the added cost. One mill department[19] tried a tapered pattern of work and 10 minute pauses. The first work period lasted for 2 hours; later the period was decreased to 1½ hours, and then to 1 hour, the assumption being that at the end of the day 1 hour is as exhausting as a longer period in the morning.

Rest periods are particularly essential to work that (1) is repetitive and unvaried, (2) requires strict attention, (3) involves constant physical exertion, (4) calls for maintained postures such as standing or even sitting more or less rigidly, (5) involves exposure to extremes in temperature, humidity, or other untoward conditions. When used judiciously, rest periods have almost invariably resulted both in greater employee satisfaction and in increased production.

When used unwisely, rest pauses may have deleterious effects. In many jobs the flow of work is not uniform, and pauses are introduced only by

[18] Moore, H.: "Psychology for Business and Industry," 2d ed., McGraw Hill Book Company, Inc., New York, 1942. Pp. 526.

[19] Mayo, E.: Revery and Industrial Fatigue, *J. Personnel Res.*, *3:* 273–281, 1924.

force of circumstance. All too often, managements assume that pauses of this sort take the place of formal rest periods. At times the nature of the work is such that employees would prefer fewer rest pauses and a shorter total working day. The manner of use of the time during rest periods may also present a problem.

Night work. Night work has also been the subject of study.[20] Some investigators strongly disfavor night work for anyone, pointing out several unfavorable conditions that it almost invariably involves. The night-worker's sleep is likely to be disturbed by the presence of daylight and the extra noise and the greater heat in the daytime. An added problem of constant readjustment is involved in the necessity of periodically changing each employee from night to day shift to equalize the disadvantages for all employees. In the case of women workers, rest is likely to be interrupted by home duties, as other members of the household live by a daytime schedule. The leisure of night workers is also curtailed, since public entertainment is not provided on a round-the-clock basis.

Poor ventilation and industrial anoxemia. Anoxemia, which is so commonly referred to in connection with special physical conditions such as those involved in high-altitude flight, may also occur under a variety of industrial conditions. In anoxemia the quantity of free oxygen in the blood is abnormally low. In industry, anoxemia is usually a mild chronic condition.

Anoxemia may develop in three ways: (1) by insufficient intake of oxygen, (2) by insufficiency in the load of available oxygen in arterial blood owing to physiological deficiency of the hemoglobin, and (3) by defective circulation. The first may arise from shallow breathing, and the last may arise from cramped posture, lack of body movement, or the lack of the stimulating effect of good ventilation. The extent to which these untoward conditions arise in various kinds of work is not well known, and slowly accumulated effects of oxygen lack are difficult to study. The situation is complicated by the fact that chronic anoxemia does not conform to any recognized disease syndrome. The cases are typically diagnosed as general debility, secondary anemia, or as pretuberculosis. Haldane suspected that shallow breathing led to the production of anoxemia, which in turn seemed a responsible factor in the cases of neurasthenia he studied in the First World War.

Various authorities recognize that anoxemia can develop under milder conditions than might be supposed. Collier[21] believes that slight anoxemia

20 Hayhurst, E. R.: Medical Argument Against Night Work Especially for Women Employees, *Am. J. Pub. Health, 9:* 367–368, 1919.

21 Collier, H. E.: "Outlines of Industrial Medical Practice," The Williams & Wilkins Company, Baltimore, 1943. Pp. 440.

is the basis for much mild chronic illness among industrial workers. He points out that apparently insignificant faults in ventilation may produce particularly marked effects upon neurasthenic and anemic workers.

The ill effects incident to poor ventilation are not initially those of diminshed oxygen supply. Ill effects occur directly from the absence of cool moving air contacting exposed body surfaces. Poor ventilation enhances any tendency to retreat into sluggishness. In the absence of moving air, the circulatory and muscular systems do not receive the necessary stimulation for maintenance of tone.

Collier says that a subjective factor is usually apparent both in the symptoms and in the origin of anoxemia. Sufferers from chronic and mild anoxemia, he claims, are usually introspective and unsocial. They are often victims of a feeling of inadequacy and inferiority. At the same time they are characteristically inclined to resist suggestions that might better their health.

Posture. The significance of posture as a factor in work situations and in everyday well-being is often overlooked. Too often the consequence of poor posture is underestimated, and the correction of the conditions inducing it neglected.

Farmer[22] studied the problem of posture in relation to fatigue and pointed out that it was advisable to determine whether shifting from sitting to standing, and vice versa, would reduce fatigue in daily work. He found that the employment of seats for work that could as well be done in a sitting position reduced fatigue and increased output. Fewer rest periods were required. In everyday work, fixed standing positions should not be maintained for long periods on account of their circulatory effects, if for no other reason.

The health of well-muscled apparently robust individuals is sometimes impaired by the task of truck driving. Not only is the doubled-up sitting position maintained for long periods, but considerable over-all muscular tenseness, the bodily concomitant of alertness, is required. Tenseness alone would be unfortunate, but its relation to retarded digestion is an additional ill consequence.

Collier[23] recognizes that liability to indigestion and anoxemia is incurred by improper posture. Collier adds that faulty posture may be one of the important contributory causes in muscular rheumatism, lumbar pain, and adolescent scoliosis.[24]

Faulty posture, whether improper in form, or too rigidly held for a long

[22] Farmer, E.: Time and Motion Study, *Indust. Health Res. Board, London, Rept.* 14, 1921.

[23] Collier, *op. cit.*

[24] Scoliosis is lateral curvature of the spine.

period of time, has both immediate and long-term cumulative effects. The immediate effects are obvious, but the long-term results are more obscure and consequently difficult to demonstrate.

An example of current fatigue classification. Collier lists five kinds of industrial fatigue: (1) physical fatigue, (2) temporary fatigue, (3) learner's fatigue, (4) subacute fatigue, and (5) chronic industrial fatigue.

Collier states that in the diagnosis of true industrial fatigue it is essential to rule out cases of "normal" tiredness that show (1) quick disappearance with rest and (2) reoccurrence only when an adequate amount of work has been performed. Collier's "normal" fatigue, in addition to being undistinguished from impairment, is an idealization. It seems parallel to the idealized type of physical deterioration or diminution in function that used to be studied by simple ergographic techniques. "Temporary" fatigue, he states, is manifested in a sudden and abrupt fall in output. Both the tired feeling and the drop in efficiency form defenses against harm to the individual in much the same way as does pain.

His learner's fatigue is an example of conflict operating to produce impairment and fatgue. Learning involves development of efficiency and harmony out of awkwardness.

A TYPICAL FIELD STUDY OF "FATIGUE"

"Fatigue" of truck drivers. This study is included here as an example of the work done in this field. The investigation was made partly under the auspices of the Interstate Commerce Commission and represents one of the most pretentious attempts of its kind on record.

A few years ago the U. S. Public Health Service undertook a study of fatigue in truck drivers.[25] The attempt was to determine the relation between hours of driving since "major sleep" and deterioration of performance in a battery of laboratory and performance tests, rather than simply to determine the relation between hours of work, impairment or fatigue, and number of accidents.

The investigation was divided into preliminary tests and a main group of field tests. A total of 889 drivers were examined. Most of the subjects were the "over-the-road" type of drivers carrying on interstate commerce. The drivers were classified according to number of hours worked per week and according to the number of hours of driving since "major sleep." The divisions of the first classification were (1) under 50 hours, (2) 50 to 59.9 hours, (3) 60 to 69.9 hours, and (4) 70 or more. The second variable was broken into three divisions, 0 hours, 0.1 to 9.9 hours, and 10 or more hours. Age trends were also noted. Over 66 per cent of the drivers were between

[25] Fatigue and Hours of Service of Interstate Truck Drivers, *Pub. Health Bull.* 265, **1941.**

20 and 35 years old, 86 per cent were below 40, 13 per cent were between 40 and 49, and 1 per cent were over 49.

The tests were not performed equally well by men of all ages, but the hours of driving constituted a greater differentiating factor. The greatest difference in relation between test performance and hours of driving since "major sleep" was shown in the older men. Except for speed of tapping, it was found that the most marked age trends were manifested in those tests which showed the greatest differences with hours of driving. The most marked age trends were manifested after long periods of driving.

The term *fatigue* as used in the study referred to a psychophysiological state imputed from deterioration in performance on the tests. Only the consistent change on a number of tests (constituting typical syndrome) was interpreted as evidence of fatigue. Decrements in single tests were ignored.

Functions showing consistent decrement with hours of driving, in order of amount, were speed of tapping, reaction coordination, body sway, manual steadiness, vigilance (steering efficiency combined with brake reaction time), simple reaction time, and flicker. Functions showing a less consistent relation to hours of driving were glare resistance, eye movement (saccadic interval), aiming, steering efficiency, heart rate, white (blood) cell count, diastolic blood pressure, and brake reaction time. Factors showing no change were blood potassium, blood total base, acidity of urine, differential white cell count, and spatial perception. The drivers did better in the test for strength of grip following driving.

At best this study succeeded in making a survey of the kinds of laboratory tests and performances that are affected by hours of truck driving. As might be expected, this procedure revealed nothing concerning the relation of fatigue to hours of driving.

The following is a quotation from Johnson's recent critique[26] of the methods used in this study:

One might have expected the study to begin with an adequate census of the distribution of hours of labor and rest among many truck drivers who have gone accident-free during a representative period. This information should have been easy to obtain if the ICC required the keeping of such records as are necessary to an intelligent evaluation of this problem. One might have expected also a census of the recent histories of work and rest of many drivers who had just been involved in accidents. A combination of the two censuses would have shown whether there is a tendency for accidents to be associated with prolongation of labor beyond limits that the census itself would set, and would indicate where the ICC would establish a reasonable margin of safety. This was not done . . . the authors began to search for Something that no one could identify if he found

[26] Johnson, H. M.: Index-numerology and Measures of Impairment, *Am. J. Psychol.,* *56:* 551–558, 1943.

it: namely, something which is *measureable* and which also corresponds to *fatigue* as defined by the legendary Man-on-the-Street. This Something has to be related in some determinable manner to hours of labor, and if possible to accident liability.

It happens, however, that the annual rate of accidents per operator of trucking companies is very low. So is its corresponding mileage rate of accidents. The variance of either rate is therefore almost exactly equal to the rate itself. Moreover, according to a very careful study made under the supervision of C. J. Tilden for the Highway Research Board of the National Research Council, on many fatal highway accidents investigated with unusual care, nearly every accident seems to be due to a set of conjoined conditions or causes, each being necessary but being in itself insufficient. If the samples are large enough, however, predisposing tendencies (when present) can be detected. Where insurance companies can detect them, there also can an agency of the federal government.

The study, as it stands, is one of the best arguments that could be found for the reexamination of the whole current outlook on the fatigue problem.

Chapter XI

DRUG ACTION IN RELATION TO FATIGUE AND IMPAIRMENT

The action and effects of drugs. Drugs act directly on tissue—the blood cells, glands, nervous system, and muscles. The particular tissues affected depend upon the avenue and rate of intake and upon the drug itself. Chemistry in the test tube is controllable and understandable. Since drugs are chemicals it is easy to assume that drug effects may be deduced fairly well in line with the predictability of chemical laws. But such an assumption is erroneous.

Drug action may be said to be localized, but *drug effects* transcend localization. Although drug action is to be understood in chemical terms, drug effects appear on the physiological and personal levels.

Various effects are commonly attributed to drugs. Drugs may expedite or check the transformation of energy; they may enhance or reduce the feeling of well-being; they may increase or decrease the urge to activity. Drugs may also influence the character of activity by raising or lowering sensory thresholds and by altering judgment and self-assessment. Drugs are effective in instigating and in reducing or obliterating pain. They may make sleep impossible or induce sleep and even total anesthesia.

Any substance that might be found to expedite the transformation of energy, enhance the feeling of well-being, and increase the urge to activity could well be looked upon as a helpful support in prolonged periods of work. Such a substance would be expected to postpone the onset and acute development of fatigue.

Any substance that lessens the degree of self-criticism precludes certain kinds or degrees of conflict. Certain conflicts fail to develop when the individual is unable to evaluate his behavior adequately. This was brought out in dealing with anoxia.

Drug effects depend, of course, upon many factors. One individual is not like another, and even when age, weight, time of day, state as gauged by amount of recent muscular exertion ("fatigue") are considered, the pertinent conditions are still not all taken into account. The individual's mood and purposes, his habitual consumption of the drug, habituation to

187

other drugs, amount of other drugs present in the body, the weather and the season, etc., are also to be considered. Generally, a number of these factors are omitted, but consideration of them is necessary to account for the lack of uniformity in the results from person to person, and from time to time in the same person.

Explanation of the contradictory outcomes in drug studies rests also on the way data are treated. In drug studies it is typical to work for a standard result, although it is recognized that uniform results are scarcely obtainable. To remedy this, a large number of subjects are used and the results averaged. In this way a "standard answer" is obtained at the price of accuracy. Individual variations are masked. Often no specific trend in drug effect is demonstrated, though under everyday conditions an effect is known to exist.

Kinds of drug studies. The biological action of drugs is studied both in isolated preparations and in the intact organism. In the latter case, two kinds of studies appear in the literature: (1) clinical and (2) experimental. In the clinical, the individual's verbal report and the physician's observations of behavior furnish the data. In the experimental, specific tests are set up by which quantitative comparisons are attempted.

It is generally felt that more precise information is obtainable in studies on isolated tissue. It is customarily assumed that the results of studies on isolated tissue also apply to the intact organism. Certain discrepancies result, however, when attempts are made either to attribute the behavior of the individual directly to what we know about tissue, or to deduce the role specific tissue effects will play in personal behavior.

Loci of drug action. The most significant location of drug action is the nervous system. The nervous system is not uniformly sensitive to drugs. The central, peripheral, and autonomic divisions are differentially affected, and even within these there is no uniformity of effect.

Drug action also involves muscle behavior. Some drugs, caffeine, for example, affect muscle tissue directly, but more commonly muscular modification occurs only through the nervous system or the neuromuscular junction.

Cushny[1] divides the drugs acting on the nervous system into three main classes: those depressing the central nervous system, those stimulating it, and those acting on the autonomic nervous system. In the first class (central depressants) six subdivisions are made : (1) narcotics of the methane series, including *alcohol* and the choloroform group; (2) the general anesthetics, including ether, chloroform, nitrous oxide, ethylene, cyclopropane and propylene, and avertin; (3) the soporifics or hypnotics of the chloral

---

[1] Edwards, C. W., and J. A. Gunn: "Cushny's Pharmacology and Therapeutics," 12th ed., Lea & Febiger, Philadelphia, 1940. Pp. 852.

and the *barbituric acid* groups; (4) *the opium series,* including apomorphine and bulbocarpine; (5) *the bromides;* and (6) cannabis. In the second class (central stimulants) are, for example, strychnine, picrotoxin, and *caffeine.* In the third class (the autonomic drugs) are four groups: (1) the *nicotine* group, (2) substances stimulating parasympathetic nerve ends, including the muscarine group, choline, acetylcholine, etc., physostigmine, and pilocarpine; (3) substances depressing parasympathetic nerve ends, including the atropine series; and (4) stimulants of sympathetic nerve ends, including epinephin, and ephedrine. Amphetamine sulfate is treated separately, but it is closely allied to these two drugs.

Substances suspected of acting on peripheral tissue (sense organs) are the salicylates and quinine. Disorders of sight and hearing are sometimes induced. Whether this arises from some vascular disturbance or through action on the nerve cells is not certain.

Quinine is somewhat different from other important alkaloids, in its greater lack of specialized action. It seems to affect the nutrition of almost all kinds of protoplasm. Quinine affects hearing more often than sight. Degenerative changes in retinal nerve cells and even optic-nerve atrophy have been attributed to continual use of quinine, but it has not been decided whether vascular effects induce this or whether the "primary lesion" is nervous.

Since most chemical substances can be tasted, it can be said that they act on the peripheral nervous system. Since the main effects of this action are sensory, they are seldom considered drug effects.

One of the most important loci of drug action is the autonomic nervous system. This system is divided into two parts, the sympathetic and the parasympathetic. Some drugs affect one part and some the other, and in so doing produce especially complex and diverse end results. The sympathetic and parasympathetic ganglia tend to act alike toward poisons such as nicotine, but postganglionically, reactions to drugs tend to be restricted to one or the other of the two innervations. They tend to be either sympathomimetic or parasympathomimetic. Epinephrin, ergotoxine, and cocaine are examples of the former, and pilocarpine, choline, muscarine, physotigmine, and atropine, of the latter. The propagation at synaptic junctions of the two systems involves specific neurohormones belonging to these two groups. The sympathetic system has been called *adrenergic,* and the parasympathetic, *cholinergic.* Although there seem to be distinguishing physico-chemical features between the two systems, there are certain drugs that act mainly on parts of one of the systems or on parts of both. Possibly most or all of the drugs that act on striated muscle directly or indirectly act on the autonomic system. Most cholinergic drugs affect striated muscle. Adrenergic substances, while not usually affecting contraction and tonus or striated muscle, are believed to affect its metabolism.[2]

The following table indicates the principal autonomic innervations. The *S* indicates sympathetic. *P* indicates parasympathetic. The small letters indicate portions of the system, such as *v* for vagal, *s* for sacral, and *t* for tectal.

PRIMARY AUTONOMIC INNERVATIONS

	Pressor action (augmentation)	Depressor action (inhibition)
Heart and blood vessels......................	S	P
Vasodermal system...........................	S	Ps
Gastric sphincters............................	Pv	Pv
Intestinal sphincters.........................	S	Ps
Intestinal muscles...........................	Pvs	S
sphincter	Pt	
Iris		
radial	Ṡ	
circular................................	Pt	
Ciliary		
radial and long...........................	S	
Autonomic ganglia (both divisions)............	P	
Genital system (uterus and ureter).............	S	S

SUBSTANCES USED TO PROMOTE ACTIVITY

Caffeine.   Caffeine and its allies have been studied not only for action upon muscle tissue, but also for many systemic effects. They have been used as analeptics in narcotic poisoning, as relaxers of bronchial spasm, as relief in asthma, as heart stimulants, and as diuretics. Caffeine belongs to what are called the methylxanthines, which include theobromine, aminophylline, and xanthine. These drugs have four general physiological actions. They increase excitability of the central nervous system, increase "ease of muscular contraction," produce vasodilatation, and produce diuresis. Caffeine is the best known though not the most powerful member of the group. It was isolated from coffee by Runge, Pelletier, and Caverton, and also by Robiquet in 1820. The alkaloid in tea was identified as caffeine in 1838 by Jobst and Muller. Since this time, the drug has been studied in many ways.

The effects of caffeine in postponing and relieving "fatigue" can be laid

[2] Sollmann, T. H.: "A Manual of Pharmacology," 6th ed. W. B. Saunders Company, Philadelphia, 1942. Pp. 1298.

in part to the peculiar combination of physiological results just mentioned. Caffeine can be said to modify tissue function; hence it bears upon what we have called impairment. In retarding impairment it postpones fatigue which might otherwise arise from the individual's realization of his own waning accomplishments and rising inadequacies. Caffeine increases the total energy output of muscle stimulated directly. Addition of the drug to unstimulated excised frog muscle multiplies its oxygen consumption four to twenty-four times.[3] Oxygen consumption in nerve is enhanced in weak concentrations and depressed in strong.[4]

Numerous studies, ranging from those on excised muscle (both smooth and skeletal) to ergographic and dynamometer experiments on the intact individual, have led preponderantly to the conclusion that the drug has a stimulating effect on muscular activity. Results have varied owing to diversity of conditions and lack of controls.

Mosso[5] was the first to note the effects of caffeine on ergographic output.

Hoch and Kraepelin (1896) [6] and Oseretzkowsky and Kraepelin (1901)[7] reported that caffeine increased the amplitude of muscle contraction, but not the number of contractions before exhaustion; hence the results were attributed to caffeine's action on muscle. This conclusion was based on the idea, then current, that the *number* of contractions of a muscle in an ergographic setup is related primarily to the state of the nervous system, while the *amplitude* of the contractions is determined by the state of the muscle. It was not long until further work revealed that the caffeine action did not pertain exclusively to contraction amplitude. Rivers and Webber[8] found that amplitude in one subject and number of contractions in another could be altered by caffeine. Since it is a well-known fact that caffeine has a decided influence on mental activity as well as on the isolated neuro-muscular preparation, it could hardly be expected that its action would be limited to muscle tissue.

[3] Saslow, G.: Oxygen Consumption and Respiratory Quotient of Caffeinized Frog Muscles, *J. Cell. & Comp. Physiol., 10:* 385–394, 1937.

[4] Sherif, M. A. F.: The Effect of Certain Drugs on the Oxidation Processes of Mammalian Nerve Tissues, *J. Pharmacol. & Exper. Therap., 38:* 11–29, 1930.

[5] Mosso, A.: Les lois de la fatigue étudiées dans les muscles de l'homme. Mémoire I, *Arch. ital. de biol., 13:* 123–186, 1890.

[6] Hoch, A., and E. Kraepelin: Über die Wirkung der Theebestandtheile auf körperliche und geistige Arbeit, *Kraep. Psychol. Arbeit., 1:* 378–488, 1896.

[7] Oseretzkowsky, A., and E. Kraepelin: Über die Beeinflussung der Muskelleistung durch verschiedene Arbeitsbedingungen. V. Der Einfluss von Alkohol und Coffein, *Kraep. Psychol. Arbeit., 3:* 587–690, 1901.

[8] Rivers, W. H. R., and H. N. Webber: The Action of Caffeine on the Capacity for Muscular Work, *J. Physiol., 36:* 33–47, 1907.

Caffeine was found to increase the creatine content of muscle,[9] even after curare, and this was attributed to increased sympathetic muscular tone. Caffeine has no effect on peripheral nervous structures when taken by mouth.[10]

Foltz, Ivy, and Barborka[11] found variation in the amount of effect in subjects given caffeine, as tested by their double-work-period technique.

Hollingworth[12] studied the effects of caffeine on motor speed (tapping), coordination (typewriting, etc.), association (color naming, opposites, calculation, etc.), and choice (size-weight illusion, cancellation, discrimination reaction time, etc.) Sixteen subjects were studied over a period of 40 days. He found that in general the effect on the motor processes comes on quickly and is only transient, whereas the effect on the "higher mental processes" develops more gradually and lasts longer. He felt that the results obtained with caffeine were definitely "drug effects" and not the results of suggestion, knowledge, or any such factor.

The table on page 193 is a modification of the original table of results.

It seems obvious that the functions investigated by Hollingworth are dependent upon neuromuscular organization rather than upon large transformations of energy. It will be noted that "stimulation" or acceleration was the most frequent effect, though in some cases no change was observable. The effects listed appeared anywhere from ¾ hour to the day following caffeine ingestion. Retardation in discrimination reaction time and cancellation were found. Since this retardation came the following day, it may have represented final depression, the early acceleration stage having been too slight to detect. On the other hand, the retardation may not have had any significant relation to the caffeine.

Although Hollingworth believes that his results are to be attributed to physiological changes brought about by the caffeine, he points out that he is unable to say whether a new supply of energy is made available, whether energy already usable is employed more efficiently, or whether organiza-

[9] Reisser, O.: Über Tonus und Kreatingehalt der Muskeln in ihren Beziehungen zu Wärmeregulation und zentral-sympathischer Erregung, *Arch. f. exper. Path. u. Pharmakol., 80:* 183–230, 1917.

[10] Aubert, H.: Über den Coffeingehalt des Kaffeegetränkes und über die Wirkungen des Coffeins, *Pflüger's Arch. f. d. ges. Physiol., 5:* 589–628, 1872.

Aubert, H., and A. Dehn: Über die Wirkungen des Kaffees, des Fleichextractes und die Kalisalze auf Herzthätigkeit und Blutdruck, *Pflüger's Arch. f. d. ges. Physiol., 9:* 115–155, 1874.

[11] Foltz, E., A. C. Ivy, and C. J. Barborka: The Use of Double Work Periods in the Study of Fatigue and the Influence of Caffeine on Recovery, *Am. J. Physiol., 136:* 79–86, 1942.

[12] Hollingworth, H. L.: The Influence of Caffeine on Mental and Motor Efficiency, *Arch. Psychol., N. Y.,* No. 22, 1912.

HOLLINGWORTH'S SUMMARY OF CAFFEINE EFFECTS*

Process	Doses			Action time, hours	Duration
	Small	Med.	Large		
Motor speed:					
1. Tapping..........	St.	St.	St.	0.75–1.5	2–4
Coordination:					
2. Three-hole........	St:	0	St.	1–1.5	3–4
3. Typewriting.......					
a. Speed........	St.	0	Ret.	Results show only in total day's work	
b. Errors........	Fewer for all doses				
Association					
4. Color naming	St.	St.	St.	2–2.5	3–4
5. Opposites.........	St.	St.	St.	2.5–3.0	Next day
6. Calculation.......	St.	St.	St.	2.5	Next day
Choice:					
7. Discrimination reaction time	Ret.	0	St.	2–4	Next day
8. Cancellation	Ret.	?	St.	3–5	No data
9. S-W illusion.......	0	0	0		
General:					
10. Steadiness........	Unsteadiness			–1–3	3–4
11. Sleep quality.... 12. Sleep quality.... 13. General health ..	Individual differences depending on body weight and conditions of administration.............			2?	

*Legend: St. = Stimulation. 0 = No effect. Ret. = Retardation.

tional changes in the direction of the elimination of interfering secondary afferent impulses are responsible. He also states that he is unable to exclude the possibility of the weakening of "fatigue" sensations. He cautions that the quantitative results could be expected to differ when caffeine was consumed as a constituent of a beverage, in which case the combined result would include the effects of sugar, etc. Some constituents would tend to enhance and some to nullify or otherwise modify the simple caffeine influence.

Thornton, Holck, and Smith[13] found improvement in tapping and in hand grip, with a decrease in steadiness. Small amounts of caffeine induced "stimulation," doses of 4 to 6 grains depressed activity and decreased efficiency after a short interval of "stimulation." Retardation was never great, but in the various results throughout the study, considerable individual variability was manifested. A tendency for effects to vary inversely with body weight was reported. Hull[14] found no statistically reliable effect of caffeine on rote learning. This by no means indicates that it does not have such an effect on some people.

Amphetamine sulfate (benzedrine). Amphetamine sulfate, commonly known as benzedrine sulfate, is somewhat like ephedrine, differing chemically by a simpler side chain. Applied locally by inhalation, it is used as a vasoconstrictor in rhinitis, etc. Oral administration relaxes spastic contraction of the digestive tract. Pharmacology texts state that it is more effective in stimulating psychic activity than ephedrine. Clinically, among other things it is used against depressive neuroses and narcolepsy. Mild overdosage is said to result in mydriasis, "inability to relax," restlessness, and insomnia. It induces rise in blood pressure and is thus contraindicated in hypertension, etc.

The Council on Pharmacy and Chemistry[15] cautions in the use of benzedrine sulfate, stating its reactions and contraindications. Care is urged in taking into account its pressor effect, tendency to disturb the gastrointestinal tract and to produce hyperexcitability, restlessness, and sleeplessness. It warns against overdosage, which may produce chills, collapse, and syncope. The dosage the council recommends is 2.5 to 10 mg., with no single dose over 20 mg., the best time of administration being in the morning.

Myerson[16] points out six common physiological reactions to benzedrine. (1) It raises blood pressure, an effect that wears off after repeated doses. (2) It fails to raise blood-sugar level. (3) It increases both the red and white blood cell counts, but it is not known to be associated with the formation of new cells. (4) When given with mecholyl, mecholyl effects first eclipse those of benzedrine. Blood pressure falls, but after an initial period of 15 to 20 minutes this and the rapid heart beat wear off, whereupon benzedrine effects become fully evident, if not exaggerated. (5) Atropine

[13] Thornton, G. R., H. G. O. Holck, and E. L. Smith: The Effect of Benzedrine and Caffeine upon Performance in Certain Psychomotor Tasks, *J. Abnorm. & Social Psychol., 34:* 96–113, 1939.

[14] Hull, C. L.: The Influence of Caffeine and Other Factors on Certain Phenomena of Rote Learning, *J. Gen. Psychol., 13:* 249–274, 1935.

[15] Council on Pharmacy and Chemistry: Present Status of Benzedrine Sulfate, *J.A.M.A., 109:* 2064–2069, 1937.

[16] Myerson, A.: The Physiological and Psychological Effects of Benzedrine, *J. Nerv. & Ment. Dis., 85:* 202–206, 1937.

is synergic with benzedrine, though not in all cases. This is to be expected since benzedrine is a sympathetic "stimulator" and atropine a parasympathetic paralyzer. Rises in blood pressure of 20 to 40 mm. Hg by benzedrine are increased to 60 to 70 mm. by the addition of $\frac{1}{50}$ grain of atropine. Heart rate is accelerated. (6) Benzedrine and amytal used together give the following results. If benzedrine is given prior to the intravenous injection of amytal for anesthesia, the final blood pressure settles at about normal. The blood-pressure rise induced by benzedrine balances the blood-pressure drop below normal induced by amytal. If the order of administration is reversed, the blood pressure may also be made to settle at normal. Myerson points out that the blood-pressure outcome and that of narcosis are largely independent, so that benzedrine seems to have little effect on the primary use of amytal.

It will be noted that at least two of these items bear quite definitely on problems of fatigue and impairment. Blood-pressure bolstering is of benefit in delaying fatigue. The fact that blood sugar does not seem to be affected leads us to look elsewhere for some of the beneficial effects on muscular activity, etc.

Myerson[17] reports beneficial effects upon mood and "fatigue" both in normal persons getting insufficient sleep and in certain depressions of the mentally unfit.

Alles and Feigen[18] studied the action of benzedrine on voluntary-work decrement and on the patellar reflex. For the former, a Mosso finger ergograph was used. The results may be summarized as follows: doses of 10, 20, or 40 mg. of benzedrine forestalled the production of voluntary-muscle exhaustion. The same dosages may obliterate complete voluntary-muscle exhaustion otherwise maintained by repeated work trials.

The effect of benzedrine on the patellar reflex was manifested either in the amplitude of contraction or in the number of contractions, or both. Its effects were more marked than those obtained with ten times the dosage of caffeine under similar conditions. In fact, the amplitude of the patellar reflex remained unchanged following caffeine, despite "jitteriness" in the one of the two subjects.

Alles and Feigen compared the effect of benzedrine on voluntary exertion and upon reflex activity. Since the effects were similar, they concluded that benzedrine acted on the central nervous system.

[17] Myerson, A.: Effect of Benzedrine Sulfate on Mood and Fatigue in Normal and in Neurotic Persons, *Arch. Neurol. & Psychiat., 36:* 816–822, 1936.

[18] Alles, G. A., and G. A. Feigen: The Influence of Benzedrine on Work-decrement and Patellar Reflex, *Am. J. Physiol., 136:* 392–400, 1942.

McNamara and Miller,[19] using written multiplication problems, found no effect either toward increasing or decreasing the number of problems worked in 12-minute periods. Likewise, the number of errors was not affected. The subjects were six undergraduates and four graduate students in the university, ranging from 20 to 25 years of age. The dosage was 20 mg., and the intervals between trials varied from 1 to 3 days. Definite experiential effects were obtained even though work output was not altered. On all days when the drug was taken, the subjects reported no tiredness or sleepiness. In a few cases this report was given on the days without the drug. None of the subjects reported that they were "nervous" on the days when a placebo (lactose) was substituted, whereas on the majority of the benzedrine days the subjects reported slight nervousness. Some tolerance was developed during the course of the experiments. The greatest amount of nervousness was reported on the first day of receiving benzedrine.

Thornton, Holck, and Smith[20] compared the effects of benzedrine and caffeine. The two drugs affected steadiness in opposite directions, benzedrine improving the test performance, caffeine making it poorer. In the other psychomotor tasks investigated, greater improvement was obtained by the use of 20 mg. of benzedrine sulfate than by 300 mg. of caffeine sodium benzoate. Not all the differences were statistically reliable. The degree of variability under the drugs correlated with the variability for the same tasks without the drugs.

These authors attempted to determine whether the improvement in performance had an identifiable connection with lessening of fatigue. As measures of "fatigue effects," certain performance ratios were computed. These were (1) the ratio of the scores on the final two trials to the initial two trials of the steadiness test, and (2) the ratio of the scores on the initial parts of certain other tests to the scores on the last parts. Supposedly, the higher the ratio, the greater the fatigue. Accordingly, to show "antifatigue" influences, the ratios on the benzedrine days should be lower than on the nonbenzedrine days. For one subject of the three this was the case. For another it was just the opposite. The same kind of results were obtained for the caffeine as for benzedrine. Thus, according to the criteria these investigators used, one subject showed more fatigue on the drug days, one showed about the same, and the other showed less. The authors concluded that the effect of the drugs is not a lessening of fatigue, but an acceleration of psychomotor activity. They reserved the possibility that the drugs might delay the onset of fatigue in tasks involving work at a fixed rate.

Here we have a good example of the application of a work-decrement

[19] McNamara, W. J., and R. E. Miller: The Effect of Benzedrine Sulfate on Mental Work, *Psychol. Rev., 1:* 78–84, 1937.

[20] Thornton, Holck, and Smith, *op. cit.*

notion of fatigue. According to such a viewpoint, a slowing up of performance is the only tangible evidence of fatigue.According to some definition, it *is* fatigue. Even in using this criterion, the authors ought to have
avoided a blanket statement regarding the drugs and the production of
fatigue.

Benzedrine sulfate effects on the individual were utilized by Barmack[21]
to test his hypothesis of boredom. In a previous paper he had proposed
that boredom was a state of conflict between the inclination to continue in
and the inclination to escape from a situation which had lost its pleasantness, mainly from inadequate motivation, which in turn had resulted in
inadequate *physiological* adjustments to the situation (see chapter on
Mental Fatigue, which contains a section on boredom). In the present
study, he states boredom to be a physiological reversion to the sleep level.
From this it was expected that an antihypnotic would preclude boredom
by preventing this reversion. Accordingly, benzedrine was chosen for the
experiment to test this hypothesis. He gave 10 mg. of benzedrine sulfate
to each of 36 individuals required to add pairs of six-place numbers. The
subjects were also required to rate themselves in certain subjective dimensions, such as bored-interested, strained-relaxed, irritated-pleased, peppy-
fatigued, sleepy-wide awake, attentive-inattentive, each on a nine-point
scale. The results in work output favored benzedrine in every way except
in number of errors. No effect on accuracy was detected. The outstanding
effect was in the number of problems attempted in the test period. Under
benzedrine, the individuals were less bored, more relaxed, less irritated,
wider awake, less fatigued, and better able to concentrate. The benzedrine
apparently tended to militate against sleeping the night following its use.
Despite loss of sleep, the individuals felt unexpectedly fresh the following
day.

Owing to the fact that Barmack did not measure the physiological supporting functions that are assumed to slump in cases of boredom, and that
Guttmann and Sargant[22] found little or no concomitancy between subjective effects and certain physiological states such as blood pressure, this
particular study failed to accomplish what it set out to do. Barmack did
not make a clear demonstration of his hypothesis that boredom is a reversion to the sleep state.

It was determined that boredom was decreased but not eliminated by
giving benzedrine. Sleepiness was also only decreased but not eliminated.
Both boredom and sleepiness increased during the course of the experi-

21 Barmack, J. E.: The Effect of Benzedrine Sulfate (Benzyl Methyl Carbinamine)
upon the Report of Boredom and Other Factors, *J. Psychol.*, 5: 125-133, 1938.
22 Guttmann, E., and W. Sargant: Observations on Benzedrine, *Brit. Med. J., 1:* 1013-
1015, 1937.

ment. This leads to the suspicion that the *nature of the task* is quite directly involved and that boredom as a unique experience does not arise as an experience induced by the suppression of vital "supporting" activities, but comes from a personal relation to the task.

Barmack states that the greatest change wrought with reference to work is in the *inclination* rather than the *ability* to do it. This and many other changes (as evidenced by the subjective symptoms) indicate the level on which benzedrine acts. This level is better spoken of as organizational than as energetic.

The following year, Barmack made a second study of the effect of benzedrine sulfate on boredom,[23] this time including measurements of blood pressure and heart rate, and comparing the effects of benzedrine with those of ephedrine. In this study, one confirmation of the previous study was made. Benzedrine was found to retard the development of an unfavorable attitude toward a repetitive task. No confirmation of the concomitancy between subjective features and expected physiological states was obtained. In fact, the results were in line with those of Guttman and Sargant.

Benzedrine delayed reports of boredom, irritation, fatigue, etc. It also (in 15-mg. doses) increased systolic pressure and heart rate. Ephedrine had a smaller and more transitory effect both on circulation and work output (accuracy of pursuit movements). Sixty milligrams of ephedrine had a greater effect on systolic pressure than 15 mg. of benzedrine, but failed to have appreciable effect on heart rate. A peculiar slump in the "sustaining" effect of ephedrine was found for most of the psychological measures used. Moreover, this failed to have its correlate in systolic pressure and in heart rate. The results of these studies nevertheless do not warrant abandonment of the idea that the circulatory and skeletal muscle tone play a role in feelings of inadequacy and in the development of fatigue.

Andrews,[24] who measured the effect of 10-mg. doses of benzedrine sulfate on syllogistic reasoning, found no reliable results in its favor, neither did he obtain any statistically significant effect on the self-ratings of his 20 subjects on mood and fatigue.

Carl and Turner[25] conducted experiments on the influence of benzedrine sulfate, using a number of tests among which were several subjective

[23] Barmack, J. E.: Studies on the Psychophysiology of Boredom. I. The Effect of 15 Mgs. of Benzedrine Sulfate and 60 Mgs. of Ephedrine Hydrochloride on Blood Pressure, Report of Boredom, and Other Factors, *J. Exper. Psychol.*, 25: 494–505, 1939.

[24] Andrews, T. G.: The Effect of Benzedrine Sulfate on Syllogistic Reasoning, *J. Exper. Psychol.*, 26: 423–431, 1940.

[25] Carl, G. P., and W. D. Turner: A Further Report on Benzedrine Sulfate (Amphetamine Sulfate); Psychophysical Effects and Supplementary Results from a Fifth Experimental Group, *J. Gen. Psychol.*, 22: 105–191, 1940.

rating scales. One of these scales was called the F-scale. It contained the dimensions of unpleasant-pleasant, pessimistic-optimistic, calm-excited, relaxed-tense, quiet-restless, fatigued-rested, dull-alert, indecisive-decisive, reserved-impulsive, and sociable-unsociable.

Carl and Turner propose that benzedrine begins to exert its effects in feelings of enhanced pleasantness, optimism, restedness, etc. This they call the "critical" period. During this period new qualities begin to arise and their achievement of full strength marks the end of the critical period. These new qualities are alertness, interest, decisiveness, sociability, and talkativeness. During this stage relaxation may be less pronounced, and still later restlessness may develop. The authors admit the absence of any clear-cut demarcation between the critical period and later stages, but insist that there are definite differences between initial and later effects, some features reaching their peak early and others later on. They suggest the possibility that the distinctions they make are attributable to two different physiological origins.

Another self-rating test used by Carl and Turner was the W-scale. It contained the following items: (1) imagination (active-inactive) ; (2) many problems intruded (rarely-constantly) ; (3) a few outside problems intruded (rarely-constantly) ; (4) assumed new tasks (with difficulty-easily) ; (5) reached full speed on tasks (slowly-quickly) ; (6) attended (with difficulty-easily) ; (7) persisted (with difficulty-easily) ; (8) work was (inaccurate-accurate) ; (9) work was (slow-rapid); (10) time passed (slowly-rapidly) ; (11) worked (conscientiously-frivolously) ; (12) tasks were (challenging-not challenging) .

Generally, benzedrine ingestion led to the following: more active imagination, assumption and achievement of full speed more easily, feeling of more rapid passage of time. Large doses led to estimation of greater accuracy and quickness. The authors believe there is evidence that benzedrine first leads to estimation of greater frivolity and later to greater seriousness in regard to work.

Wilbur, MacLean, and Allen[26] reported improvement after administration of benzedrine in 25 patients out of 32 suffering from *chronic exhaustion*. This included increased capacity for mental and physical activity, in some cases reaching the spectacular. Certain vague pains and aches disappeared. The use of 2.5 to 20 mg. once or twice daily resulted in marked tolerance in 4 months if not before. Of a group of 30 patients suffering from *depression,* 21 experienced immediate relief. Of 20 patients having simple depression, 14 obtained marked benefits, 4 showed no change, and

[26] Wilbur, D. L., A. R. MacLean, and E. V. Allen: Clinical Observations on the Effect of Benzedrine Sulfate: A Study of Patients with States of Chronic Exhaustion, Depression, and Psychoneurosis, *J.A.M.A., 109:* 549–554, 1937.

2 became worse. Of 10 patients in the depressed stage of manic depressive psychosis, 7 showed definite improvement and 3 experienced exaggeration of their symptoms.

Benzedrine sulfate has also been used to combat orthostatic hypotension[27] and enabled those who manifested incapacity to return to work.

Reifenstein and Davidoff[28] were led to conclude from a study of 200 clinical cases that the effects of the drug are likely to be variable, unpredictable, and even paradoxical. The basis of this is to be sought in the complex effects upon the different parts of the nervous system (an alleged pseudo-sympathomimetic effect), even apart from the question of idiosyncrasies arising from other supposed sources.

From their study one is unable to determine just what the criteria for their assertions are. They report "stimulation" of four different functions: (1) "mental response," (2) speech, (3) motor activity, and (4) "affectual function." In each category, the effects are divided into two types, the major and the paradoxical. Examples of some of the major effects are the following: acceleration in activity, increase in mental efficiency, increase in alertness, improvement in perception, decrease in sleep requirements, decrease in fatigue, and decrease in reticence. Paradoxical effects such as forgetfulness, dullness, increase in fatigue, malaise and drowsiness, as well as many others, sometimes appeared. Benzedrine sulfate obliterated mutism, induced loquaciousness, increased willingness to discuss personal problems, improved coherence in speech in many cases, whereas in other cases it was associated with the opposite effect. Benzedrine also increased or decreased motor activity and increased or decreased the coordination of physical activity, depending upon the individual.

Benzedrine also in some cases elevated mood and feeling of well-being. It resulted in euphoria and increase in confidence. It also increased impatience and impulsiveness and homicidal tendencies in mentally sick individuals. Depression was sometimes induced. Uncontrolled fits of weeping occurred. Anxiety and suicidal tendencies were aggravated. Not only did individuals differ from one another, but unpredictable combinations of effects in the same individual were seen.

Guttmann and Sargant[29] report findings that are somewhat like those of Reifenstein and Davidoff. Psychological effects are stressed. For example, increase in confidence, in initiative, ease in making decisions, and produc-

[27] Davis, P. L., and M. Shumway-Davis: Orthostatic Hypotension, the Treatment of Two Cases with Benzedrine Sulfate, *J.A.M.A.*, 108: 1247–1249, 1937.

See hypotension under Posture in Chap. XII.

[28] Reifenstein, E. C., and E. Davidoff: The Psychological Effects of Benzedrine Sulfate, *Am. J. Psychol.*, 52: 56–64, 1939.

[29] Guttmann and Sargant, *op. cit.*

tion of euphoria were some of the results obtained. These and other effects are said to make the drug useful in mild retardation, depression, hesitation, and in the relief of "mental fatigue" brought on by worry. Even though overdosage may interfere with sleep, it is claimed that this is not always unpleasant. Observations on individual cases indicate that the personal effects do not always coincide with physiological changes, such as rise in blood pressure. These authors, too, point out the development of tolerance and the loss of the euphorizing effect after a few days.

The effects of d-desoxyephedrine. This drug, known in Europe by several shorter commercial names such as pervitin and methedrine,[30] is chemically related to ephedrine and amphetamine (benzedrine).

The influence of pervitin on fatigue and physical performance is represented by very meager scientific data. The reports have come mostly from foreign sources. The claims regarding its effects are somewhat contradictory, owing partly to lack of controls, differences is dosage, etc. Ivy and Goetzl[31] have published a review of what little is known.

From the information on hand it would seem that the effects are somewhat similar to those of benzedrine, with possibly a greater toxic effect and a smaller dosage required to obtain analogous results.

Pervitin apparently elevates the individual's mood, induces the urge to activity, counteracts sleepiness, and in general dispels bodily feelings which are a part of the "feeling of fatigue." Mood elevation sets in in about 20 to 60 minutes after the oral intake. This effect lasts 6 to 36 hours. In conjunction with this is the disturbance to sleep involved the first night even if ingestion is at breakfast time.

Certain comparisons with benzedrine and caffeine tended to show it to be more effective than caffeine in influencing writing, drawing, addition, and attention. Since information is so meager, general conclusions regarding comparisons are as yet unwarranted. However, caffeine and pervitin are said to be synergistic as are caffeine and benzedrine.

Foltz, Ivy, and Barborka[32] have made a well-controlled study of the effects of certain drugs on work output and recovery when trained subjects undergo quickly exhausting exercise. A bicycle erograph was used on subjects whose diet, etc., was under control by the experimenters. Exhaus-

[30] Other names for this substance are n-methylphenylisopropylamine, 1-phenyl-2-methylaminopropine (dextrorotatory), d-phenylisopropylmethylamine, methyl-benzedrine, and methylisomyn.

[31] Ivy, A. C., and F. R. Goetzl: d-Desoxyephedrine: A Review, *War Med., 3:* 60–77, 1943.

[32] Foltz, E. E., A. C. Ivy, and C. J. Barborka: The Influence of Amphetamine (Benzedrine) Sulfate, d-Desoxyephedrine Hydrochloride (Pervitin), and Caffeine upon Work Output and Recovery when Rapidly Exhausting Work is Done by Trained Subjects, *J. Lab. & Clin. Med., 28:* 603–606, 1943.

tion in each case was measured by the point at which the subject could no longer pedal the ergograph at the required speed. None of the subjects failed to react differently to the drugs than to control substances. As might be expected, it was found that the benzedrine, pervitin, and caffeine not only influenced work output and recovery from exertion, but produced subjective effects hard to evaluate by physiological procedures. It was found that the subjects differed from one another, so that no single description would fit them.

Pervitin tended to induce insomnia in a majority of the subjects used. When administered to subjects fatigued by the first work period, the pervitin seemed to obliterate the bodily feelings of fatigue. Nevertheless, when these individuals were put into the second work period, indications in output showed that recovery from the first work period was by no means so complete as implied by the subjective advantages. In contrast to this, caffeine, in the doses used in the experiments, produced both the subjective "lift" and physiological evidence of enhanced recovery. All individuals reported stronger subjective effects from both the pervitin and the caffeine when administered before the first workout than afterward.

This effect of caffeine is in line with the daily experience of some individuals who experience more pronounced effects from caffeine when taken in the morning than at night. Here, again, there may be a pronounced difference in people, not only as to personal idiosyncrasy but also as to their actual bodily state when awakening in the morning.

Recently, certain relations between alcohol and pervitin have been reported.[33] Pervitin was said to have no influence upon the alcohol concentration in the blood. Alcohol given alone resulted in the deterioration of motor performance (pegging of rings), but alcohol preceded by pervitin failed to produce this result. "Sober" limits of performance were maintained. With considerable alcohol, a discrepancy between motivation and ability to perform was characteristic. This divergence was enhanced by the addition of pervitin. Self-assessment became even more discrepant when pervitin was used, although performance was improved. Pervitin, in inducing a simulation of sobriety, precluded the development of certain symptoms by which the individual would ordinarily deduce the extent of his intoxication. It precluded the individual from becoming aware of the danger signs of intoxication.

SUBSTANCES USED TO QUIET THE INDIVIDUAL

In addition to drugs that play a role in the retardation and alleviation of fatigue and impairment by promoting activity, our discussion must

[33] Elbel, H.: Pervitin und Alkohol, *Deutsche Ztschr. f. d. ges. gerichtl. Med., 36:* 90–100, 1942.

include others that are used on account of some quieting effect. Drugs in this category allay pain, promote relaxation, and induce sleep.

Many difficulties lie in the transitions from "rest" to work and from work to full detachment from it. It is often as difficult to relax from the personal stances taken in regard to one's responsibilities as it is to mobilize one's resources in order to accomplish the tasks in the first place. The quieting drugs are useful, for example, to an individual who, having completed his work, cannot easily disengage himself from the discomforts developed in activity.

It is appropriate here to deal only briefly with several classes of drugs used for their quieting action. They are the antipyretic analgetics, the barbiturates, the bromides, and the opiates. Commonly one, or a combination, of three effects is sought in the use of these drugs: (1) relief from aches and pains, without the clouding of perception; (2) reduction of tenseness and other symptoms of overexcitation; and (3) the facilitation or the induction of sleep. It is obvious that these three effects would tend to aid in recovery from fatigue and impairment by providing for "rest." Since not all fatigue is curable through rest, however, they may often fail to do all that is expected of them.

Antipyretic analgetics. The antipyretic analgetics include, primarily, three groups of drugs: (1) salicylates, (2) paramidophenol derivatives, and (3) pyrazolon derivatives.

What occurs in analgesia is little understood. The antipyretic analgetics are not particularly effective in alleviating traumatic pain. In the case of headache, it has been suggested that the alleviation may occur through relief of intracranial pressure by mobilization of excess water.[34] Tactile sensibility is not greatly lessened by this group of drugs, although sensitivity to thermal stimulation is reduced. The degree of analgesia has been tested in man by the amount of thermal radiation required to produce pain when applied to the forehead. Certain psychological experiments indicate that maximum medicinal doses of some of the analgetics decrease mental alertness as measured by tests. Analgesic doses of some of the group do not deteriorate neuromuscular coordination.[35] Auditory acuity is said to be reduced by the salicylates but is supposed to be increased by some of the other antipyretics.[36] Small amounts of the drugs of this group presum-

[34] Sollmann, T. H.: "A Manual of Pharmacology," 6th ed., W. B. Saunders Company, Philadelphia, 1942. Pp. 1298.

[35] Macht, D. I., S. Isaacs, and J. P. Greenberg: On the Influence of Some Antipyretics on the Neuromuscular Coordination Test of "Tapping," *Proc. Soc. Exper. Biol. & Med., 15:* 61–62, 1918.

[36] Macht, D. I., S. Isaacs, and J. P. Greenberg: Concerning the Influence of Antipyretics on the Acuity of Hearing, *Proc. Soc. Exper. Biol & Med., 17:* 22–23, 1920.

ably enhance the sedative effect of hypnotics,[37] but the practical advantage of combinations of the two is not great. It is alleged that the analgetic effect is reduced and not augmented.[38]

The salicylates are quite specific remedies for rheumatic pains. Their action in allaying the symptoms in rheumatic fever is so uniform that, when they fail, suspicion is cast upon the diagnosis. They obliterate both the pain and the fever. The local inflammation, redness, and swelling are reduced in a few days, and the person as a whole shows great improvement. Strangely enough the symptoms reappear upon discontinuance of the drug, and the term of hospitalization does not seem to be reduced.

The commonest of the salicylic compounds is the much-used aspirin. It, like the other salicylates, may in rare cases produce alarming allergic symptoms. These include acute local or general edema of the skin and mucous membranes, urticaria, bronchial spasm, erythemia, pruritus, etc. The other salicylates besides aspirin include methyl salicylate and phenol salicylate (salol). Allied to this general group of compounds are the benzoates and cinchophen, etc.

The paramidophenol or "coal-tar antipyretics" are commonly exemplified in acetanilid and phenacetin. These, too, at times induce untoward side reactions such as cyanosis and anemia. Persistent use tends to induce headache; hence addiction to these drugs may become part of a vicious cycle.

The pyrazolon derivatives, amidopyrine (pyramidon) and antipyrine (phenazone), likewise, in addition to their antipyretic and analgesic influences, at times induce dangerous side reactions such as collapse. These drugs have less influence on blood than acetanilid but are more likely to induce cutaneous symptoms.

The barbiturates.   The barbiturates belong to a class of drugs called the aliphatic hypnotics, which include the urethanes, the carbamides, sulfonal, paraldehyde, chloral hydrate, etc. The barbiturates are more commonly used than the others just mentioned. Until recently, they could be purchased without prescription, and overdosage was a common method for attempting suicide. The most important barbiturates include barbital (veronal), dial, amytal, pentobarbital, neonal, phanodorn, pernoston,

---

[37] Starkenstein, E.: Kombinationsversuche in der Analgetikareihe, *Therap. Halbmonatsh., 35:* 629–636, 1921.

Loewi, S., E. Kaer, and H. Muischnek: Über Kombinationswirkungen: VII. Anwendung auf Phenazetin-Azetylsalizylsäure-Codeinmischungen, *Arch. f. exp. Path. u. Pharmakol., 120:* 25–40, 1927.

Steinmetzer, K.: Versuche mit Schlafmittelkombinationen, *Arch. f. exp. Path. u. Pharmakol., 132:* 172–192, 1928.

[38] Pohle, K., and A. Nietschmann: Über die kombinatrischen Eigenschaften des Veramons, *Arch. f. exp. Path. u. Pharmakol., 188:* 611–632, 1938.

and ipral. They vary over a range that is roughly 3 to 1 in minimum fatal dose and minimum anesthetic dose, and over a range of about 2 to 1 in therapeutic breadth (minimum fatal dose ÷ minimum therapeutic dose).

The barbiturates appear to be cortical and subcortical depressants. The bulbospinal reflexes are little affected. The barbiturates have distinct effects on the autonomic nervous system.[39] Amytal, pernoston, and pentobarbital obliterate peripheral vagus response to faradic stimulation. On the other hand, the thiobarbiturates (pentathol sodium) have been found by some to augment vagal action,[40] while others were unable to demonstrate increased sensitivity from its use on the isolated intestine.[41] The barbiturates are generally used as somnifacients. Administered every 4 to 6 hours in small quantities, they are used for sedation. In surgery, they are used for their anesthetic effects.

Curran[42] believes that barbiturate intoxication presents a specific syndrome. In acute cases, the individual is generally in deep coma, varying from hours to several days. Following coma, drowsiness and "resistance to approach" are manifested. Disorientation is usual at this stage, and euphoria is said to be common. Nystagmus, asynergia, hypotonia, and adiadochinesia may develop. The symptoms of chronic poisoning are drowsiness and silly euphoria which resembles that of general paresis. Nystagmus and cerebellar and vestibular signs also develop. Delirium is rare. Hypomania may occur and lasts from 3 days to a week, during which period restlessness, overtalkativeness, facetiousness, petulance, sarcasm, etc., characterize behavior.

While there are a fair number of studies of the barbiturates in the literature, it is difficult if not impossible to find the kind of investigation ideally required by our interest in fatigue.

The bromides. The bromides depress both cortical functions and reflexes, leading to dullness and apathy. They produce a general state conducive to sleep, hence are often employed in various forms of nervous hyperexcitabilities. Formerly they were used against epilepsy, but now have largely been displaced by phenobarbital. The bromides require continuous administration, since they are rapidly eliminated in the urine.

[39] Linegar, C. R., J. M. Dille, and T. Kappanyi: Studies on Barbiturates. XVIII. Analysis of a Peripheral Action of Barbiturates, *J. Pharm. & Exper. Therap., 58:* 128-134, 1936.

[40] Gruber, C. M., C. M. Gruber, Jr., and N. H. Culosi: The Irritability of the Cardiac Vagus Nerves as Influenced by the Intravenous Injection of Barbiturates, Thio-barbiturates, and Picrotoxin, *J. Pharm. & Exper. Therap., 63:* 215-228, 1938.

[41] Kohn-Richards, R., and C. Grimes: Effect of Certain Barbiturates on the Response to Vasoactive Substances, *Anesth. & Analg., 19:* 31-34, 1940.

[42] Curran, F. J.: Current Views on Neuropsychiatric Effects of Barbiturates and Bromides, *J. Nerv. & Ment. Dis., 100:* 142-169, 1944.

Acute bromide poisoning is rare, but untoward effects may result from chronic use. Curran[43] states that the commonest development from chronic overdosage is delirium.

Bromides tend to reduce or obliterate aftercontraction in skeletal muscle. Aftercontraction is the phenomenon demonstrated by Sapirstein, Herman, and Wallace,[44] who had 10 subjects stand on one foot and raise a weight with the other limb by means of a pulley system. After a latent period following the release of the weight, the limb tended to rise quite spontaneously. When the experiment was repeated under the administration of bromides, these investigators obtained reduction of aftercontraction in all the subjects and its obliteration in seven. The effect became identifiable in 30 minutes and lasted for several hours. There were said to be no subjective symptoms accompanying this aftercontraction reduction, and no change in the knee jerk was obtained.

It is interesting that these same experimenters found that caffeine, in contrast to bromides, left aftercontraction appreciably unaffected in five cases. In two, a moderate increase was found, and in one a fivefold increase.

In a later experiment, barbital was given to six subjects in doses of 3 to 6 grains. In three cases, no effect was identified, in two a slight decrease in aftercontraction resulted, and in one no aftercontraction was obtained. Two of the subjects were used in both the bromide and barbital experiments. In both of them, the bromides obliterated aftercontraction and were said to induce no subjective symptoms, whereas barbital failed to change aftercontraction and the subjects were reported to be depressed.

It should be noted that in all these experiments variation from person to person was revealed. The number of cases, however, was few, and the possibility of variation in effects from time to time was not ruled out. Although no statistical justification of the results were given, it is likely that these experiments do represent a rough indication of the differences in the effects of certain drugs.

Berger[45] reported that bromides damped the alpha waves in the electroencephalogram. These, of course, are characteristically enhanced in epileptiform attacks.

Opiates.   The three main opium alkaloids are papaverine, narcotine, and morphine. Of these, the most widely used is morphine, because of its powerful analgesic effects. Our discussion here will be limited to morphine and its derivatives.

[43] Curran, *op. cit.*

[44] Sapirstein, M. R., R. C. Herman, and G. B. Wallace: Effect of Certain Drugs on After-contraction, *Proc. Soc. Exper. Biol. & Med., 35:* 163–165, 1936.

[45] Berger, H.: Über das Elektrenkephalogramm des Menschen, *Arch. f. Psychiat., 101:* 452–469, 1933.

Morphine acts most obviously on the central nervous system. Medullary centers are initially stimulated and later depressed, whereas reflexes and spinal action are primarily enhanced. Hyperglycemia is induced, possibly through stimulation of the posterior hypothalamus. With use of the drug over a period of a few weeks, this effect disappears. Morphine derivatives, in acting on the midbrain, tend to produce catatonic rigidity. This is especially marked in certain animals below man.

Morphine is rapidly absorbed. About a fifth of it is excreted in the urine, and the major portion of the rest is destroyed in the liver.

When applied directly to muscle preparations, morphine results in some curare action. Currents inducing tetanus in normal preparations result in a series of rapid discrete contractions when morphine is used.

Administered in small doses, morphine is said to diminish the ability to hold lasting impressions, presumably leading to emotional tranquillity. In larger doses there is likely to be an excitant action, some individuals evidencing this much more than others. Euphoria may occur. The excitant action is supposedly best explained as a release from restraint. Flights of imagination are produced by certain amounts of the drug. Sudden changes tend to produce exaggerated response, whereas gradual changes or persistent "stimuli" tend to be much less effective than normally. In large doses, morphine clearly affects concentration, judgment, and memorizing ability. A tendency toward torpor is induced. Morphine sometimes induces violent pain experiences, as well as those of heat and itching.

One of the most common morphine derivatives is codeine. Although not quite so effective in producing analgesia as morphine, it is less given to unpleasant side reactions and also less likely to induce addiction.

Demerol. Demerol,[46] known in Germany as dolantin, is one of the many piperidine compounds. Because of its analgesic properties, it has recently been used to alleviate pain. Demerol, in addition to being analgesic, is both sedative and spasmolytic.

While the salicylates, acetanilide, and amidopyrine are somewhat specific in the types of pain they affect, demerol is said to be quite general. In contrast to the barbiturates, the analgesic property of demerol dominates the hypnotic.

As a sedative, demerol is only moderately effective. The sedative action is fairly inconsistent and unpredictable. With large parenteral doses, sleep is likely to be induced and lasts for about 2 hours. The patient is said to experience no mental confusion on awakening. Although demerol usually

[46] Batterman, R. C., and C. K. Himmelsback: Demerol—A New Synthetic Analgesic, *J.A.M.A.*, *122:* 222–226, 1943.

Hoffman, R.: Demerol, a New Departure in Analgesia: An Evaluation of Present Therapeutic Claims, *Anesth. & Analg.*, *22:* 336–340, 1943.

aids in sleep induction for bed patients, it is likely to induce only slight drowsiness in ambulatory patients.

Demerol does not affect blood pressure, blood-sugar level, or blood-cell count. It tends to relax smooth muscle of the gastrointestinal tract, bladder, uterus, and bronchi. Curiously it tends to decrease segmental peristalsis while promoting propulsive peristalsis. Demerol has proved effective in alleviating smooth-muscle spasm.

Whether the effects of demerol are pleasant or unpleasant appears to depend upon a number of factors. The personality of the individual is obviously an important determinant. Some people complain of a feeling of insecurity, while others express a mild euphoria. These effects are inconsistent, however, even for the same individual at different times.

Demerol is likely to have an epinephrin-like effect, which deters its usage in higher doses and works against chronic dependence upon it. "Habituation" has been found in a small number of cases, but demerol is considered less likely to induce "physical dependence" than the opiates.

To summarize, the quieting drugs, of which there are many examples, have numerous diverse actions and effects. These drugs in general are considered too dangerous to be purchasable without restriction. But under the direction of the specialist, they are capable of being of enormous aid in relieving pain, abolishing discomfort, and aiding in various kinds of regulation often needed by the individual.

The literature, however, is scant in insightful studies relating to subjective effects, yet the results of such studies are needed to clarify their connection with fatigue and impairment. At the present time, little may be said about the detailed and subtle effects of the quieting drugs on human experience and personality.

OTHER SUBSTANCES COMMONLY USED

Nicotine. Nicotine given directly has no therapeutic use in pharmacology or medicine, but owing to its presence in tobacco, which is habitually and widely used in the population, it deserves attention. Nicotine effects are induced in functional combinations with the other aspects of smoking and chewing tobacco. It is well known that marked changes occur, both centrally and peripherally, when nicotine is given in experimental doses.

In experimental doses, nicotine acts both on the central and autonomic nervous systems and on the muscles themselves. Centrally, stimulation precedes depression of the entire cerebrospinal axis, beginning from above. In general, the symptoms are similar to asphyxia and hydrocyanic poisoning. The respiratory, vasomotor, vagus, and emetic centers are strongly affected, partly through involvement of the carotid sinus and cardioaortic reactions. Small doses result in transient stimulation of respiration followed by acapnia; larger doses result in complete arrest. Initially the pulse is slowed; later the heart rate is accelerated and blood pressure rises. Various complex results in rate and amplitude of heart action occur. Blood-sugar concentration is first increased and then diminished by nicotine. The rise is laid to the increase in epinephrin output brought about by nicotine, the fall to paralysis of ganglia or lowered blood pressure. Tissue oxidation is reduced by nicotine. Nausea, emesis, and diarrhea may be produced, the gastric action being mainly central, the intestinal largely peripheral. Fibrillar contractions in skeletal muscle are induced in mammals, but no central convulsions. Nicotine has a curare-like effect, though nicotine is antagonistic to curare and other substances having a curare-like action.

What is to be expected from the daily use of subacute doses of nicotine taken by inhalation or into the digestive tract is the appropriate question for the present discussion of fatigue and impairment. Since it is well known that a degree of tolerance to the drug may be developed, our problem involves the effect of continued usage after tolerance has been developed. It must be understood that tolerance in this case involves mainly the eradication of the major unpleasant reactions that are characteristic of the first contacts with the drug.

Baumberger, Perry, and Martin[47] reported that habitual smoking, off the job, apparently did not reduce the work output of glass blowers. Palmén[48] noted an initial increase in muscular work from cigarette smoking, following which fatigue set in earlier so that total work output was reduced.

Vasoconstriction in the skin has been shown to set in promptly by microscopic observation of the nailfold. Effects from a single cigarette have been observed.[49] Inhalation was not necessary, but increased the degree of effect. Lowering of skin temperature has also been observed by others.

Smoking produces a slight nicotine effect on blood-sugar level. Although little effect appears at normal levels, the fasting level is raised. The fasting R.Q. is likewise raised. The blood-sugar effect wears off in about $\frac{1}{2}$ hour after smoking.

[47] Baumberger, J. P., E. E. Perry, and E. G. Martin: An Output Study of Users and Non-users of Tobacco in a Strenuous Physical Occupation, *J. Indust. Hyg. & Toxicol.*, *3:* 1–10, 1921.

[48] Palmén, E.: Über die Einwirkung des Tabakrauchens auf die körperliche Leistungsfähigkeit, *Skandinav. Arch. f. Physiol.*, 24: 187–196, 1911.

[49] Wright, I. S., and D. Moffat: The Effects of Tobacco on the Peripheral Vascular System, *J.A.M.A.*, *103:* 318–323, 1934.

The effects of smoking on blood pressure were found to differ greatly.[50]
The extremes were a rise of 35 mm. in systolic pressure and 22 mm. in
pulse pressure, to a drop of 30 mm. in systolic and 34 mm. in pulse pressure. The same patient did not always respond in the same way. The rises,
falls, and cases of indifference were about equal. Arrythmia in the form
of extrasystoles is sometimes attributed to tobacco.

Chronic digestive disturbances have also been laid to the habitual use
of tobacco. "Nervous dyspepsia," loss of appetite, hyperchlorhydria, and
alternation between constipation and diarrhea are some of the symptoms.

Raymond Pearl[51] found an unfavorable correlation between smoking
and longevity. Hull[52] in his monograph on the influence of tobacco smoking on mental and motor efficiency reports the work of a series of earlier
investigators who have concluded that smoking reduces the precision of
voluntary movement. Among others, he cites the following: (1) Blickley,
who in 1914 found the smoking of two cigars had a disadvantageous effect
on line tracing and also on lunging at a target with a foil. (2) Froeberg,
who in 1920 found loss of precision and steadiness and a very slight increase in the efficiency of tapping. (3) Lombard, who in 1892 made the
earliest study of the effects of tobacco on muscular fatigue. About 29 per
cent decrease in work output occurred on the days he smoked. (Hull, com-
puting the statistical reliability, found Lombard's results could have happened by pure chance only once in a hundred cases.) (4) Bush, who in
1914 studied the effect of tobacco on mental processes. All but 2 of the
15 subjects he used were habitual smokers. Loss in cancellation, free association, controlled association, a genus-species test, addition, subtraction,
etc., were reported. No control tests were run on the subjects themselves;
the results of an individual not among the smokers were used for comparison.

A large number of tests have shown that, in general, nonsmokers receive better school marks than smokers. One study cited by Hull as the best
showed deficiencies in planning and statistical treatment which render
the results open to question.

The weakness of all the previous studies, regardless of their variety and
their relative uniformity in reporting loss in efficiency through smoking,
was a factor that led Hull to perform a study of his own. Hull chose 12
typical mental and motor functions, which were tested following a 25-
minute period of smoking a pipe of mild tobacco begun 1½ hours after

[50] Thompson, W. G., and W. R. Sheldon: Tobacco Smoking and Blood Pressure, *N.
Y. State J. Med., 17:* 55–58, 1917.

[51] Pearl, R.: Tobacco Smoking and Longevity, *Science, 87:* 216–217, 1938.

[52] Hull, C. L.: The Influence of Tobacco Smoking on Mental and Motor Efficiency,
Psychol. Monogr., 33: 1–159, 1924. No. 150.

a meal. The smoke was not inhaled. The effects were followed for 1¾ hours after the end of smoking.

Four problems were considered: (1) the effect of smoking on the non-smokers with gastric tolerance, (2) the effect on habitual smokers, (3) the comparative recovery rates of the tested mental and motor functions, and (4) the extent of possible tolerance developed by habituation, as revealed in improvements in the tested functions. Most of the generalizations given by Hull in his conclusions pertain to the habitual smokers. Many subjects were unfavorably affected by the use of tobacco, but, since others were not, a statistical analysis of the data to reveal general trends resulted in a cancellation of the two types. The effects on most of the functions varied so much from individual to individual that they were treated as virtually nonexistent. Only 3 out of the 12 functions showed consistent enough effects to permit generalization. Two of these were physiological effects, change in pulse rate and tremor, and the other was change in ability to do addition. Certain other psychological functions showed some effects in favor of tobacco. They, as Hull put it, involved the functioning of *old* associative bonds. The results relative to rote learning, memory span, etc., involving *new* associative bonds, tended to be unfavorable to the use of tobacco.

Alcohol. There is so much to be said about human behavior in connection with alcohol that only a rather unsatisfactory résumé can be condensed into short space. The significance of alcohol, like nicotine and caffeine, is derived from its widespread use.

Alcohol is a fuel as well as a drug, for it is absorbable without modification and may replace carbohydrate or other nutrients in furnishing energy. Alcohol cannot be transformed and stored as are other fuels. It remains alcohol until oxidized and continues to exert its influence as a drug. Alcohol is quickly absorbed and is thereby a quickly available source of energy in collapse.

Alcohol as a drug is a depressant, acting primarily on the brain and spinal cord. The acidosis that results from ingestion of large amounts is thought to arise from the depression of the respiratory center in the brain.[53] Difference of opinion still exists as to whether or not small doses of alcohol are initially stimulating. But however this may be, the chief action is one of depression,[54] beginning from the top of the neuroaxis downward.

[53] Himwich, H. E., L. H. Nahum, N. Rakieten, J. F. Fazikas, and D. DuBois: The Effects of Alcohol on Metabolism, *Am. J. Physiol.*, *101:* 57, 1932.

[54] Since some of the functions of the nervous system are inhibitory and regulatory, when they begin to be depressed the net effect is the display of greater activity and momentum. When this is overlooked, the observed result appears to be stimulation.

Since alcohol has a depressant effect on cellular respiration, its effects extend to muscle as well as to nerve tissue. The inadequate oxidation in muscle leads to lactic acid accumulation and a diminution of work capacity. Despite lessened capacity for strenuous muscular exertion, the individual is likely to have a feeling of well-being and of relief from tension and under some circumstances may be more willing to carry on a task. There is at the same time lessened discomfort in muscular exertion. Under alcohol, lessened productivity does not represent so much of a conscious threat to the worker as normally. The individual tends to overlook his own mistakes. Or he fails to see his actions as faulty. For this reason, fatigue is greatly postponed, when not entirely avoided.

Although much is already known about alcohol effects, there is still a need for further investigation. Studies should be performed on individuals in natural situations. We are not aware of any such studies.

Typological views on drugs. In typological studies the constitution of the individual is of focal importance. Unlike the studies previously cited, in typological studies of drugs the person is always used as the reference point. The primary consideration of the individual is a step in the right direction.

One of the more recent typologies is Sheldon's temperament scheme.[55] This scheme involves 20 traits for each of three clusters: viscerotonia, somatotonia, and cerebrotonia. It was not possible to find related traits in each of the three categories in all cases. Although the traits of few if any individuals fall in one category, the author refers to viscerotonic, somatotonic, and cerebrotonic individuals. Viscerotonic individuals are characterized by "general relaxation, love of comfort, sociability, conviviality, gluttony for food, people, and for affection." In somatotonia there is a "predominance of muscular activity and of vigorous bodily assertiveness." In cerebrotonia "the element of restraint, inhibition, and of the desire for concealment" prevails.

Viscerotonic individuals are said to enjoy alcohol and like tobacco. It is supposed to be good for them in moderate amounts. Cerebrotonics, on the other hand, dislike alcohol, and for them it is a poison. Alcoholism is said to develop in those individuals whose cerebrotonic and somatotonic components are in struggle for ascendency. Resistance to hypnotic drugs is one of the 16 diagnostic clinical symptoms of the cerebrotonic, and the use of such drugs is said to be of little avail except in large doses for acute emergencies.

It is probable that individuals possess different sorts of neural organization. Some may be so structured as to involve greater cerebral dominance

[55] Sheldon, W. H.: "The Varieties of Temperament," 2d ed., Harper & Brothers, New York, 1944. Pp. 520.

than others. To the extent to which the neural organization of one individual can be said to be more extensively characterized by cerebral
dominance, alcohol would be expected to be a liberating influence. The
results, however, vary greatly, and the release from restraint in some cases
will prove as harmful as it is beneficial in others.

Effect of drugs on the resting state. Jacobson[56] performed an important general demonstration on the effects of drugs under "resting"
conditions. His subjects were tested while lying with closed eyes in a
semisoundproof room. Action potentials were recorded from the flexors
of the arm. Fifteen grains of bromides had virtually no effect on the action
potentials in the 30-minute test period. Larger doses produced a diminution of the potentials within 2 hours. Intramuscular injections of $1\frac{3}{8}$
grains of sodium amytal were more effective than the bromides, and caffeine sodium benzoate induced definite enhancement of the potentials as
compared with controls of sterile water. From this it may be deduced that
various drugs alter the tonal state of the skeletal musculature while the
individual is in a quiet "nonworking" state. To such changes of tone can
be ascribed a partial basis for feelings of relaxation,·etc., or their opposites,
uneasiness, etc.

CONCLUSIONS

The organism may be ordinarily thought of as needing only nutritive
substances, in addition to sensory stimulation from its surroundings, to
provide for its activity, but substances for purposes other than nutrition
are constantly employed by virtually everyone. These range from condi-
ments to spur the appetite, beverages to provide "pick-up," and other
stimulants to relieve lassitude and "fatigue," to sedatives for "quieting
the nerves," analgesics to relieve pain (particularly headaches), and
hypnotics to promote sleep. Spasmolytics are often taken to relieve spastic
conditions of the gastrointestinal tract induced as a part of the picture
of tension and worry. In addition, popular habits, such as smoking, involve
the use of drugs. The individual through a kind of momentum is often
either too active or too inactive to meet his obligations. It is apparent
that, whether by deliberation or by accident, the individual is constantly
subjecting himself or being subjected to the influence of drugs.

In his search for "stimulation" and its opposite, and for relief from experienced pain and tension, the individual comes to expect standard
effects from the substances he employs. The tendency to view the use of
drugs in terms of fixed standards of effect also is obvious in the planning
of specialized investigations. Yet standard effects are seldom obtained.

[56] Jacobson, E.: Direct Measurements of the Effects of Bromides, Sodium Amytal and
of Caffeine in Man, *Ann. Int. Med., 21:* 455–468, 1944.

Despite the antiquity of some drugs, their effects on the individual as well as those of drugs of more recent origin are not too well understood. Knowledge of the action of these substances on excised tissue has not correspondingly increased knowledge of the effects on the whole individual.

This gap in our knowledge seems to arise from an unwillingness to abandon the taxonomic viewpoint for the strictly functional one now required. The customary description of any drug involves a list of fixed effects to be expected from it. An individual is said to be idiosyncratic if the effects on his behavior deviate from these.

When drugs enter the body, they become part of a larger physico-chemical system that is already in action. Even when no more than this physico-chemical system is being observed in drug studies, the drug should not be taken as the point of reference, for it has become only a part of this total system. The old logic of relating the effects to the drug should be replaced by the diametric viewpoint of relating the drug to the system of which it has been made a part. In dealing with the organism, we cannot legitimately stop at the physico-chemical level. Since our interest lies in determining the behavior of the individual, description of what occurs must be made in appropriate terms. These we call "personal" terms (see Chap. III).

The subtleties of the personal outcomes which could be obtained by introspective accounts have been masked in the determination to maintain objectification. It is out of the massing of "subjective" information that these subtleties evolve and from this that more significantly functional classifications can be constructed.

The meaningful approach to understanding the individual is the same regardless of what particular factors are being considered. When the individual is studied under the influence of drugs, and whether or not fatigue is the central point, the over-all logical framework remains unchanged.

A criticism of current experiments on drugs is that too few conditions are handled concurrently. Experimenters often feel relieved of obligation after stating the limitations of the conditions analyzed. They rarely appear to recognize that their results cannot be related to the findings of others without vitiating any over-all conclusions that might be drawn.

Chapter XII

ORGANIZATION IN NEUROMUSCULAR ACTIVITY

THERE SEEM to be two broad alternatives used in accounting for action, explaining its course, and making intelligible its variations and diminutions which are generally put into the category of fatigue. The one stresses the question of the existence and availability of energy supplies, limitations of which are crucial for behavioral end results. The other assumes the general adequacy of energy resources, and seeks not only to ascertain the course of the energy flow but more especially to disclose the character of arrangements by which activity is carried on. This is the study of organization.

The term "organization," in referring to the interrelations between functioning parts, tends to direct the attention immediately to the structural elements involved. Although we might wish for more information about the activity of the structural elements, the first requirement, both in this chapter and in actual research, is a consideration of the broader aspects of organization. At least from a biological standpoint it is only in terms of function that structure may be understood. A grasp of the general functional principles manifested by the organism is the only framework within which the details of behavior may be coherently placed.

The significance of a consideration of organization in biological thinking is emphasized by the fact that organic behavior, even under the most abnormal circumstances, is never *un*organized. The *essential* characteristics of the organism are most clearly revealed by its functional organization. Organic behavior manifests a decided continuity in the face of external changes. Occurring at one moment, it may be clearly connected with outside events long past and with those which will take place in the future.

The organism, in possessing momentum and directionality, initiates behavior. Thus the organism itself should be taken as the starting point. When this is done, the outside influences, which are continually present, must be viewed merely as indicators for the responses, the main determinants of which lie within the organism. When the organism is considered in the light of its over-all functional organization, no simple causal relationships may be assumed between the organism and what is known as the physical world.

BROAD ASPECTS OF ORGANIZATION

As we proceed with the broader questions regarding neuromuscular organization, four distinct attributes come to light, *viz.,* variability, equivalence or substitution, stereotypy, and disjunction or incompatibility between functional parts. These, of course, are to be considered in the light of each other, and each has its bearing on fatigue.

Variability is the change in rate, precision, or appropriateness of action as features of action are repeated, or in any situation in which standards for these three features are available for the experimenter's use. In tasks such as typing or doing a number of "equally difficult" arithmetic problems, the factor of variability comes to light quite distinctly. A later section will deal at length with this attribute of neuromuscular organization.

Equivalence refers to the fact that strict localization of function does not exist. Instead, there is lability in the utilization of elements to achieve ends even where rigid mechanization has often been thought to be demanded. It is as though a pattern were playing over a bank of lights. The pattern has its identity, but the particular lights (elements) used vary from moment to moment.

Both brain structures and the receptor surfaces, such as those of the retina and skin, do not function twice alike, nor are the same components necessary on separate occasions to achieve the same end result. Repetition is only nominal. For example, "local signs" of space and quality are fictions as fixed entities. Pseudofoveae have been shown to develop in cases of complete hemianopsia. The center of fixation shifts from the anatomical fovea to the peripheral retina in which a greater visual acuity can be shown than in the anatomical macula.[1] Rats, for example, in learning to run a maze, never proceed alike from trial to trial. If experimentally deprived of brain tissue degrading their manner of locomotion, the animals will successfully hobble, roll, or twist their way through.

Stereotypy refers to the fact that the organism uses fixed modes of doing various jobs. The fixity pertains more particularly to component rather than to over-all performances. Stereotypy, although it may seem to be a contradiction of equivalence, is by no means that. Even in acts that are outwardly quite uniform, functional elements vary. Stereotypy is testimony for the persistence of pattern rather than literal repeti-

[1] Fuchs, W.: Untersuchungen über das Sehen der Hemianopiker und Hemiamblyopiker, in A. Gelb, und K. Goldstein: "Psychologische Analysen hirnpathologischer Fälle," Leipzig, 1920.

tion of act. In this way it emphasizes the durability of the schema, which, though its literal structural agency changes, continues to maintain its identity.

Stereotypy is illustrated in reflexes and in conditioned responses (habits). Both equivalence and stereotypy emphasize directionality in the organism's acts, stereotypy stressing momentum as well.

Disjunction or *incompatibility* occurs within and between reflexes and in the components of deliberate activity. It amounts to being a competition between directionalities, for with a single well-established alignment, incompatibilities are logically and automatically ruled out. That incompatibilities can occur is to be taken as evidence of subsystems of alignment in the organism—degrees of cleavage. Upon occasion the elements that are able to function now in one pattern and now in another are called upon to become parts of both at once and are unable to do so. With all the fluidity that is suggested in the principle of equivalence, disjunction is bound to occur, and the study of the organism from this point of view is extremely important in coming to understand fatigue.

The organism is endowed with a great many predetermined modes of doing things. Graphic among these are reflexes, modes of behavior arising phylogenetically as adequate responses to the more unequivocal organism-physical world relations. Although streotypy is manifested in a way enabling the observer to classify reflexes, this does not interfere with the principle of equivalence. Reflexes are legitimate abstractions in the sense that we know that some activities are indeliberate, unconscious, arise very early in life without intentional practice and that we can trace their character to morphological design.

If it were our purpose to describe in detail the structure of the neuromuscular system and the modes of its function, there would be several classes of reflexes to describe. Some reflexes are spinal, and of these there are three kinds, the segmental, the intersegmental, and the suprasegmental. In the intersegmental, there are cooperative reflexes and competitive reflexes. The common description of the outcome in the interplay of two competitive reflexes is that one of three things may happen: (1) The first of two reflexes may dominate, while inhibiting the other. (2) The second may dominate. (3) The domination may not be so complete, and alternation between the expression of the two occurs. Since only one can be expressed at a time (*a*) resolution can be complete, in which case one or the other of the two reflexes occupies the final common path; or (*b*) resolution can be incomplete, in which case neither is able to retain use of the final common path. More or less rapid alternation then takes place. In connection with this, forms of momentary "blocking" may occur. Each of these situations is a form of incompatibility.

Among antagonistic (competitive) spinal reflexes, there is also what is called "successive induction." It is the name for the fact that such reflexes may support each other and actually become cooperational when they occur in certain time relations. If one stimulus has elicited action for a time, it is easier for an antagonistic reflex to be elicited than before. So runs the conventional description[2] of waking and other forms of locomotion.

Although forms of disjunction (conflict) and incompatibility in the function of spinal reflexes can be observed, certain simpler reflexes show this even better. The pupillary light reflex is quite striking in this respect.[3] Slow changes in level of illumination elicit changes in the size of the pupillary aperture by means of the reciprocal action of the opposing muscles. One set of muscles upon contracting dilates the aperture, and the contraction of the other set constricts it. If alternations from light to dark are rapid enough, both sets of muscles may come to contract simultaneously and a clear-cut and simple example of incompatibility occurs. The concept of the final common path, if applicable at all here, becomes rather loose and figurative.

While reflexes furnish some of the more concrete examples of possible disharmony, incompatibilities may arise in all kinds of skeletal muscle activity, the voluntary as well as the reflexive. However, muscular activity is so varied and complex that it is not even possible to demonstrate quantitatively all forms of incompatibility. Suggestions of incompatibility arise in the course of investigations motivated by other experimental objectives. Still others would naturally come to light were the objectives of inquiry those of attempting to disclose them.

Muscular incoordination has its origin in the behavior of the nervous system. Although this, considered simply from the standpoint of neurophysiological theory, may not merit the term incompatibility, the muscular end result may be most aptly described as disharmony. Nervous activity is related not only to muscle behavior, but also to personal behavior, descriptions of which have a character all their own. Various forms of incompatibility (conflict) tend toward several personal consequences: (1) discomfort and (2) thwarted accomplishment. Both of these play their part in fatigue.

VARIABILITY

Variability as already defined is a manifestation of complex organization and not a simple unidimensional change as the supply of energy is

2 Fulton, J. F.: "The Physiology of the Nervous System," Oxford University Press, New York, 1938. Pp. 675.

3 Bartley, S. H.: A Factor in Visual Fatigue, *Psychosomatic Med., 4:* 369–375, 1942.

being depleted. The analysis of the various displays of variability should give some clue to the nature of the organization underlying the performance in question. For our purposes, variability is significant insofar as it furthers insight into organization.

Examples of variability in performance. Regardless of the type of work measured, variability in performance occurs in some degree. Arai[4] presents 12-hour work curves for problem solving in which this factor is evident, especially after the first hour. During the first hour the difference in solution time from problem to problem was always 1 minute or less. During the second hour this variation increased to 2 minutes. Later on, variations of 4 or 5 minutes developed. Even when relative rather than absolute values of the variations were considered, the growth in variation was large as work progressed.

Weinland[5] made a study of variability in simple ergographic situations. He found that variability was manifested in three ways: (1) in incidental features of a single work curve, (2) between work curves of different individuals, and (3) between a work curve of any given individual and the average curve of work under the given conditions. All these were more pronounced in the final phases of the curves. Those who identify fatigue with the prolongation of activity make the statement that variability increases with fatigue. No doubt the statement is true when we substitute the word *impairment* for fatigue.

The main conclusion Weinland drew from his study was that the variations manifested gave evidence of lack of control rather than exhaustion of muscle tissue. An experiment supporting this conclusion was one in which it was shown that, as work progressed, the subject was less and less able to keep pace with a metronome. Granting this lack of control, we have in variability a demonstration of the organizational origin of the deterioration of performance, which we have mentioned elsewhere in accounting for fatigue.

Variability during the course of improvement in performance ought to be somehow related to variability during deterioration of performance. Variability in performance during learning has been studied by a number of workers, two of whose results are especially pertinent here. Asch[6] found no relation between the subject's change in learning level and the extent of his variability. Variations during learning were similar in some

---

[4] Arai, T.: "Mental Fatigue," Teachers' College Contribution to Education No. 54, Columbia University, New York, 1912. Pp. 117.

[5] Weinland, J. D.: Variability in Performance in the Curve of Work, *Arch. Psychol.*, No. 87, 1927.

[6] Asch, S. E.: An Experimental Study of Variability in Learning, *Arch. Psychol.*, No. 143, 1932.

respects to those during no learning. The distribution of variation scores was symmetrical in both.

Thurstone[7] found that the variability in typewriting speed for any individual tends to diminish with practice. However, if the subject is a fast writer, he tends to be more variable in speed than does a slow writer, even when measurements are made in relative terms.

Asch and Thurstone agree in their finding that relative deviations decrease with practice, but differ in their findings on absolute deviations with practice. Asch points out several possibilities in methodology, etc., that might account for this.

Our purpose in including learning studies has been to compare certain characteristics of activity when improvement is a salient characteristic with those when deterioration in activity sets in. Although we have not been able to take examples of both improvement and deterioration from the same task, we might gather even from the scant information now existing that one cannot lump all variability into one category. Not all variability is similarly related to the matter of control, or in other words to the organization needed in the rapid and efficient execution of a required task. It is only in general that variability and lack of control are equivalent. In certain more restricted ways, variability has more than one relation to standards of excellence of performance. This was exemplified in Thurstone's finding that the rapid typists made the greatest number of mistakes per unit time, but not necessarily for the total amount typed.

Periodicity and variability are distinguishable aspects of performance. Whereas variability of one kind or another is the most common feature of activity, the existence of periodicity is not nearly so common. Freeman and Wonderlic,[8] examining the literature for examples of periodicity, found them absent as often as present in ergographic studies. Wheeler,[9] in experiments requiring consecutive trials in blindfold stylus maze tracing, found considerable variability in times required. These were far from being random. A definite break seemed to occur about every 40 trials. Though this may be spoken of as periodicity, it pertains directly to number of trials rather than time.

The outcome of Freeman and Wonderlic's study shows that, for their ergographic conditions (finger), subjects exhibiting the greatest variability in work output manifested the least periodicity. They found that

[7] Thurstone, L. L.: The Learning Curve Equation, *Psychol. Monogr.*, *26:* 11–51, 1919. (No. 114.)

[8] Freeman, G. L., and E. F. Wonderlic: Periodicity in Performance, *Am. J. Psychol.*, *47:* 149–151, 1935.

[9] Wheeler, R. H.: "The Science of Psychology," The Thomas Y. Crowell Company, New York, 1929. Pp. 556.

some individuals did not show periodicity at all and that there are conditions even in a well-controlled experimental situation that tend to disguise periodicity.

This leads us to the question of whether, if variability is a common outcome in prolonged continuous activity, and if periodicity and amount of variability are negatively related, periodicity might be an expression of maximum control or orderliness in behavior.

Philip,[10] in his series of studies on the features of continuous tapping, describes periodicity as appearing at the beginning of the "semiautomatic" stage. In his experiments this came on after the elapse of 25 minutes or more. The essential feature he believed to underlie the oscillations he observed was the grouping of sets of factors that tend to work in the same direction, these being able to destroy or bolster accomplishment only within limits, before compensatory factors begin to group for the opposite outcome.

Early decline in the work curve, Philip believes, may be associated with temporary boredom or decreased motivation. Effort with concomitant intrusion of experiential factors, cramping of muscles, and blocking, may work in the same direction—the reduction of efficiency. Pseudo rest periods are thus automatically injected by the subject. The results begin to eliminate the conditions that had made for lowered efficiency, and activity tends toward its effective level. Under pressure, performance that remains nearly constant for a time functions as a standard. Variations from this seem to occur in the direction of diminished efficiency rather than as spurts in the opposite direction.[11] Whether or not this is always true, there is a tendency on the part of the individual to recognize loss of efficiency which may result in motivation to regain an effective level. This tends to carry him beyond his effective working speed, with the involvement of greater physiological demands than can be continuously met, and once more the downswing of the efficiency cycle occurs.

In summarizing, it may be said that performance is observed to change with time. If the required task consists in "repeating" certain operations again and again, this change may not only be exemplified in a slow upward or downward trend, but may also manifest a superimposed variability. This variability may be great or small in either an absolute or a relative sense. As activity goes on, variability may increase or decrease, depending upon many factors, among which is whether improvement or deterioration is occurring.

10 Philip, B. R.: Studies in High Speed Continuous Work. I. Periodicity, *J. Exper. Psychol., 24:* 499–510, 1939.

11 Flügel, J. C.: Practice, Fatigue and Oscillation, *Brit. J. Psychol., Monogr. Suppl.* 13, 1928. Pp. 80.

It would seem that if we were able to gain a picture of periodicity and variability as normal attributes of system action accruing from the *inter-related* functioning of a number of parts, we should have arrived at a far greater understanding of the organism's action. In this picture, diminution is not to be called fatigue, and need not even be a function of what we have defined as impairment. Certain alignments contain the prediction of conditions that will eventuate in diminution and termination of action. For example, as one reaches for something, and one's hand comes to rest, the explanation of cessation of movement is neither fatigue nor exhaustion, but is the change of alignment in the organization of the activity. Thus diminution and variability, like other changes, are inherent aspects of a determined pattern. This limits the ways activity can be profitably studied. It requires that all the sequential implications in activity be recognized, and this can be done only when the aim is to deal with all the parts in the light of each other.

MEASUREMENT OF MUSCLE ACTIVITY

One expression of neuromuscular organization is muscular movement. This movement is understood through analysis of the contributions of the component muscles involved. Movement is measured and described in terms of direction, rate, tension, etc., of the muscular components. Thus the more precise study of muscular activity has been limited to a certain few procedures, *viz.,* (1) *the ergographic,* in which movement is repetitive and confined to one dimension, or at least to the limited motions allowed by the apparatus involved; (2) *the pursuit,* in which records of the accuracy in following a moving target are taken; (3) *the fixation,* in which the particular static balance in tension between two or more opposing muscles is compared under two or more conditions; (4) *the reflex,* in which sensory stimulation evoking a more or less fixed set of movements is studied; and (5) *the isolated nerve-muscle preparation,* in which electrical stimulation is applied to the motor nerve in nerve-muscle tissue removed from the body. Information from this type of study has already been dealt with in the chapter on electrophysiology. Studies that involve the first four methods will be included in the present chapter.

Muscular activity *as movement* in time and space is so complex and elusive to the experimenter that he is obliged to use every device possible to simplify conditions in order to gain an experimental foothold. On this account it is easy to run into the artifactual. Indeed, most if not all the concepts used as tools for understanding motor behavior are abstractions.

Muscle activity not as movement but *as the manifestation* of properties of the organism or as means for carrying out certain long-term functions is also an elusive affair. While the use of such concepts as purpose has long been tabooed in science, we find that statements having to do with direction, goal, action with respect to the future, etc., are becoming used more frequently. Temporal orientation seems to be inescapable if meaning is to exist for the experimenter himself.

The description of any function, muscular activity being no exception, involves some form of representation beyond the original recordings. Graphic representation in the form of curves describing the relation of two variables is commonly practiced in certain kinds of muscle studies.

Representation of activity. In studying muscle activity, motion itself is often not the primary consideration. Measurement of energy expenditure and rates and kinds of performance with reference to arbitrary standards are the more common objectives. Certain representations of these are called *work curves*. Work curves are only one of three general kinds of activity curves. The other two are those of *learning* and of *forgetting*. In each, units of product are plotted against units of time. It is presumed that, from the curves, deductions can be made about the nature of the processes described.

At this point, a few remarks about work curves are in order. Work curves may be plotted to show rate of accomplishment, degree of accuracy, and certain other features such as quality of output.

Certain features are typical of the work curves usually found in experimental studies. These are initial spurt, warming-up period, steady state, general decrement, and end spurt.

Generally, maximum accomplishment is the goal in such experimental studies. For the subject beginning work, this maximum is yet to be determined. Since it is typical[12] to find little or no relation between the individual's estimates and his actual performance, rise is given to what is known as the "initial spurt." The individual tends to plunge into a task at a higher rate than can be maintained, and in a short time a slump sets in. Often a very large proportion of the loss indicated on the first hour's work curve appears in the first few minutes. That the initial spurt is not totally eliminated by familiarity with the task suggests that the phenomenon is not merely a matter of judgment of a maintainable rate but is determined by the over-all state (enthusiasm, etc.) of the individual at the time of beginning the work.

Curves of both physical and "mental" work exhibit another typical characteristic, that of a "warming-up" period. This is a period, often of 20 minutes to ½ hour, during which improvement in performing the task is manifested. This phenomenon is accounted for in various ways, depending in part upon what the task is. In physical work it has been alleged that

12 Filter, R. O.: Estimates of Amount of Work One Can Do, *J. Appl. Psychol., 11:* 58–67, 1927.

lactic acid, one of the products of activity, acts in turn as a stimulant. Robinson and Heron[13] showed how warming-up could be manipulated. When the "continuity of the performance" is great, it is minimized, and when rest periods are injected frequently into the work during its early course, it is exaggerated.

General decrement is, nevertheless, the most salient and characteristic feature of continuous activity. Rest periods injected at various points, however, have a marked effect on the shape of the curve. Since tasks and their demands are so varied, no short description of the decrement covers the diverse results known to occur. With few exceptions, work decrement is taken to be the evidence for fatigue, whereas increase in productivity is often attributed to learning of some sort, learning being as varied in definition as fatigue itself. Some curves level off and remain horizontal for a time, indicating the achievement of a "steady state."

"End spurt" is another well-known feature of the work curve. It is the improvement in output or performance when the worker realizes the end of the work period is near. No better evidence for the "personal" nature of activity could be had than the phenomenon of end spurt. When decrement is attributed to personal factors, some have argued that it is not true fatigue and should not appear in the work curve. This argument, of course, depends upon the definition of fatigue. In fact, by use of definition, any of the features of the work curve can be made either significant or irrelevant. When the personal nature of activity is recognized, reversals in the curve are legitimate and not at all paradoxical. They do not signify a falsity in the manner of measuring fatigue. They show that the individual cannot be studied by *machine* logic. Fatigue is always as much a matter of drop in incentive, etc., as it may be a correlate of accumulating impairment. It may be a quickly changing affair. Whether the task is pleasant or abhorrent, whether its duration is known or unknown, whether it is considered worth while or not by the worker, are some of the many ways of describing the process of working.

Spurts are not confined to the beginning and end of the task performance. They may appear at any time, depending upon a number of factors. Actually few work curves are smooth, if the temporal units in plotting them are small. Spurts often represent a phase of variation of which distraction is sometimes the opposite phase.

It must be remembered that whether a curve plotting activity against time is to be called a work curve (in which evidences of fatigue are looked for) or a learning curve depends upon its trend, and upon the part of the total curve considered. In most formal studies of activity in which curves

13 Robinson, E. S., and W. T. Heron: The Warming-up Effect, *J. Exper. Psychol.*, 7: 81–97, 1924.

are plotted, a number of arbitrary features are present as conditions under which performance takes place. The features that have been described here necessarily partake of the arbitrariness of the experimental setups. Any performance curve involves learning aspects. Learning, impairment, and fatigue are intermingled in the course of almost any prolonged activity.

NEUROMUSCULAR ARRANGEMENTS PROVIDING FOR INCOMPATIBILITY

It is now appropriate to deal with some of the arrangements whereby overt action eventuates. Description will show that incompatibility is predetermined by the very nature of these arrangements. Intrinsic properties of neuromuscular arrangements, as well as providing for incompatibility, form a basis for personal conflict. The basic plan in skeletal-muscle grouping (as well as in some smooth muscle) is that of *pairing for mutually opposing action*. Consideration of this is a dominant part of understanding organismic action, as is a knowledge of the interrelations *between* nerve and muscle.

The motor unit. The literal connections between the nervous and muscular systems are through the relations of single nerve fibers to the muscle fibers they supply. The several muscle fibers taken together with the nerve fiber and its fibrils are called a *motor unit*. The cell bodies of motor neurons innervating striated muscle lie in the ventral horn cells of the spinal cord and in the motor nuclei of the brain stem. Their axons divide into a number of fibrils before reaching the muscle fibers they serve. Generally, only one fibril supplies each muscle fiber, and one neuron is connected to a number of muscle fibers. These fibrils are distributed throughout the muscle and may vary within the limits of about 3 to 150 per neuron. Bulky muscles involved in gross bodily movements tend to have the higher ratios.

Kinds of muscle. Skeletal-muscle fibers are of two kinds, the white and the red. The red fibers take their color from the presence of large amounts of muscle hemoglobin. They likewise contain a large number of fat particles. Presumably these two characteristics permit long-sustained action. White fibers seem to have somewhat the opposite characteristics and would seem fitted only for intermittent activity. Flexor muscles are made up predominantly of white fibers, while red fibers are most numerous in extensors. As usually classified, muscle action is of two kinds, *phasic* and *postural*. The former constitutes the quickly executed adjustments, the latter, the sustained tensions.

There are two kinds of muscle in addition to the striated skeletal muscles just described. They are smooth and heart muscle. Smooth muscle, innervated by the autonomic nervous system, is distributed throughout the body in glands and the circulatory and visceral systems, taking care of the maintenance functions of the organism. Such muscle is slower in action than skeletal. Skeletal muscle possesses a dual innervation. It is supplied not only by the somatic motor system, but also by the sympathetic.

Reciprocal innervation. Between the years of 1893 and 1909, Sherrington, in a series of papers, laid the broad pattern of what has been known ever since as reciprocal innervation. For centuries prior to that time, ideas with reference to the action of muscle in producing motility were put forth. Galen gave attention to this matter and believed that when a muscle contracted to move a limb its antagonist became "dormant" or passive. Descartes believed that in this contraction the antagonist relaxed simultaneously. Winslow later added the idea that opposing muscles in a pair may concurrently contract to offer, as he put it, a moderating resistance. Sir Charles Bell and J. B. Pettigrew argued on the theoretical basis of economy (the unnecessary wasting of energy) that simultaneous contraction of the opposing muscles does not take place.

As Fulton[14] points out, the law of reciprocal innervation admits the existence of contraction in opposing muscles. The essence of the law is that the *augmentation* in contraction of the one is accompanied by the *diminution* of contraction in the other.

While Sherrington's studies marked large and important steps in clarifying what actually happens in skeletal muscle behavior, his interpretations have been criticized. Tilney and Pike[15] believe that they have shown Sherrington's idea of reciprocal innervation to be inadequate to describe their observations. They found opposing muscles contracting simultaneously in some behavior.

With his spinal and decerebrate preparations, Sherrington was able to study what would happen if two afferent nerves instead of only one were stimulated.[16] Sherrington calls the nerve supply *double reciprocal innervation.* He used the nerves that have to do with knee flexion and extension. Such nerves have not only an ipsilateral effect but also a contralateral. Each produces knee flexion contralaterally. If these homologous nerves (on both sides of the animal) are stimulated concurrently, one of three types of result is produced. If the stimulation of the ipsilateral afferents is strong and the contralateral not so strong, then the mechanical result is

[14] Fulton, J. F.: "Muscular Contraction and the Reflex Control of Movement," The Williams & Wilkins Company, Baltimore, 1926. Pp. 644.

[15] Tilney, F., and F. H. Pike: Muscular Coordination Experimentally Studied in Its Relation to the Cerebellum, *Arch. Neurol. & Psychiat., 13:* 289–334, 1925.

[16] Sherrington, C. S.: On Reciprocal Innervation of Antagonistic Muscles. 14th Note: On Double Reciprocal Innervation, *Proc. Roy. Soc., London, 81B:* 249–268, 1909.

flexion of the knees, with apparent complete relaxation of the extensors. If the stimulation of the contralateral afferents is relatively strong, the opposite happens, and the flexors are virtually completely relaxed. If one of the opposing muscles is found at rest, it does not enter into contraction, or if it had been contracting, it is thrown into relaxation. Although two sources of concurrent afferent stimulation are used together, the result simulates the mechanical outcome from stimulating either one or the other of the opposing afferents by itself. The third general type of result ensues when both the contralateral and ipsilateral afferents are strongly stimulated nearly equally. Both flexor and extensor muscles go into contraction and remain for some time.

Sherrington, in describing the limitations of method and qualifications of interpretations thus implied, pointed out the fact that the stimulation of one nerve while all others remained quiet was artificial. Under ordinary circumstances, no single restricted activity of the organism is excited upon a background of inactivity. In natural situations, the skeletal muscles are receiving stimulation involving almost all of them.

Although Sherrington pointed out that simple reciprocal innervation was but an ideal, most of the thinking up to the present day has partaken of many of the qualities of that idealization. It is obvious from the three cases of double reciprocal innervation that many combinations of action could be' expected, ranging from those expressing maximum efficiency to cases of extreme inefficiency. Even slight incompatibilities, when prolonged or repeated, would, in the cumulative nature of their effects, exact considerable toll.

One of the more clear-cut studies on the organization of muscle activity is that of Wilson,[17] who made an analysis of the behavior of the paired components under several types of task, viz., (1) fixation (attempted rigid posture), (2) pursuit movement, (3) ballistic movements, and (4) involuntary extension. In all cases, change from rest to effort rather than from effort to rest was studied. The major characteristics studied were the direction of action of both the protagonist and the antagonist and the time relations involved. The information is of the very kind from which notions regarding voluntary muscle behavior, with its potential kinds of incompatibility and discord, can begin to be conceived.

Results when fixed posture is attempted. In these experiments, an increasing load was placed upon a finger. With voluntary resistance to the increasing load, both the protagonist and the antagonist systems invariably contracted. At no stage of the contraction of the former did the latter relax.

[17] Wilson, D. J.: Antagonistic Muscle Action during the Initiatory Stages of Voluntary Effort, *Arch. Psychol.*, 24: 1-42, 1933-1934. (No. 160.)

The time intervals between the initial action of the opposed muscles for both flexor and extensor loads are generally much too great to suggest simple reciprocal innervation, which requires approximate simultaneity. The time elapsing between the action of the protagonist and the antagonist is sometimes more than 25 seconds. According to Wilson's interpretation, such a temporal dissociation in the action of the two muscles is scarcely compatible with the idea of fullest coordination. Even if it were assumed that this immobility was a resultant of positive and negative tendencies that balanced for this considerable interval, the result would not represent simple reciprocal innervation.

The characteristics of muscle reciprocation depend in part upon the nature of the external task. The facts seem to indicate that the slower the rate of development of load, the greater the temporal dissociation of the opposing muscle systems.

Irregularities of timing also appear in the data. The order of the acting of the units is variable—as are also the time intervals between beginning action when the order is the same. Despite these irregularities, there are some general trends. Thus, for example, there is a predominating though different order of events for both flexor and extensor loads. In flexor fixation, the antagonist succeeds the protagonist slightly more often than it precedes or equals it, whereas in extensor fixation the antagonist never precedes and is rarely simultaneous with the protagonist.

In fixed posture the time interval between the beginning of load and the beginning of the first muscle action is generally shorter and more regular than the latency between the action of the two muscles. Wilson suggests that the subject's stage of "readiness" with its associated tonicity of the muscles at the time of application of the load plays a role in the irregularities.

A marked feature of the postural records is the stepwise contractions of both muscles to a smoothly increasing load. This is especially true of the protagonist. These steps are fewer and smaller the slower the application of the load, and only the large steps are concomitant in the opposed muscles. Wilson suggests from this that the term "relaxation" is relative, since each of the steps is an analogue to the initial relaxation point, the beginning of the load.

Pursuit movements. The latency between the action of the two muscle systems in pursuit movement again is greater than for simple reciprocal innervation. In one instance it was 2.24 seconds. In flexion pursuit, the average interval between the two muscle systems is 0.37 ± 0.37 seconds, and in the extension pursuit it is 0.33 ± 0.27, dependent somewhat upon the speed of the target pointer, a relation more evident in extension. The results are taken to mean that the slower the demand, the greater the temporal dissociation of the opposing muscles in getting under way.

There is again irregularity in time and order. In pursuit, the extensor muscle moves first or currently with the flexor, both for flexion and extension of the finger. As in posture maintenance, there are no instances of finger extension in which the flexor moved first. In finger flexion, the antagonist moved first in 85 per cent of the cases. Wilson suggests that this may show (1) that the extensor system is more unstable than the flexor system and tends always to act first regardless of the direction of the overt movement, or (2) that the action may be adaptive for coordinated action, in that the extensor, being the weaker system, is given an appropriate advantage.

In some cases, both muscle systems acted prior to movement of the visual target pointer. One or the other muscle "jumped the gun" in more than one-quarter of the cases. Since in the experiments the subject was aware of the direction in which the target pointer was to move, they apparently represent a concrete demonstration of the muscular phase of "readiness," imputed to the "foreperiod" preceding voluntary reactions. This favorable "set" by the extensor muscle is predominantly assumed even when the movement is to be flexion.

Ballistic muscle movements. In voluntary ballistic movements both muscle systems invariably contract.

The temporal separations between the antagonist and protagonist are smaller in the ballistic type of movement than in either of the former types. They are, nevertheless, great enough to differ from the short latency of simple reciprocal activity.

Wilson points out two tendencies. (1) The difference in order of action of the units is greater under flexion than under extension. (2) There is a difference in order of action depending upon the size of load. Under zero load, the finger generally moves before the antagonist, particularly in extension, whereas in a large majority of the cases under larger loads, both opposing muscles act before the finger moves.

Velocity of finger movement is unrelated to the latencies between the muscles. This is in contrast to relationships previously stated for posture maintenance and for pursuit. In ballistic movements it was indicated that the greater the energy required for a given task, the more intense the antagonistic action.

Wilson pointed out that none of his findings substantiated the view that in typing, piano playing, etc., the protagonist relaxes while the finger is on its way toward the end of the excursion. He found that the motion was not completed by momentum. The prime mover, having attained as great a degree of contraction as his markers would indicate, remained contracted throughout the stroke and until the individual voluntarily relaxed. Whether intensive training would allow relaxation of the protagonist in ballistic movements before completion of finger movement was not discovered.

Involuntary extension. In finger extension induced by electrical stimulation, time intervals between the action of separate muscles depended upon load and intensity of stimulation. With zero load and weak stimulation, no flexor contraction resulted, although mild extensor contraction occurred with little-finger displacement. With moderate intensities, slight flexor contraction occurred about 0.2 to 0.4 seconds after protagonist (extensor) contraction. Flexor contraction preceded finger movement in the large majority of cases. With strong intensity, pronounced flexor contraction occurred 0.05 to 0.033 seconds after extensor contraction.

The facts seem to emphasize that, in ordinary muscle behavior, relations between the activities of the various muscles involved are on the verge of inefficiency and need only undergo slight changes to be incomptaible and inefficient. This is quite different from the view commonly held in which decided changes in time-tension relations would be necessary to constitute incompatibility and inefficiency.

It may be concluded from the character of the prime mover and its antagonist that the organization behind it is far from simple reciprocal innervation. Although initial action of the antagonist in contracting, when not overdone, contributes to stability of limb motion and other features of motor control, it would seem to represent a condition most susceptible to discord. Only slight changes would represent this decline. With initial action of both members of the pair being contraction, all that is necessary for beginning discord is the failure of antagonistic contraction to remain within small time and intensity proportions. With this failure, work is excessive and discomfort can be expected. On the other hand, were the timing and character of both members of the pair to represent simple reciprocal activity (with initial antagonist action as relaxation), a much grosser change would be required to bring about internal incompatibility in the muscle system.

Wilson's study on the contractional features of the antagonist has made it clear why, although gross overt movement of a member fails to disclose inherent incompatibilities, a considerable amount of discord between the parts of the system may exist. This when recognized would account for certain end results, such as feelings of tension, cramp, and other forms of discomfort. Since tension breeds tension, it is easy to conceive of extreme amounts of difficulty developing from small beginnings.

Irradiation. The information provided by Wilson's study pertains to the *particulars* of the behavior of specific muscle groups. It showed that some degree of incompatibility always exists and that, even in ordinary activity, conditions are laid for the possible eventuation of considerably more. While Wilson's study was analytical, other observations have disclosed gross events in neuromuscular activity which tend to indicate the development of incompatibility.

One of these is irradiation. Irradiation, as used here, is the progressive involvement of more and more tissue in aspects of activity that were originally more localized. Although, strictly speaking, irradiation is a term used to refer to neural activity, its evidences come to light in forms of overt behavior and in introspective data. It is manifested in spreading patterns of muscular tension and movement and in the subjective accompaniments. General modes of behavior peculiar to certain instances of irradiation are described by Snoddy[18] in his study of mirror tracing. He found that mirror drawing involved a progressive difference in the manner of perceiving the geometrical form that was being traced.

Irradiation was used by Berstein and by Pavlov to refer to the spreading of cortical activity. Irradiation as used in other instances may employ the idea of "spread" not in a spatiotemporal sense but in the sense of finding the excitation or other activity beyond the bounds expected of it. For example, irradiation has been used as a term applying to neuroretinal events underlying certain perceptual phenomena. Sharp boundaries between active and inactive areas corresponding to the images cast on the retina were presumed not to be maintained. Activity is said to have irradiated from the highly stimulated area to adjacent less stimulated ones. It is probable that, in prolonged performance, activity that could be said to have been more or less localized becomes more general. Originally existing barriers break down.

Some activity when "localized" is represented by awkwardness, lack of smoothness, etc., in overt behavior. Localization in this case is but a specific example of incoordination. With practice there is a more general participation of tissue and better coordination. This was the case in Snoddy's subjects, and such is the description that could be applied to learning how to dance.

At other times the precise application of a restricted set of muscles would seem to be required. The individual seems to have good control in performing such tasks at first. Neglecting the general postural participation involved, it can well be said that the performance is localized. In some ways, though not all, the neural events that lie behind the performance

[18] Snoddy, G. S.: An Experimental Analysis of a Case of Trial and Error Learning in the Human Subject, *Psychol. Monogr.*, *28:* No. 124, 1920. Pp. 78.

have localized aspects. As performance continues, the distinction between the localized areas and adjacent or more distant ones begins to diminish. Instead of a growing coordination, the outward results seem to indicate the opposite. This is manifest in feelings of muscle tension and cramp in various parts of the body and in a lessened ability to perform the task precisely.

Thus we see that irradiation may lead to two forms of outward manifestation. The spreading of activity may be characterized by increasing coordination or by the opposite. Barring the inordinate increase in intensity of activity as irradiation continues, it is probable that the performance of tasks involving motion of only limited musculature tends to be hurt by irradiation and that of tasks requiring the most fluid participation of large groups or all musculature tends to be benefited by this change.

Given a functioning nervous system, some degree of irradiation is inevitable. Irradiation is another example of the fact that change is predetermined by the nature of the nervous system itself. This predisposition to change is not fully recognized in the customary systematic treatment of nervous phenomena. There seems rather to be an inclination to look upon change as an outcome of impairment, deterioration, and breakdown. Hence it cannot be emphasized too strongly that nervous activity is something that flows from the specific character it has at the moment, to something that is very different in specific details every succeeding instant. Although impairment is likely to be involved, it participates only incidentally, and not as the sole explanation of change.

Irradiation, although it represents a possible form of compensation within nerve and muscle tissue, in many instances represents for the individual a state in which he is less comfortable and less able to perform the task. The individual judges himself to be inefficient. His symptoms are likely to be something that he cannot long tolerate, and thus he uses them as the reason for abandoning the activity he is engaged in.

The symptoms of irradiation are seen to be clearly involved as a factor in fatigue. Although irradiation is a common factor in the fatigue situation, it must not be looked upon as evidence of necessary tissue impairment. As was pointed out, the features of neural organization itself must account for it. The antecedent arrangements predetermine, under certain conditions, shifts in the ways of doing things.

EARLY SYMPTOMS OF MUSCULAR "FATIGUE"

When "fatigue" develops in muscle, the phenomenon expected would be partial or total loss of ability to contract. Diminution in the power of contraction would be the first symptom expected. Ergographic experiments, in their usual limited form, bear on nothing but the amplitude of contraction in a series of trials. Since the relation of the changes occurring in the various component muscles in a group is not disclosed, information on problems of organization is not obtained.

A number of years ago Ash,[19] in studying the development of "fatigue" from muscular exertion, performed some simple but ingenious experiments to demonstrate what he called "loss of control." He used a modified ergograph, which measured not only the voluntary movements of one finger, but also the involuntary movements of some of the others. The records appeared side by side on the kymograph. It was Ash's belief that activity was not precluded by the exhaustion of energy supplies or the accumulation of toxins. Fatigue was not brought about in these ways. He believed that fatigue, even in its first appearance, was evidenced as a loss of control, developing as a result of activity.

Ash required flexions of the second finger at a paced rate of one per 2 seconds under load. With repetition of such flexions, the first and third fingers became increasingly involved. At the outset, some individuals were able to hold their first and third fingers motionless. All individuals sooner or later were flexing the first and third fingers over even greater amplitudes than the second finger which had become less and less able to move. To Ash this constituted an obvious loss of control, inasmuch as the intent of the individual was to move only the second finger. The loss of control originated in the nervous system. The other fingers received more and more involuntary innervation and finally came to move relatively more than the one intended.

Ash's next experiment was intended to show whether decrement in control over movement develops before the test finger is "entirely exhausted or before resistance in the motor tracts leading to these muscles had developed to a point which the organism could not overcome . . . ." Instead of allowing the first and third fingers to move under load, they were held down in the manner customary in ergograph experiments. When the second finger had reached the point at which it was no longer able to raise the weight, the index finger was released, while the subject continued his efforts to raise the weight with the second finger. This was done without interrupting the paced rhythm. The kymograph records showed that the second finger was again able to lift the weight. In some cases the lift was higher than at the outset, and successful trials continued for a period as long as or longer than the first one. When the finger again became totally unable to lift the weight, the third finger was released and allowed freedom of movement. Again the test finger was enabled to flex and lift the weight for another period of trials.

[19] Ash, I. E.: Fatigue and Its Effects upon Control, *Arch. Psychol.,* No. 31, pp. 1–61, 1914.

It appears from Ash's experiments that, in the course of prolonged exertion of specific groups of muscles, voluntary contraction comes to an end long before factors intrinsic to the muscles themselves become responsible. This inability to contract, he speaks of as loss of "control." Since with the involvement of other elements in the innervational pattern, the muscle that was unable to contract immediately became able to contract again, it would seem that innervational *patterns* are involved. The factor necessary in restoring contraction seems to be that of innervational reorganization. The most frequent example of this is possibly what has been called irradiation, the spreading of innervation to collateral channels originally uninvolved. Whereas this change has been thought of exclusively as a kind of overflow, it may partake of the nature of a reorganization. In our use of the term irradiation, repatterning is recognized as an important aspect.

A significant aspect of the situation described by Ash is the innervation supplied proprioceptively when the fingers are released and able to move. Proprioception may supply an "energizing" factor for the movement of the test finger, through the central neural connections involved. Or it may, under usual conditions, provide a stabilizing effect tending to prevent test-finger innervation from shifting into other channels. Thus in Ash's second experiment, the introduction of proprioceptive stimulation from the other fingers may have helped to reestablish the focus in the organization, enabling the test finger again to become active.

The introduction of a proprioceptive factor in accounting for "fatigue" of voluntary muscular activity has some justification in the work of Reid,[20] who concluded its involvement in his experiments.

POSTURE

Posture is a pervasive affair in the existence of the organism. It can be considered from each of several standpoints: (1) as a *body position* that involves varying degrees of muscular exertion and circulatory support for its maintenance, depending upon whether the position is erect, recumbent, etc.; (2) as a *pattern of neuromuscular coordinations,* (a) for maintenance against gravity, (b) for preparation, etc., for activity, and (c) for accomplishing the task at hand; and (3) as a *personal stance* expressing the general character of the individual and his particular relations (attitude, etc.) to the job, etc., at the moment. In attempting to do justice to the problem of fatigue and impairment, we cannot fail to examine posture from each of these angles.

Posture as position—its consequences. Poor posture is the maintenance of a position or state of fixed or nearly fixed rigidity, in which various body

[20] Reid, C.: The Mechanism of Voluntary Muscular Fatigue, *Quart. J. Exper. Physiol.,* *19:* 17-42, 1928.

or limb segments often bear unfortunate positional relations to each other. This immobility applies also to relaxed positions in which muscular tension is not involved. The weight of the member upon its support impedes circulation and gives rise to the need for periodic change of position if not of constant motion of some sort.

In posture not only muscle, bone, and cartilage, but also the respiratory system, the circulation of the blood, and the supply of fuel to the central and peripheral nervous systems are involved. Poor posture may impoverish respiration and disturb the circulation of the blood by retarding blood flow and by involving the body in difficulty with gravitational influences. The brain may be deprived of the fuel supply, and personal alertness, or at times even consciousness, may be lost.

When an individual rises from a reclining to a standing position, gravitational reduction in the pressure on the carotid sinuses and a lessening of the distention in the large veins near the heart, associated with the impedance of venous return, occur. Along with this is an increase in arterial pressure in the lower parts of the body, compensation for which induces reflex acceleration of pulse rate and general, but not uniform, vasoconstriction, which raises blood pressure if cardiac output is maintained. The arterial gravitational pressure provides for the circulation of an undue fraction of the blood through the lower parts of the body, unless the arterioles in these parts constrict more than those in upper portions. Although venous return is indirectly aided by even slight movements of the limbs, rise of venous pressure in the limbs in the absence of muscular movements may compensate the effect of gravity in the arterioles. Postural sway is, however, a common constituent of vertical stance and is of considerable aid to the maintenance of proper circulation.[21]

If an individual is tilted on a movable table with muscular movements absent, the rise in tissue-fluid pressure within the muscles may fail to take place. The individual is likely to faint. It is thought that absence of active muscle movements permits pooling of the blood in the veins of the lower body parts, resulting in insufficient available fluid to enhance the pressure within the muscle. The approximately linear increase in heart rate is taken by some[22] as demonstrating that small changes in blood distribution are not adequately compensated. Krogh[23] agrees that in passive standing there

[21] Hellebrandt, F. A., E. F. Crigler, and L. E. A. Kelso: Variations in Intramuscular Pressure during Postural and Phasic Contraction of Human Muscle, *Am. J. Physiol.*, 126: 247–253, 1939.

[22] Asmussen, E., E. H. Christensen, and M. Nielsen: Pulsfrequenz und Körperstellung, *Skandinav. Arch. f. Physiol.*, 81: 190–203, 1939. Also following articles in same volume.

[23] Krogh, A.: Effect of Posture on Regulation of Circulation, *Proc. Inst. Med. Chicago*, 12: 398–399, 1939.

is inadequate adaptation. Regardless of muscular movements, accumulation of fluid in subcutaneous tissues is not only sluggish, but occurs also without sizable change in tissue fluid pressure. Low intramuscular tissue pressure is a sizable underlying factor in postural syncope. Sitting postures, although they may entail some reduced cardiac output, in general show only slight differences from the reclining.

Temperature of the environment when taken in conjunction with posture leads to observable effects. With high temperatures and their associated dilatation of the superficial veins, the venous return to the heart is more difficult than otherwise. The usual increase in pulse rate and diminution in stroke volume are exaggerated. The mean blood pressure which might otherwise remain the same tends to fall. However, adaptation to the higher temperature may take place, and the circulatory shifts on standing may become smaller rather than greater than usual. This seems to be connected with increased blood volume and results in a lessened effect from pooling of blood in the limbs.

From these details it should be apparent that the individual's shift from horizontal to erect posture is a matter of consequence, especially if adequate movement is not allowed, and if the individual is having difficulty in adjusting to high temperature. In a sense, the adjustments necessary for heat loss and for adequate circulation through the central nervous system are somewhat in opposition. The outcome depends upon the specific patterns of compensation for gravity and for heat loss and upon the relations of the two to each other. For more details, see McDowall's monograph.[24]

The energy expenditure of verticality is definitely greater than that of recumbency. Hellebrandt, Brogden, and Tepper[25] found an average increase of 5.71 kcal. per sq. m. per hr. in 75 women during passive standing. This represented a 16.3 per cent increase over recumbency. The increase on standing varied greatly from one individual to another. This finding emphasizes the need for approaching the problem from the point of view of the individual.

To offset the implication that energy expenditure is the crucial factor in postural difficulty, it should be mentioned that the expenditure in the upright position has been found to be no greater for some individuals than that for others in recumbency. Tepper and Hellebrandt[26] investigated the expenditure for upright posture under several different conditions, including vertical suspension of the body in water, mechanical sus-

[24] McDowall, R. J. S.: "The Control of the Circulation of the Blood," Longmans, Green and Company, New York, 1938. Pp. 619.

[25] Hellebrandt, F. A., E. Brogden, and R. H. Tepper: Posture and Its Cost, *Am. J. Physiol.*, *129:* 773–781, 1940.

[26] Tepper, R. H. and F. A. Hellebrandt: The Influence of the Upright Posture on the Metabolic Rate, *Am. J. Physiol.*, *122:* 563–568, 1938.

pension on a tilting board, and ordinary standing with swaying. Under the first conditions, the caloric cost was 2.58 kcal. per hr., under the second 5.42 kcal. per hr., and under the third 19.23 kcal. per hr. Since the expenditure at no time was great enough to account for metabolite accumulation, the postural distress in motionless standing was attributed to cerebral anemia from the absence of the peripheral pumping effect of postural sway.

Unfortunate posture may affect circulation, digestion, muscular efficiency, and the fuel supply to the brain and the rest of the central nervous system. The effect on circulation has already been described with the inference that fainting and lesser forms of insufficiency and discomfort can be induced by rigidily maintained standing positions. It is not difficult to see how certain symptoms of distress arising from circulatory insufficiencies could contribute to the experience of fatigue.

The apparent stereotypy of circulatory insufficiency or other systemic inadequacies develops through gradual conditioning. Much of the considerable distress that may ensue is in a sense unwittingly self-imposed.

Posture as an example of neuromuscular organization. Posture considered from the standpoint of neuromuscular organization is one of the most important aspects of activity. In fact, as Fulton[27] points out, postural determination of tonus and the participation of the proprioceptive system is one of the greatest recognitions of modern physiology. We have already pictured posture in terms of the type of innervation necessary to maintain continuous muscular contraction so that bodily support may be had at all times. The present consideration of posture is an inquiry into the relations between tonic and phasic activity. Contact with, and reaction to, the surroundings is generally thought of in terms of what is called "phasic" response. But it has become apparent to many workers over the past decades that the phasic develops only out of the tonic as a background. "Reactivity levels,"[28] "excitation backgrounds,"[29] and "postural substrates,"[30] etc., have been postulated in accordance with this belief.

The initial distinction between what is tonic and what is phasic arises from the following observations. The tonic is generally slower in developing, outlasts and is more diffuse and extensive than the phasic. The two are centrally controlled by separate channels, the great pyramidal for the phasic, and the extrapyramidal for the tonic. Tonic processes are initiated

[27] Fulton, *op cit.*, p. 383.

[28] Freeman, G. L.: The Postural Substrate, *Psychol. Rev., 45:* 324–334, 1938.

[29] Darrow, G. W.: The Equation of the Galvanic Skin Reflex Curve: I. The Dynamics of Reaction in Relation to Excitation Background, *J. Gen. Psychol., 16:* 285–309, 1937.

[30] Freeman, *op cit.*, defines it as "the general organic background (neuromuscular-glandular) which operates to sustain and energize phasic responses."

through introceptive channels and the phasic through exteroceptive. Some workers extend the differentiation even further. Hunt[31] asserts his belief in the duplicity of muscle-fiber structure and function having to do with tonic and phasic reactions. Even so, the tonic and the phasic are not fully isolated. The phasic can be expected to be largely mobilized and maintained by the tonic.

Kempf[32] pictured the tonic-phasic dichotomy in his autonomic-projicient doctrine. He put forth the idea that whenever the sensorimotor apparatus of the autonomic system is disturbed (through growth, metabolism, or other "stimuli") the projicient system must adjust to receptors in the surroundings so as to be provided with "stimuli" to produce satisfactory "postural" adjustments in the autonomic system. The autonomic disturbances were supposed to sustain and regulate the efficiency of the overt responses as well as to start off the phasic activity for restoring organic equilibrium. The persistent tendency of the tonic system was to maintain the phasic apparatus so as to acquire the greatest satisfaction with the least cost in energy.

Freeman supposes that the relation of the "activity level" to overt performance is determined by two factors: (1) the individual's resources as an energy system, and (2) the appropriateness with which the systems of phasic response can channel the activity. The latter he wishes to call "inhibitory control," relating it to the integrational activity of the higher cortical centers. He thinks overt performance scores are largely representative of "control," while measures of postural activity are reflectors of "drive." Their relation should yield an inflected curve showing that, up to a certain point, additions in postural "output" have to do with an increasingly effective overt performance, but beyond which the relations are reversed. He points out that the ends of the curve would represent, respectively, sleep and collapse. He interpreted experimental work[33] in line with these ideas.

It should be called to the reader's attention that notions about the energizing of activity have crept into what might have been expected to be an inquiry on functional relationship between parts. Freeman has classed the postural (tonic reactions) as the energizers, mobilizers, and maintainers of the phasic responses. The tonic response represents "drive,"

---

[31] Hunt, J. R.: The Dual Nature of the Efferent Nervous System, *Arch. Neurol. & Psychiat.*, *10:* 37–82, 1923.

[32] Kempf, E. J.: The Autonomic Function of the Personality, *Nerv. & Ment. Dis.*, Monogr. Series 28, 1921.

[33] Freeman, G. L.: The Optimal Muscular Tensions for Various Performances, *Am. J. Psychol.*, *51:* 146–150, 1938.

Freeman, G. L.: The Facilitative and Inhibitory Effects of Muscular Tension upon Performance, *Am. J. Psychol.*, *45:* 17–52, 1933.

while he attributes to the phasic responses "control." This procedure side-tracks the task of analyzing the active relationships between the various parts of the neuromuscular system.

Posture as a personal stance. Certain individuals are far more prone to difficulties in maintaining posture than others. Persons who suffer from what Alexander[34] calls *vegetative retreat* are among the most likely to exemplify these difficulties. Alexander has described patients who have become inadequate to meet the demands of their social environments. These individuals characteristically manifest physiological symptoms that indicate a parasympathetic dominance. As this dominance would suggest, their behavioral alignment tends to be distinctly conservational. These individuals behave as if they were attempting to retreat from obligation, lack of tonus being one expression of this retreat.

The inability to stand for long, or to walk any great distance without exhaustion or collapse, is a recognized clinical entity. It is called postural hypotension, or *orthostatic hypotension,*[35] and is known by the following group of symptoms: (1) the failure of the pulse rate to rise when the individual rises to a standing position, (2) diminution or absence of sweating, (3) loss of sexual desire, (4) pallor, (5) high blood urea, and (6) low basal metabolism.

MacLean, Horton, and Moersch[36] have reported cases of exhaustion in connection with standing postures and walking. Headaches, tachycardia, blurring of vision, dizziness, and nausea occurred in all three of the cases cited. In two of the cases there were no other postive medical findings; the other was diagnosed as myasthenia gravis.

Despite the definiteness of the hypotension symptoms, the specialist sometimes has difficulty in relating them to a broader set of conditions. In other words, he is often unable to account for hypotension by discovering the "syndromic origin." It is plausible that a type of "conditioning" may have been responsible. In this case the symptoms would become a meaningful part of a larger picture following a broader and more penetrating insight into the personality as a whole. It is interesting in this connection that one of the three patients reported above was a psychoneurotic.

One of the treatments recommended is benzedrine sulfate used for the purpose of maintaining blood pressure above symptomatic level.[37]

[34] Alexander, F.: Fundamental Concepts and Psychosomatic Research, *Psychosomatic Med., 5:* 205–210, 1943.

[35] Chew, E. M., E. V. Allen, and N. W. Barker: Orthostatic Hypotension: Report of Six Cases and a Review of the Literature, *Northwest Med., 35:* 297–303, 1936.

[36] MacLean, A. R., B. T. Horton, and F. P. Moersch: The Importance of Postural Vascular Studies in Exhaustive States, *Proc. Staff Meet., Mayo Clin., 14:* 620–624, 1939.

[37] Davis, P. E., and M. Shumway-Davis: Orthostatic Hypotension, the Treatment of Two Cases with Benzedrine Sulfate, *J.A.M.A., 108:* 1247–1249, 1937.

Chapter XIII

SLEEP AND OTHER PERIODICITIES

NATURE in general is characterized by variations, alternations, intermittencies, and rhythms. The definite cycles that have been identified pertain both to inanimate nature and to biological activity, including human behavior. In human activity there are several well-known variations that would seem to have some bearing on fitness for work and upon fatigue. In addition to the diurnal sleep-waking cycle, there are various cycles such as the gastric-motility rhythm,[1] recurrent changes in temperament,[2] and the variations in ability to sleep as influenced by weather and climate.[3]

EFFECTS OF THE SEASONS AND RECURRENT FEATURES OF WEATHER, ETC.

Climatic effects are studied mainly by observing the differences in populations as wholes in different climates. Selected individuals have never been followed for prolonged periods in a variety of climates. Day-to-day weather conditions and the concomitant changes in physiological function, feeling of well-being, and in work output have been studied, however. The information from these studies along with that from climate studies is used to show that meteorological changes are potent factors in organism function and in the personal outcome. Climate as reflected in temperature, humidity, and other such conditions has been studied by Mills,[4] and day-to-

[1] Kleitman, N., F. J. Mullin, N. R. Cooperman, and S. Titelbaum: "Sleep Characteristics," University of Chicago Press, Chicago, 1937. Pp. 86.

Richter, C. P.: Cyclic Manifestations in the Sleep Curves of Psychotic Patients, *Arch. Neurol. & Psychiat., 31:* 149–151, 1934.

Rubenstein, B. B.: The Relation of Cyclic Changes in Human Vaginal Smears to Body Temperature and Basal Metabolic Rate, *Am. J. Physiol., 119:* 635–641, 1937.

[2] Hersey, R. B.: "Selle und Gefühl des Arbeiters," Konkordia, Leipzig, 1935. Pp. 171.

[3] Erwin, D.: An Analytical Study of Children's Sleep, *J. Genetic Psychol., 45:* 199–226, 1934.

Kleitman, N., N. R. Cooperman, and F. J. Mullin: Studies on the Physiology of Sleep. IX. Motility and Body Temperature during Sleep, *Am. J. Physiol., 105:* 574–584, 1933.

Kleitman, Mullin, Cooperman, and Titelbaum, *op. cit.*

[4] Mills, C. A.: "Climate Makes the Man," Harper & Brothers, New York, 1942. Pp. 320. Also many articles in medical journals.

day weather conditions, by Petersen.[5] The effects of the broad geographical and meteorological, as well as those of some more nearly cosmological, conditions upon human activity and enterprise have been studied by Huntington[6] and by Wheeler.[7]

Seasons. Over most of the earth's surface, climate can be divided into seasons. Sometimes the primary differentiation is made in terms of rainfall, in which case there is a wet season and a dry, for example. Most populations live in regions in which seasons can be distinguished.

It would not be surprising if decided seasonal variations in behavior were to occur, inasmuch as the seasons exemplify shifts of whole groups of conditions (temperature, humidity, sunlight, barometric pressure, etc.), almost any one of which can be shown to influence behavior.

There is as yet little agreement regarding the influence of season upon any single phase of activity. One investigator[8] finds that sleep is longest in winter and shortest in summer in some peoples. Whether this was directly climatic, or whether the work or other social obligations of the individual were different in the two seasons was not determined. While several investigators have found seasonal differences, others[9] have failed to find them.

Kleitman[10] discusses the matter of seasonal variation in sleep and shows how certain measures may be used to indicate a fairly stable pattern of sleep movements throughout the year, and how certain others will indicate seasonal variation. He concludes by saying that a fair opinion would be that the sleep pattern of a given individual expresses more similarities throughout the year than it shows seasonal differences.

Huntington,[11] in one of his earlier works, presents a diagram to indicate seasonal differences in factory workers in two American cities. It is given here as Fig. 37. The smoothed curves, representing results corrected for practice, represent work over a period of four successive years. They show

[5] Petersen, W. F., *et al.:* "The Patient and the Weather," Edwards Bros., Inc., Ann Arbor, Mich., 1934–1936.

[6] Huntington, E.: "Civilization and Climate," Yale University Press, New Haven, 1915. Pp. 333.

Huntington, E.: "Mainsprings of Civilization," John Wiley & Sons, Inc., New York, 1945. Pp. 660.

[7] Wheeler, R. H.: The Effect of Climate on Human Behavior in History, *Tr. Kansas Acad. Sc., 46:* 33–51, 1943.

[8] Hayashi, Y.: On the Sleep Hours of School Children Aged 6 to 20 Years. *Jido Jatshi (Child's J.)* , 1925.

[9] Garvey, C. R.: An Experimental Study of the Sleep of Pre-school Children, *Proc. Ninth Int. Cong. Psychol.,* pp. 176–177, 1929.

[10] Kleitman, N.: "Sleep and Wakefulness," University of Chicago Press, Chicago, 1939. Pp. 638.

[11] Huntington, E.: "Civilization and Climate," Yale University Press, New Haven, 1915. Pp. 333.

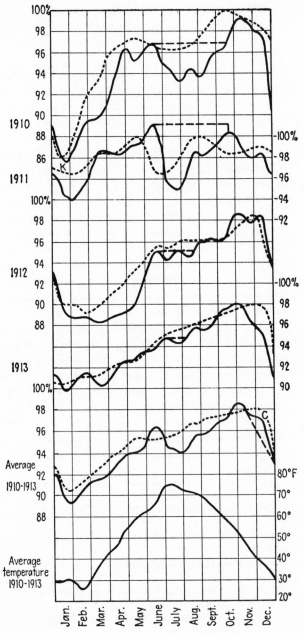

Fig. 37.—The effect of the seasons on factory operatives in Connecticut (solid lines) and in Pittsburgh (dotted lines). (*Huntington: "Civilization and Climate," Yale University Press.*)

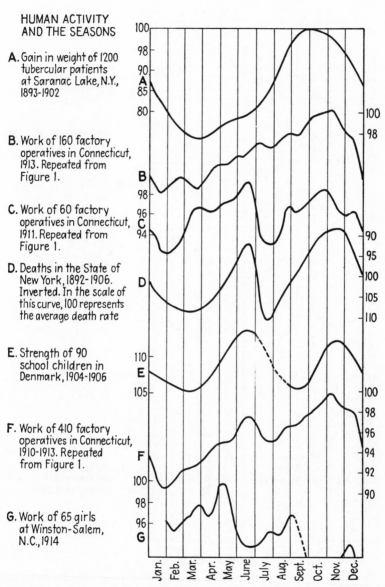

HUMAN ACTIVITY
AND THE SEASONS

A. Gain in weight of 1200
tubercular patients
at Saranac Lake, N.Y.,
1893-1902

B. Work of 160 factory
operatives in Connecticut,
1913. Repeated from
Figure 1.

C. Work of 60 factory
operatives in Connecticut,
1911. Repeated from
Figure 1.

D. Deaths in the State of
New York, 1892-1906.
Inverted. In the scale of
this curve, 100 represents
the average death rate

E. Strength of 90
school children in
Denmark, 1904-1906

F. Work of 410 factory
operatives in Connecticut,
1910-1913. Repeated
from Figure 1.

G. Work of 65 girls
at Winston-Salem,
N.C., 1914

Fig. 38.—The relation of the seasons to productivity in workers. (*Huntington:
"Civilization and Climate," Yale University Press.*)

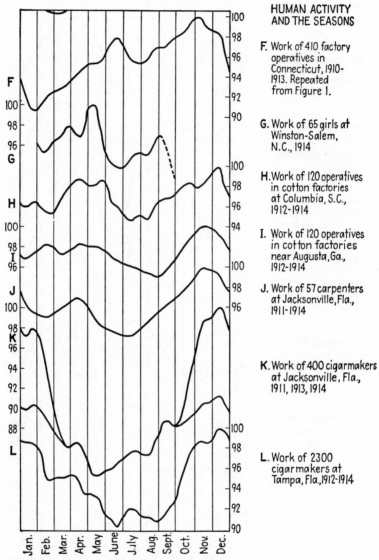

HUMAN ACTIVITY
AND THE SEASONS

F. Work of 410 factory
operatives in
Connecticut, 1910-
1913. Repeated
from Figure 1.

G. Work of 65 girls at
Winston-Salem,
N.C., 1914

H. Work of 120 operatives
in cotton factories
at Columbia, S.C.,
1912-1914

I. Work of 120 operatives
in cotton factories
near Augusta, Ga.,
1912-1914

J. Work of 57 carpenters
at Jacksonville, Fla.,
1911-1914

K. Work of 400 cigarmakers
at Jacksonville, Fla.,
1911, 1913, 1914

L. Work of 2300
cigarmakers at
Tampa, Fla., 1912-1914

Fig. 39.—The relation of the seasons to productivity in workers (*continued*).
(*Huntington: "Civilization and Climate," Yale University Press.*)

consistent trends from low activity in the early spring to maximum activity in the late fall.

In Figs. 38 and 39, the seasonal differences in the activity of workers of various sorts are pictured in two overlapping diagrams. Huntington has arranged the curves to range from those representing cooler climates at the top to those representing warmer climates at the bottom. There is a

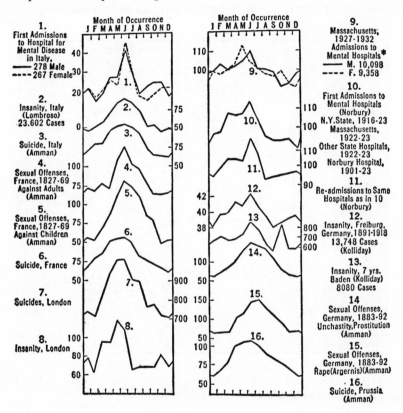

FIG. 40.—The relation between seasons and crime and insanity. (*After Dexter*). (*Reprinted by permission from Huntington, E.: "Mainsprings of Civilization," John Wiley & Sons, Inc.*)

remarkable similarity in the several curves, especially when the temperature factor in climate is taken into account. The curves for the cooler climates manifest the trend of increasing activity from about February to about October, whereas the low period of activity in the warmer climates occurs in the middle of the summer, and the high period in the midwinter months. The length of time spent in relatively low activity is longer for the warmer climates.

Taking the United States as a whole, there are seasonal variations in conception and in length of life of individuals conceived in different months of the year. In Fig. 40, from Huntington,[12] annual distribution of the suicides, admissions to insane hospitals, readmissions, and crime is shown. In every case the late spring and early summer months furnish the maximums. The year cannot be considered as a uniformity, and hot weather is a difficult condition for the individual to contend with.

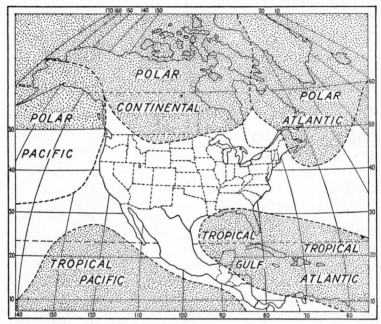

Fig. 41.—The source regions of air masses common to North America. (*Finch, Trewortha, Shearer and Caudle: "Elementary Meteorology," McGraw-Hill Book Company, Inc. After Transcontinental and Western Air, Inc.*)

Weather.   Day-to-day weather changes are often variations of considerable magnitude. Extremes of temperature, sunlight, barometric pressure, humidity, air movement, etc., may occur. Regions vary greatly from one another, both in the magnitude and frequency of change. Some regions (of the United States, for example) are much more unstable in temperature and barometric pressure than others. Some characteristically receive more rainfall than others, whether this is measured in single seasons or in totals for the year.

[12] Huntington, "Mainsprings of Civilization."

America, for instance, is traversed by storm tracks.[13] Major meteorological changes, the alternations of conditions determined by movements of great air masses (with the water vapor they carry), sweep across the continent in fairly predictable paths. Figure 41 indicates the chief air masses from which originate the meteorological changes in North America. The centers of such changes (storms) do not all follow exactly the same course, but most of them cluster well enough to mark out a predominant band across the continent. This band can be spoken of as the region of the storm

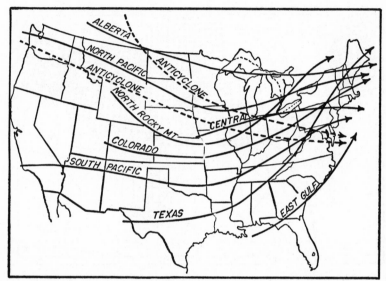

Fig. 42.—The principal tracks of cyclones. (*Finch, Trewartha, Shearer and Caudle: "Elementary Meteorology," McGraw-Hill Book Company, Inc. After map by U.S. Weather Bureau.*)

tracks. It begins in the Canadian Northwest and dips southeastward extending eastward through the North Central and Central states, and veering northeasterly to the North Atlantic and New England states and the Atlantic Ocean. The map in Fig. 42 indicates the named storm tracks. As will be seen, certain storm tracks lie outside this band, but taken as a whole the bulk of cyclonic changes center within it. A greater number of storms traverse the Alberta and North Pacific tracks than any other two.

Petersen,[14] among others, has studied the influence of meteorological

[13] The term "storm" is the broad label given to a pattern of meteorological change, and is measured primarily barometrically, but entails certain other features incident to changes of temperature and pressure.

[14] Petersen, *op. cit.*

changes on the well-being, health, and course of disease in the human organism. In connection with the study of the effects of day-to-day meteorological changes upon the human organism, Petersen has constructed a map that he believes indicates the regions of greatest meteorological demand. This is reproduced in Fig. 43. This map is to be inspected in the light of several other sets of information, such as cold, cloudiness, rainfall, and barometric variability. Petersen has superimposed three maps in which these factors were plotted separately in shades of gray.

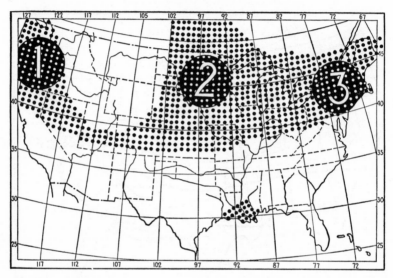

FIG. 43.—The regions of greatest meteorological demand on the organism. (*Petersen: "The Patient and the Weather," Edwards Bros., Inc.*)

Several other maps that bear on the matter of meteorological demand are also included. Figure 44 is a map indicating the average annual number of cloudy days. Figure 45 shows the average annual number of days with thunderstorms. In Fig. 46 the average annual precipitation in the United States is given. It will be seen that precipitation in a given area and its coverage by numerous storm tracks do not necessarily go hand in hand.

Geographers divide the world into a number of climates. The classification given by Finch, Trewartha, Shearer, and Caudle[15] in their "Elementary Meteorology" is shown in Fig. 47. From this map it can be seen that the climatic differentiation of the continental United States depends upon many factors. The maps taken as a group serve to emphasize that physical influences upon individuals are a complex problem.

[15] Finch, V. C., G. T. Trewartha, M. H. Shearer, and F. L. Caudle: "Elementary Meteorology," McGraw-Hill Book Company, Inc., New York, 1942. Pp. 301.

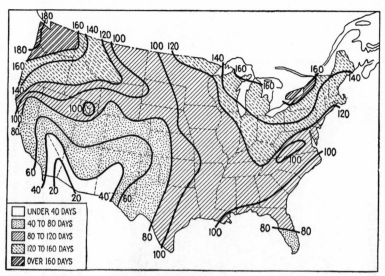

Fig. 44.—The average number of cloudy days per year. Note that the regions having the greater average number of cloudy days lie within Petersen's areas of greatest meteorological demand on the organism. (*Finch, Trewartha, Shearer and Caudle: "Elementary Meteorology," McGraw-Hill Book Company, Inc.*)

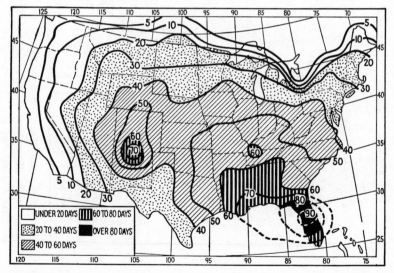

Fig. 45.—The average annual number of days with thunderstorms. (*Finch, Trewartha, Shearer and Caudle: "Elementary Meteorology," McGraw-Hill Book Company, Inc. After Alexander.*)

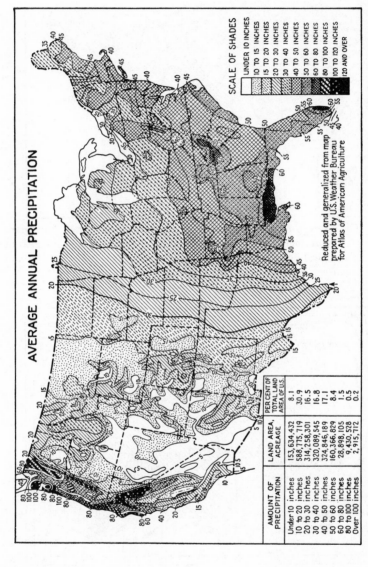

AVERAGE ANNUAL PRECIPITATION

SCALE OF SHADES

UNDER 10 INCHES
10 TO 15 INCHES
15 TO 20 INCHES
20 TO 30 INCHES
30 TO 40 INCHES
40 TO 50 INCHES
50 TO 60 INCHES
60 TO 80 INCHES
80 TO 100 INCHES
100 TO 120 INCHES
120 AND OVER

Reduced and generalized from map
prepared by U.S. Weather Bureau
for Atlas of American Agriculture

AMOUNT OF PRECIPITATION	LAND AREA, ACREAGE	PER CENT OF TOTAL LAND AREA OF U.S.
Under 10 inches	153,634,432	8.1
10 to 20 inches	588,775,719	30.9
20 to 30 inches	314,258,301	16.5
30 to 40 inches	320,089,545	16.8
40 to 50 inches	324,846,189	17.1
50 to 60 inches	160,366,829	8.4
60 to 80 inches	28,898,105	1.5
80 to 100 inches	9,430,528	0.5
Over 100 inches	2,915,712	0.2

FIG. 46.— The average annual rainfall in the United States. *(Finch, Trewartha, Shearer and Caudle: "Elementary Meteorology," McGraw-Hill Book Company, Inc. Reduced and generalized from U.S. Weather Bureau map.)*

Petersen's experimental procedure has included the measurement of blood pressure, acid-base balance, water and salt balance, etc. He has found that these basic characteristics as well as others shift in keeping with the meteorological changes characteristic of our cyclonic weather in the United States. Alkalosis alternates with acidosis, high with low blood pressure, high salt content with low, and positive with negative water balance in the tissues.

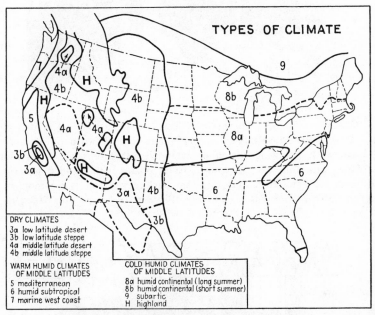

FIG. 47.—The types of climate of the United States. (*Finch, Trewartha, Shearer and Caudle: "Elementary Meteorology," McGraw-Hill Book Company, Inc.*)

In polar fronts and in tropical fronts certain bodily changes are said to be induced. Whereas in the polar front the barometric pressure rises and atmospheric temperature falls, in the tropical front there is high temperature, high humidity, and low barometric pressure. Both fronts are said to induce a series of bodily changes that are reversed as the weather shifts to its opposite cyclonic phase. The first phase Petersen calls the anabolism, chemical reduction, spasm (ARS) phase and the second, the catabolism, oxidation, dilatation (COD) phase.

In the ARS phase (see Fig. 48), the blood pressure rises, and closure in parts of the vascular bed occurs. During this, relative anoxemia, anabolism, chemical reduction, and spasm are said to predominate. The pH of the

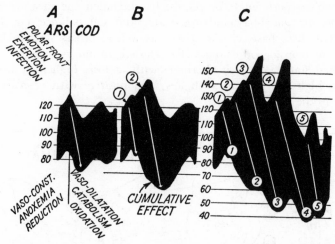

Fig. 48.—Pressor curves with varying effects of repeated environmental alterations. (*A*) A single ARS-COD cycle. (*B*) Summation of two impulses, a double ARS phase with following period of extended dilatation. (*C*) Summation of ARS phases with following prolonged COD phases with decided lowering of blood pressure. Petersen points out that such a reaction is common in the spring. (*Petersen: "The Patient and the Weather," Edwards Bros., Inc.*)

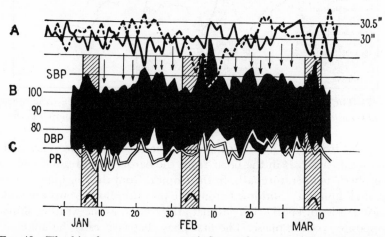

Fig. 49.—The blood pressure curve as influenced by storm. Heavy black curve (*A*) is the barograph. The dotted curve is the average daily temperature. The upper edge of the broad black curve (*B*) is the systolic blood pressure. Lower edge (*C*) is the diastolic blood pressure. The double curve below is the pulse rate. Arrows indicate periods of polar infalls. Note pressor peaks synchronous with them. (*Petersen: "The Patient and the Weather," Edwards Bros., Inc.*)

blood is raised, and adrenal effectiveness is increased. This phase is also called the sympathetico-tonic phase, since the hypophysis and adrenals presumably play a prepotent role among the endocrines.

After the polar front has passed, the "corrective" or COD phase develops in the individual. In it, catabolism, oxidation, dilatation, and acidity are greatest. During this phase there is said to be "thyroid preponderance." An illustration of certain relations between weather changes and changes in bodily processes is given in Fig. 49.

Untoward results ensue in the individual when certain organs of the body are not able to adjust to the basic changes in body chemistry induced by the meteorological variations. Vascular constrictions and oxygen hunger may result in impairment or in injury.

Whereas the storm-track areas induce alternations in degree of oxygen utilization, certain other more quiescent regions may induce conditions slowly leading to chronic oxygen deficiency, and thereby also be detrimental.

Not only systemic effects clustering around and ensuing from the basic meteorological shifts are involved in this picture, but also bacterial diseases. Penetration of bacteria into regions suitable for their life and growth depends upon the mucous membranes and skin relaxing their barrier functions. When the alternations (in blood pressure, for example) occur, the mucous membranes are brought into corresponding functional states, which amount to an oscillation of varying resistance to bacterial penetration.

The complexity of the interrelations among meteorological conditions, bodily processes, and personal behavior is further recognized by Petersen in his attempt to show that there are two extremes among individuals in the way they are affected by the weather.

Granting the efficacy of physical factors in influencing body functions, it can be said that weather alternations are no respecters of persons. They may appear in very rapid progression, in which case various summative effects occur, and they may occur at unfortunate moments. Petersen shows, for example, that certain ARS phases coming in quick succession tend to lower the general blood-pressure level, both diastolic and systolic. This cumulative effect is shown in *B* and *C* of Fig. 48.

LONGER PERIODIC VARIATIONS OF THE INDIVIDUAL

A number of more or less periodic variations have been reported from time to time to characterize the individual. Some of these are organic manifestations, some have to do with mood, and some are variations of the over-all tendency to activity. Among the briefer rhythms is the gastric-motility cycle, for example, covering periods of 4 to 6 hours. Sleep, which we look upon as a phase of a diurnal cycle, has been reported to vary, at least in some individuals, so as to manifest a 4-day rhythm.[16] Rhythms in mood covering 4- to 6-week periods have been reported by Hersey.[17] These rhythms were of different lengths in various individuals and bore a relation to fatigability and efficiency. They tended to be shorter in the young, in the extrovert, in the dull, in the submissive, and in the unmarried.

The menstrual cycle. One of the more significant longer rhythms is the female menstrual cycle. The menstrual cycle may be regarded from several standpoints, among which are (1) the ovarian cycle, with the ripening of the follicle and the expulsion of the ovum, the development of the corpus luteum, and the activity of hormones; (2) the uterine cycle, with tissue changes culminating in the breakdown of the membranes and the characteristic bleeding; (3) the cycle of changes in the tendency toward overt activity, etc.; and (4) the cycle of more intricate personality changes in which the individual varies in her social and psychosexual outlook.

Each of these four related cycles may be divided into periods. The period beginning with the end of uterine hemorrhage and ending at the expulsion of the ovum from its follicle is known as the *interval* period. This is sometimes broken into the *resting stage* and the *interval*. The interval period is usually one of intense activity. During this time the production of estrogenic hormones is at its height, and both ovarian and uterine changes are occurring. The next stage is that of *ovulation* itself. The expulsion of the ovum may or may not occur. If it does not, the cycle is spoken of as an anovulatory one. Whereas during the ripening of the follicle preceding ovulation, estrogenic hormones were produced at their peak, this activity begins to fall off at ovulation. If the ovum is expelled, the corpus luteum develops and the hormonal product is progesterone. Both estrogen and progesterone have effects on certain organs of the body, the uterus in particular. The next period is called the *premenstrual* period. It has been recommended[18] that this be called the *progestational* period. This period, whether it follows ovulation or the retention of the ovum (ovulation or anovulation), terminates in hemorrhage, the *menstrual* period, a uterine event brought about under the influence of estrogen and progesterone. After ovulation, it follows the withdrawal of progesterone or a combination of progesterone and estrogen. After anovulation it follows the withdrawal or diminution of estrogen alone.

In the attempt to associate psychic or personality phenomena with hor-

[16] Richter, *op. cit.*

[17] Hersey, *op. cit.*

[18] Allen, E., F. L. Hisaw, and W. U. Gardner: Endocrine Functions of the Ovaries, in Allen, Danforth, and Doisy's "Sex and Internal Secretions," 2d ed., Williams & Wilkins Company, Baltimore, 1939. Pp. 1346.

monal chemistry, the cycle is often divided roughly into the *estrogenic,* the *progesteronogenic,* and the *menstrual* periods.

The overt activity character of the cycle. One of the primary considerations in dealing with the menstrual cycle here is a description of it in terms of the tendency to overt activity.

Altmann, Knowles, and Bull[19] studied 10 college women (22 to 26 years of age) over a period of 5 months. They found that the most typical "energy" pattern consisted in a burst of motor and mental activity just before the onset of menstruation. "Tensiveness" and irritability preceded or accompanied by depression were a part of this pattern. A secondary high-activity phase dominated the ovulation phase of the cycle. This activity was different in character, being devoid of "nervous tension," and was frequently accompanied by a mood of elation.

The following study suggests that not all the subjective and overt characteristics of the menstrual cycle can be laid to hormone variations. Measures[20] of fatigue, steadiness, rate of tapping, color naming, free association, etc., as well as of sleep, "energy," and mood, on women passing through the menopause, failed to reveal any consistent differences when estrogenic hormonal injections were given and when saline water was substituted.

The gross amount of motor activity measured in six psychiatric patients by means of a pedometer showed a consistent postmenstrual burst of activity that declined gradually up to the time of the succeeding menstrual period.[21]

Other characteristics. From a questionnaire given to 100 women, the following symptoms associated with menstruation were reported:[22] headache, 14 per cent; backache, 40 per cent; cramps, 60 per cent; feeling of well-being, 15 per cent; feeling of anxiety, 21 per cent; increased fatigue, 63 per cent; desire toward extra activity, 34 per cent; emotional or crying spells, 25 per cent; let-down or depressed, 49 per cent; increased irritability, 59 per cent; reconciled to period, 83 per cent.

About half of the group had been told to reduce activity during the period. About one-fourth had been advised to take no baths. Between one-fourth and one-third actually carried on less than average activity. About two-thirds or more carried on average activity. Three or four did even

[19] Altmann, M., E. Knowles, and H. D. Bull: A Psychsomatic Study of the Sex Cycle in Women, *Psychosomatic Med., 3:* 199–225, 1941.

[20] Seward J. P., and G. H. Seward: Psychological Effects of Estrogenic Hormone Therapy in the Menopause, *J. Comp. Psychol., 24:* 377–392, 1937.

[21] Billings, E. G.: The Occurrence of Cyclic Variations in Motor Activity in Relation to the Menstrual Cycle in the Human Female, *Johns Hopkins Hospital Bull., 54:* 440–454, 1934.

[22] Brush, A. L.: Attitudes, Emotional and Physical Symptoms Commonly Associated with Menstruation in 100 Women, *Am. J. Orthopsychiat., 8:* 286–301, 1938.

more than usual. About one-sixth reported that they felt better if quiet, and about one-fourth felt better if active.

Bloech and Bergel[23] are among those who hold the view that the menstrual cycle involves changes in carbohydrate metabolism. Their observations show that during the premenstrual and menstrual stages a dextrose tolerance test is different from one made during the interval. Near the menstrual stage there is an exaggerated hyperglycemia, a decided subsequent hypoglycemia with an occasional second peak, all of which is interpreted as an increased irritability of the autonomic nervous system. In some diabetics an impairment of carbohydrate tolerance occurs during the menstrual period.[24] Exaggerated hunger, feelings of anxiety and depression, tremors, and increased irritability may be associated with low blood sugar and low blood calcium.

Irregularity. If the menstrual cycle is influential in the distribution of feelings of well-being and tendency toward activity and their opposites, its length becomes an important consideration here. Recognition of and knowledge about irregularities in the menstrual cycle may be of value in distinguishing "normal" from anomalous kinds of personal organization. The fact that irregularity occurs implies that the whole train of events known as the menstrual cycle is determined by the larger situation of which it is only a part. The cycle itself, or rather, certain features of it, can scarcely be taken as a fixed natural point from which to reason causally, though this has often been done.

There has been a long-standing tendency to consider the length of the menstrual cycle in terms of 28 days, and irregularities in it in terms of multiples of 7 days. The outstanding result of various studies has been the disclosure that the cycle for the majority of women is not 28 days, nor are consecutive periods of equal length.

A study[25] of 747 menstrual cycles of 76 normal women showed their range to vary from 11 to 100 days, with the vast majority between 18 and 42 days. The mean for the total was 30.4 days, the standard deviation being ±11.53. Fluhmann divided the cases into two principal groups. One-third of the subjects constituted the first group, for whom there was a relatively regular succession of cycles. The cycle length for nine individuals in this group ranged from 26 to 30 days. The cycles of 6 individuals tended to be

[23] Bloech, J., and A. Bergel: Ovarieller Zyklus und Kohlehydratstoffwechsel; der Ablauf der glykämischen Reaktion nach Dextrosebelastung im normalen Zyklus, *Wien. Arch. f. inn. Med., 26:* 233–240, 1935.

[24] Cramer, H. I.: The Influence of Menstruation on Carbohydrate Tolerance in Diabetes Mellitus, *Canad. M.A.J., 47:* 51–55, 1942.

[25] Fluhmann, C. F.: The Length of the Human Menstrual Cycle, *Am. J. Obst. & Gynec., 27:* 73–78, 1934.

shorter than this, and the cycles of 13 tended to be longer. The second, or "irregular," group contained 48 subjects, or two-thirds of the cases. Irregularity was thus more common than regularity.

Another study[26] likewise emphasized the irregularity in the occurrence of menstruation in normal women. The same author had previously collected detailed menstrual records of 17 women, covering 523 intervals. Sixteen of the subjects were college women, the majority being students. The age range was from 19 to 35 years. In the present study, 37 industrial and

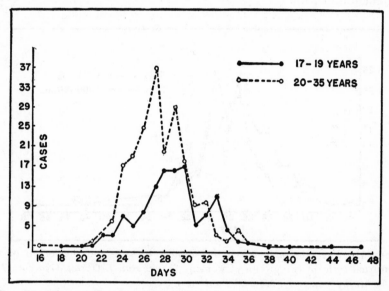

Fig. 50.—The relation between the number of cases and the length of the menstrual cycle in two age ranges. (*King: Am. J. Obstet. Gynecol., The C. V. Mosby Company, Medical Publishers.*)

college women were observed, the series including 354 cycles. The author was able to draw no conclusions as to the differences between college and industrial groups. In the first series of cases, 18½ per cent of the cycles were 27 days. In the second series, the most frequent interval was likewise 27 days, but the percentage manifesting this interval was only 14. Of the 354 menstruations 56.7 per cent occurred on the twenty-sixth to the thirtieth day. Figures 50 and 51 show the results.

Another author[27] collected 1,414 records from 131 members of a nurses' training school. The most striking feature of these records was the marked

[26] King, J. L.: Menstrual Intervals, *Am. J. Obst. & Gynec., 25:* 583–587, 1933.

[27] Allen, E.: The Irregularity of the Menstrual Function, *Am. J. Obst. & Gynec., 25:* 705–709, 1933.

irregularity manifested in the length of the cycle. Out of of the group, 87 subjects had previously thought they were absolutely regular, but the study showed this not to be the case. Fifty-three of the group had previously recognized that they were somewhat irregular, but were surprised by the degree of irregularity shown in the records. Variations in occupation did not seem to alter the general cycle appreciably or vary the amount of dysmenorrhea, with one exception—duty in the general diet kitchen or drug room, where going in and out of large refrigerators seemed to enhance the amount of pain.

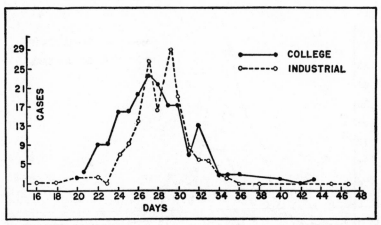

Fɪɢ. 51.—The relation between the number of cases and the length of the menstrual cycle in two groups of women. (*King: Am. J. Obstet. Gynecol., The C. V. Mosby Company, Medical Publishers.*)

Two-thousand four-hundred and sixty records of 150 presumably normal women indicated that the most common cycle was about 28 days, occurring in 15 per cent of the cycles.[28] The average length of the cycles was 28.4 days. In all these cases there was no single instance of absolute regularity. There was no instance of the periods occurring in multiples of 7. The distribution of the cycle lengths was found to follow the normal probability curve (see Fig. 52).

Gunn, Jenkin, and Gunn[29] also made a study of a large sampling of normal cases of menstrual periodicity. A progressive decrease of one day

[28] Haman, J. O.: The Length of the Menstrual Cycle, *Am. J. Obst. & Gynec., 43:* 870–873, 1942.

[29] Gunn, D. L., P. M. Jenkin, and A. L. Gunn: Menstrual Periodicity: Statistical Observations on a Large Sample of Normal Cases, *J. Obst. & Gynaec. Brit. Emp., 44:* 839–879, 1937.

in 5 or 6 years as the subject grows older was found. A slight tendency for menstruation to begin in the latter part of the work week also was detected. They concluded that the duration of one cycle is not affected by that of the previous cycle.

The effect of the form of imposed personal activity (work, etc.). It is difficult to make any useful generalizations pertaining to women in industry or in other work in and outside the home. Too little study has been made in this country which is usable for this purpose. It would be expected that classification of subjects would have to be made upon the basis not only of types of work, but upon the individual's adjustments to the work. This

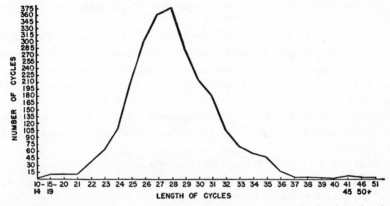

Fig. 52.—The relation between the number of cases and the length of the menstrual cycle. (*Haman: Am. J. Obstet. Gynecol., The C. V. Mosby Company, Medical Publishers.*)

mode of approach assumes that the organism as a whole expresses itself in somatic ways, such as in variations of metabolism, and ostensibly in variations in the menstrual cycle.

The following will serve as an example of an industrial study. Many women who had had no previous difficulty with menstruation began, after work in a large war plant, to seek medical aid for relief from menstrual disorder, or discomfort.[30] The work in this plant was not considered heavy, 20 lb. being the maximal allowable lift. The work week was 48 hours and required standing most of the time. Two hundred and fourteen women who had been employed 6 months or longer were given a short questionnaire. From this it was found that 30 per cent of the workers had noticed some change in the cycle since beginning work in the plant. Twenty-five

[30] Parkes, M.: A Survey of the Effects on Menstruation of Working in a War Plant, *Indust. Med., 13:* 150, 1944.

per cent reported its lengthening. Fourteen per cent reported having more pain than they had had previous to working. Twelve per cent reported an increased flow. The answers of 15 per cent of the women stated their monthly loss of time prior to working in this plant was one day, and the plant found that about 15 per cent were losing time per month, averaging one day per individual. It is likely, although not certain, that a considerable fraction of the workers were previously housewives by occupation. If so, these findings would indicate that work in plants of the kind in question has some effect on the individual. It would be expected that adjustments incident to shifting to a radically different type of work might be expressed in alterations of the menstrual cycle. It seems, however, that in the present illustration such changes did not result in increased work interference.

Skerlj's investigation[31] on 152 girls showed that as a result of strenuous exercise, chiefly skiing, approximately 80 per cent showed at least a temporary effect on menstruation, and in about 50 per cent of these the effects became permanent. In the latter group about 50 per cent showed lengthening of the intervals, with increase in duration of flow.

Vogt[32] thinks that women trained to athletic sport can safely continue exercise during the flow, but that their muscular strength is somewhat impaired at the time.

It might be presumed that any changes which occur in keeping with the work week are indices of the effect of activity. Weekly and longer term cycles in women's weight have been disclosed.[33] The longer weight cycles were found to correspond to the menstrual cycle. Weight reached a peak just before or at the onset of the menstrual period. Weekly weight cycles were typically minimum on Saturday night and weight rose sharply during the week ends.

Personality and mood changes. In order to understand the problem of menstrual rhythms as related to fatigue and impairment, an understanding of personality is required. There are few studies bearing on the relations of personality and the menstrual cycle.

Benedek and Rubenstein,[34] in a psychiatric study, summarize the female stances during various portions of the cycle in a general way. It is believed

31 Skerlj, B.: Menstruationszyklen und Leibesübungen. (Ein Beitrag zum Problem), *Arch. f. Gynäk., 162:* 516–537, 1936.

32 Vogt, E.: Über die Bedeutung der Leibesübungen für die Physiologie der Fortpflanzungsorgane der Frau, *Med. Klin., 32:* 857–859, 1936.

33 Tinklepaugh, O. L., and M. B. Mitchell: Monthly and Weekly Weight Cycles in Women and Their Relations to Behavioral and Physiological Functions, *J. Genetic Psychol., 54:* 3–16, 1939.

34 Benedek, T., and B. B. Rubenstein: The Correlation between Ovarian Activity and Psychodynamic Processes. I. The Ovulative Phase, *Psychosomatic Med., 1:* 245–270, 1939.

that in the "minimally neurotic" woman a rise in estrogen production and an increase in heterosexual tension and heterosexual fantasies and dreams occur together. Euphoria often develops just prior to ovulation, and with ovulation transient release from tension occurs. A feeling of freedom and contentment tends to develop and predisposition toward erotic sensations to emerge. When the production of progesterone rises, tension reappears. The individual now becomes oriented toward her own body, and eroticism is accompanied by a tendency toward exhibitionism. Wishes are now directed toward being loved and cared for. In the neurotic woman, personal conflicts become enhanced at the peak of the estrogen and progesterone levels. Specific symptoms may appear or chronic ones become exaggerated.

While these particulars are not focused on fatigue, they are expressions of alignments which, when work is involved, might be expected to affect reactions to such obligation. Were investigations directed toward clarifying such conditions as fatigue, certain important facts would undoubtedly be disclosed.

There are mood changes during the menstrual cycle that might be expected to bear upon the ability to do work. In some studies, mental depression was found to be at a maximum two days before menstruation began. McCance *et al.*[35] report that depression tends to diminish until the eleventh day, when it increases somewhat until the seventeenth day, diminishes again until the twentieth day, and then rises. They state that the tendency to irritability is least on the sixth day. Balázs,[36] on the basis of 3,110 cases, claims that successful and unsuccessful attempts at suicide in women are mostly committed during the menstrual period. The suicidal tendency is seen as greatest during the first day of the period. During the premenstruum, the number of suicides is lowest.

Daniels[37] found that psychiatric interviews during times of "hormonal pressure" (times of tension associated with certain chemical phases of the cycle) yielded marked changes in the individual. Spontaneous production of introspective material was induced, tension was relieved, and better social adjustments resulted.

SLEEP

The diurnal variations in man, where the 24-hour cycle of day and night functions as a unit of behavior, are the most highly accentuated of all

35 McCance, R. A., M. C. Luff, and E. E. Widdowson: Physical and Emotional Periodicity in Woman, *J. Hyg., 37:* 571–611, 1937.

36 Balázs, J. v.: Menstruation und Selbstmord, *Psychiat. neurol. Wchnschr., 38:* 407–409, 1936.

37 Daniels, G. E.: An Approach to Psychological Control Studies of Urinary Sex Hormones, *Am. J. Psychiat., 100:* 231–239, 1943–1944.

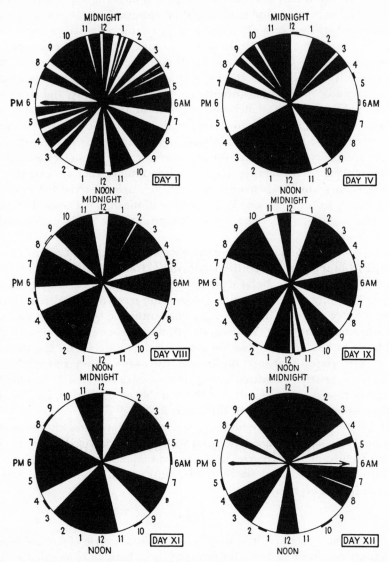

FIG. 53.—The sleep-waking activity of a newborn infant at various times between the third and twelfth days. The dark portions of the discs indicate periods of sleep—the light portions, waking. (*Gesell: "The Embryology of Behavior,"* Harper & Brothers.)

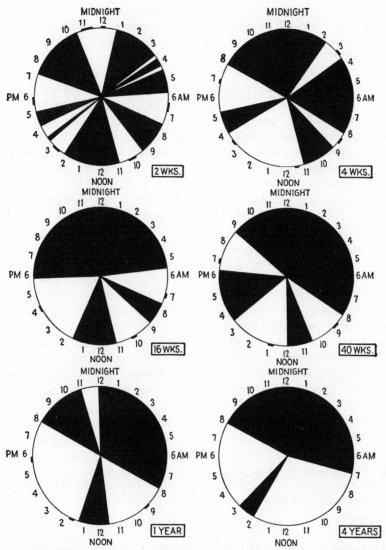

Fig. 54.—The sleep-waking activity of the same child at various periods from the age of 2 weeks to 4 years. (*Gesell: "The Embryology of Behavior," Harper & Brothers.*)

recurrent patterns. We are particularly concerned with the character of this cycle and must consider the kinds of behavior variations that constitute the 24-hour period. The activity-rest alternations of lower animals have not all been found to coincide in a simple way with the diurnal cycle of day and night. Two general types of adjustment have been distinguished, the "polyphasic" and the "monophasic." Polyphasic animals have several periods of quiescence and activity (white rats, 10 cycles; rabbits, 16 to 21; etc.) during the 24 hours. Monophasic animals have one cycle. This includes one unbroken period of rest during the dark of the night, the development of the dominance of the visual sense apparently having been largely responsible for the monophasic evolution. In this connection it should be noted that human infants sleep most of the time; a regular diurnal cycle is only gradually learned. Figures 53 and 54, showing typical findings of Gesell[38] in his study of infant behavior, illustrate this shift from the polyphasic mode of life to the monophasic. In the circles, each representing 24 hours, the black portions indicate the times spent in sleep.

To begin with, newborn infants sleep nearly all the time, the "awake" periods adding up to about 2 hours, which are mostly devoted to feeding. The baby when a few months old is awake much longer (4 to 6 hours), and the main period of sleep occurs during the night.

From about 2 years until school age, the child sleeps about 13 to 14 hours. Reynolds[39] reports that in spite of a variation from day to day in the amount of sleep taken by a preschool child there is a fairly consistent average over a few weeks. Reynolds and others have observed no consistency in the variations of different children, however. A negative relation between intelligence (M.A.) and amount of sleep has been found by several workers.[40]

Diurnal rhythms. The most obvious differentiation that can be made in the diurnal pattern is a gross division into sleep and wakefulness. Such a division does not rest on any strictly quantitative difference, nor even upon a full set of qualitative specifications. It has been possible to distinguish intermediary stages, frequently called hypnogogic states, between sleep and wakefulness.

[38] Gesell, A. L.: "The Embryology of Behavior," Harper & Brothers, New York, 1945. Pp. 289.

[39] Reynolds, M. M.: Sleep of Young Children in a 24-hour Nursery School, *Ment. Hyg., 19:* 602–609, 1935.

[40] Wagner, M. A.: Day and Night Sleep in a Group of Young Orphanage Children, *J. Genetic Psychol., 42:* 442–459, 1933.

White, M. R.: Some Factors Affecting the Night Sleep of Children, *Child Development, 2:* 234–235, 1931.

Shinn, A. V.: A Study of Slep Habits of Two Groups of Pre-school Children, One in Hawaii and One on the Mainland, *Child Development, 3:* 159–166, 1932.

Though sleep should be considered simply as the complement of wakefulness, merely the less active phase of the diurnal activity cycle,[41] it has been generally assumed that waking is the "normal" state. The irregular polyphasic diurnal activity of young babies would seem to indicate that wakefulness is a state to which the organism must *ascend,* rather than sleep being a state to which the organism must *descend,* periodically.

The sleep-wakefulness behavior of the infant is customarily explained by the lack of full development of the nervous system. The waking state may be thought of as an achievement of maturation. The individual is sensitive to a great many kinds of external events that affect him nowise in direct proportion to their physical intensity. It is highly plausible that were the individual not trained to respond to the events around him, he would spend a great deal more of this time sleeping than he does. The sleep state, requiring little external stimulation or antigravity postural innervation, and only the minimum sensory connection with the surroundings, is more easily maintained than is the waking state which exists only under favorable circumstances.

Both common experience and a number of investigations of various sorts show that there is constant change throughout the activity cycle. Neither the sleep nor the waking periods are homogeneous. There appear to be fairly regular patterns of variation, which differ for different individuals and are somewhat modifiable,[42] upon which are superimposed minor and less regular variations. The diagrams in Fig. 55 may be said to represent variations of "alertness" and will serve to illustrate possible forms of diurnal periodicities.

In diagrams 1 to 5, the diurnal cycle is pictured in two parts, the waking (*W*) and the sleep (*S*) phases, with an arbitrary boundary line between them. Diagram 1 is a hypothetical alertness curve. There is no basis in fact for the relative levelness of both *W* and *S* shown in rhythm *A*. Four possible rhythms, *B, C, D,* and *E,* are pictured in diagrams 2 and 3. They are all similar to rhythm *A* in that they manifest a maximum in the sleep state, but they differ from *A* in exhibiting no plateaus, or constant periods of equal alertness. Rhythms of this type, unlike *A,* are in accord with the known facts. Rhythms *B, C, D,* and *E* differ from each other in their exact maximum and minimum periods and might be said to represent the diurnal periodicity of four different individuals. Rhythm *E,* for example, illustrates the diurnal pattern of an individual who wakes early and does

[41] Kleitman, N.: "Sleep and Wakefulness," University of Chicago Press, Chicago, 1939. Pp. 638.

[42] Welsh, J. H.: Diurnal Rhythms, *Quart. Rev. Biol., 13:* 123–139, 1938.

Freeman, G. L.: "Diurnal Variations in Performance and Energy Expenditure," Northwestern University Press, Chicago, 1935. Pp. 27.

his best work in the morning, slowing down in the late afternoon and early evening and reaching minimum alertness early in the sleep period. Rhythm F in diagram 4 is a modification of B, and G in diagram 5 is a modification of E. These curves show two possible low periods, one about noontime and one late in the afternoon, which momentarily alter the general trends.

Obviously, there is no measure for degree of alertness, and the curves given here merely represent a general over-all expression of activity. It should be emphasized that the diagrams are schematic and do not represent any particular measure. However, measures of various sorts have been made in attempts to study diurnal periodicity, some of them at intervals

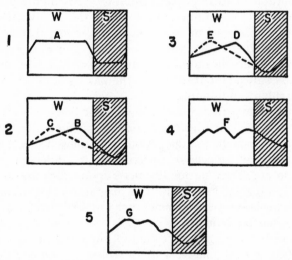

FIG. 55.—Various diurnal activity cycles. (See text for explanation.)

throughout the 24-hour period.[43] These show fairly consistently periodicities more or less of the type represented in diagrams 2 to 5. Testing individuals on various kinds of performance has led investigators to believe that the waking period is not homogenous.[44] A given task is not equally

[43] Kleitman, N., S. Titelbaum, and H. Hoffman: The Establishment of the Diurnal Temperature Cycle, *Am. J. Physiol.*, *119:* 48–54, 1937.

Woodhead, G. S., and P. C. Varrier-Jones: Investigations on Clinical Thermometry: Continuous and Quasi-continuous Temperature Records in Man and Animals in Health and Disease. Part IV, *Lancet, 190* (I) : 450–453, 1916.

[44] Freeman, G. L., and C. I. Hovland: Diurnal Variations in Performance and Related Physiological Processes, *Psychol. Bull., 31:* 777–799, 1934.

Gates, A. I.: Diurnal Variations in Memory and Association, *Univ. California Publ., Psychol., 1:* 323–344, 1916.

Omwake, K. T.: Effect of Varying Periods of Sleep on Nervous Stability, *J. Appl. Psychol., 16:* 623–632, 1932.

well done during all portions of it. Although the pattern for different tasks is not the same, nor are all individuals alike, the existence of pattern as such is to be taken as fact in the case of performance.

The most frequently and accurately measured diurnal functions are organic ones. For example, 24-hour body temperature curves have been well worked out and show clearly a diurnal periodicity, individually established and very similar to the type represented in the diagrams. Although it has been alleged that activity or alertness is dependent upon body temperature, the reverse dependency is just as plausible as the one alleged. As it is, the strict concomitance of body temperature level and height of any specific activity has not been demonstrated.

Physiological differences between wakefulness and sleep. A rather extensive though incomplete relaxation of the skeletal musculature is characteristic of sleep, postural reflexes being usually inoperative. Characteristic sleeping positions vary during the sleeping period for one individual, as well as from individual to individual.

During sleep the pupils of the eyes are constricted. The eyeballs themselves tend to diverge outward.

Deep sleep has a specific brain potential, the delta rhythm. This is a counterpart to the alpha rhythm usually present when the individual is fully awake. Various types of "brain waves" have been said to characterize the semisleep stages.

Minor changes in the chemical constituents of the blood, probably due almost entirely to the horizontal position, occur during sleep, and blood volume is increased. With "parasympathetic dominance" and lessened sensori-motor activity, heart rate is markedly slowed. Except for this retardation, circulation seems unaffected. Basal heat production is usually decreased, and body temperature, in line with the diurnal cycle, is at its lowest ebb during sleep.

Except for a general reduction in sensitivity, reflex excitability is the same as during the waking state, with one notable exception, *viz.*, a positive Babinski response, which is frequently elicited from normal individuals in deep sleep.

The decreased irritability which in general characterizes sleep is marked in the respiratory center. Breathing becomes deeper and more regular, generally speaking, but many changes in the condition of the respiratory center occur, as it is still affected by both external and internal "stimuli."

Most of the early studies of characteristics of the sleep phase pertained to questions of "depth" of sleep, the amount of sleep characteristic of various groups, the relation of motility to depth, and the amount of sleep necessary for the human being. Many of the questions that are still being studied are expressions of these major points, although they are somewhat more specialized.

Notable in this series are the study of Kohlschütter in 1862, developing the first depth-of-sleep curve that was based on the intensity of sound necessary to awaken the sleeper; the work of Endres and von Frey developing the idea of the amount of sleep as a product of depth and time; the study of depth and motility by Mullin, Kleitman, and Cooperman,[45] in which the threshold sound was the criterion of depth.

A great wealth of detail on the course certain sleep variables tend to take may be garnered from these and other studies. All the work reveals vast individual differences and shows clearly that sleep is not a fixed entity, but that it changes continuously throughout its course.

Motility. Since the development of Szymanski's recording apparatus in 1914, a great many studies have been performed on motility during sleep. Johnson[46] and colleagues found an average of 11.5 minutes between the movements in 11 subjects based on 15,000 measurements, although they did not measure how much time a subject spent in motility during a night, since they used a standard 5-minute duration as a period of motility. Actually, the periods of motility were much shorter.

Kleitman,[47] with a large number of subjects, showed that the average manifested only about 30 seconds of motility per hour asleep, or 3 to 5 minutes of motility per night (20 to 60 movements). He and his coworkers found a greater number of movements during the second half of the night. This does not agree with Johnson's conclusion that distribution of movements depends upon the individuality of the sleeper.

Motility during sleep has been shown to be influenced by various external and internal conditions, both in children and adults.

Laird and Drexel[48] used motility in the attempt to define quality of sleep. Such a procedure does not seem justified.

Meteorological and seasonal influences. Climatic and seasonal changes have been found to influence sleep to some extent. But the individual character of a given person's sleep is nearly always recognizable under the changed conditions, and the pattern of the diurnal cycle is not essentially altered.

[45] Mullin, F. J., N. Kleitman, and N. R. Cooperman: Studies on the Physiology of Sleep. Changes in Irritability to Auditory Stimuli during Sleep, *J. Exper. Psychol., 21:* 88–96, 1937.

[46] Johnson, H. M.: Rhythms and Patterns of Nocturnal Motility, *Proc. Ninth Int. Cong. Psychol.,* 238–239, 1929.

[47] Kleitman, N.: New Methods for Studying Motility during Sleep, *Proc. Soc. Exper. Biol. & Med., 29:* 389–391, 1932.

[48] Laird, D. A., and H. Drexel: Experiments with Foods and Sleep, *J. Am. Dietet. A., 10:* 89–99, 1934.

A few studies have been performed on humidity, precipitation, room temperature, and other short-term variables in sleeping conditions. Most of these report no significant effects on the characteristics of sleep, at least in the subjects studied.

More positive results have been obtained from studies of the effects of the seasonal cycle on sleep. The findings are somewhat contradictory and are handicapped by the fact that different experimenters used different criteria for depth of sleep, etc., but a general trend is apparent.

Sleep has been reported to be deepest in winter. Erwin,[49] from studies based on the sleep of 409 children, concluded that sleep is longer in fall and winter than it is in spring and summer. Garvey,[50] however, also studying children's sleep, was unable to find seasonal changes.

Kleitman, Cooperman, and Mullin[51] reported a lower body temperature and less motility in winter and spring. The colder part of the year is less conducive to sleep motility than the warmer. This conclusion has been substantiated in subsequent studies, although it is not certain whether all the sleep characteristics are influenced by seasonal changes.

As would be expected, various internal cycles such as the menstrual cycle and the gastric-motility rhythm have also been shown to influence the character of sleep.

Influence of habits and attitudes. The importance of habits and attitudes as factors affecting the character of sleep and the sleep-wakefulness cycle can hardly be overestimated. In spite of this, they have been nearly always neglected in studies of sleep. A purely physiological approach to the sleep problem can never reveal more than a partial picture of events.

Studies that approach the sleep-wakefulness cycle from the point of view of mental hygiene are by and large no more satisfactory than the purely physiological ones. Questions such as, How much sleep is necessary? and At what hours should sleep be taken? are of the type about which everyone feels free to venture opinions. In general, regular habits, especially eating and retiring habits, along with "proper" distribution of work, play, and rest, are given highest importance for "good" sleep in children. But an adequate criterion for "good" sleep has never been established.

Increased sleep motility has been used as a criterion for disturbed sleep

[49] Erwin, D.: An Analytical Study of Children's Sleep, *J. Genetic Psychol., 45:* 199–226, 1934.

[50] Garvey, C. R.: An Experimental Study of the Sleep of Preschool Children. *Proc. Ninth Int. Cong. Psychol.,* pp. 176–177, 1929.

[51] Kleitman, N., N. R. Cooperman, and F. J. Mullin: Studies on the Physiology of Sleep. IX. Motility and Body Temperature during Sleep, *Am. J. Physiol., 105:* 574–583, 1933.

in children by a number of workers. Laird and Drexel and others report that children show an increased motility during sleep following a heavy meal. Using the same method, some find sleep disturbed following mental work or exciting games, and Renshaw, Miller, and Marquis,[52] after certain types of movies. Giddings[53] reports sleep disturbances following (or during?) emotional states, but finds no disturbance after an hour's exercise.

The amount of sleep required by adults is undoubtedly a question to which there can never be a general answer. Yet many hygienists seem unaware of the vast individual differences. Some believe that most adults do not sleep enough. Others, like Camp,[54] think that most people sleep too much. Camp holds that oversleeping is just as detrimental as overeating. Between these two extremes in opinion, all gradations may be found. On the other hand, some authors conclude that different individuals require different amounts of sleep; they add that some people who are sleeping enough believe they are not.

The old idea that 1 hour of sleep before midnight is worth 2 after midnight still has many supporters. Such an opinion, however, is not in line with our present knowledge of the individual nature of the diurnal cycle. Wuth[55] and others recognize the relation of sleep to the diurnal cycle. Two types of sleepers are distinguished by Wuth: (1) the individual who is wide awake in the evening, has a delayed onset of sleep, does not reach his greatest depth of sleep until near morning, and wakes up feeling tired; (2) the individual who becomes drowsy early in the evening, falls asleep quickly, reaches deep sleep early, and awakes feeling well rested. Wuth has pointed out only the two extreme cases. It is likely that most individuals show at least a tendency in the direction of one or another of these extremes. Schultz[56] refers to "monophasic" and "diphasic" sleepers, people who have one period and two periods of deep sleep, respectively.

Many opinions have been expressed about various circumstances conducive to "good" sleep. Such items as ventilation, type of bed and mattress, eating habits, positions assumed, and number of bedcovers all seem in the last analysis to be matters of individual taste. Suggestions of the type thrown out by the hygienists, for example, undoubtedly may play some role in making specific settings for sleep important to certain persons. The

[52] Renshaw, S., V. L. Miller, and D. P. Marquis: "Children's Sleep," The Macmillan Company, New York, 1933. Pp. 242.

[53] Giddings, G.: The Effect of Emotional Disturbance on Sleep, *J. Med. Assn. Georgia,* 25: 351–357, 1936.

[54] Camp, C. D.: Disturbance of Sleep, *J. Michigan M. Soc.,* 22: 133–138, 1938.

[55] Wuth, O.: Klinik und Therapie der Schlafstörungen, *Schweiz. med. Wchnschr.,* 61: 833–837, 1931.

[56] Schultz, J. H.: Die Psychopathologie und Psychotherapie des Schlafes, *Ztschr. f. örtzl. Fortbild.,* 30: 225–228, 1933.

recipients of these suggestions acquire an attitude toward the conditions required for sleep. The effectiveness of such opinions or attitudes in influencing sleep cannot be questioned.

The problem of what constitutes "good sleep" has been approached by Kleitman and his coworkers.[57] Six sleep characteristics were chosen which, it was thought, might collectively throw some light on the question. These were (1) ease of falling asleep, (2) motility, (3) awakenings during the sleep period, (4) dreaming, (5) length of sleep, and (6) subjective state (rested or tired) on awakening. They found each of the six sleep characteristics to vary not only from subject to subject, but also from night to night for the same subject. Having established a control pattern on the basis of the six characteristics, the influence of a number of conditions, internal and external, on these characteristics was investigated. They concluded that none of the factors examined affected all the characteristics in a desirable manner. Different individuals attach unequal importance to one or another of these characteristics.

Fatigue is not to be viewed as the result of impairment. Nor is sleep, although its relationship to impairment is probably different from that of fatigue, necessarily the result of impairment. After certain limits of impairment, both fatigue and sleep become inevitable, but the relationship among these three factors is certainly not nearly so simple or direct as it is often taken to be.

EXPERIMENTAL PRODUCTION OF SLEEP

In general, there are two ways of "artificially" inducing sleep. The first is by immobilization and a reduction of afferent sensory responses. The second is the more drastic method of cortical assault (chemical, mechanical, or electrical). Work under the second category has been, for obvious reasons, nearly all restricted to animals.

Sleep, or a state closely resembling sleep, may be induced in animals and persons by immobilization alone. Sidis,[58] employing children and a variety of animal species, induced a sleeplike state by a degree of immobilization. Part of the time he also used a continuous monotonous sound. Sidis concluded that "diminution in the variability of the volume of sensory impressions" was the "cause" of sleep. That the monotonous sound was purely gratuitous was demonstrated by Kleitman[59] and Coriat[60] who found that,

[57] Kleitman, N., F. J. Mullin, N. R. Cooperman, and S. Titelbaum: "Sleep Characteristics," University of Chicago Press, Chicago, 1937. Pp. 86.

[58] Sidis, B.: An Experimental Study of Sleep, *J. Abnorm. Psychol., 3:* 1-32; 63-96; 170-207, 1908.

[59] Kleitman, N.: Studies on the Physiology of Sleep, I, *Am. J. Physiol., 66:* 67-92, 1923.

[60] Coriat, I. H.: The Nature of Sleep, *J. Abnorm. Psychol., 6:* 329-367, 1912.

both in humans and animals, relaxed skeletal musculature is sufficient to induce sleep. Miller[61] added the finding that relaxation of the skeletal musculature decreases sensory acuity. That uniformity of surroundings is a sleep-inducing factor has been shown by a number of workers.

Sleep has also been experimentally produced by destruction of regions of the brain stem and by the injection of various substances into the blood stream or into the brain. Marinesco, Sager, and Kreindler[62] obtained sleep in somewhat less than half of their cats by passing a polarizing current through the brain stem. The polarization caused detectable lesions. Ranson, Kabat, and Magoun[63] obtained a state of excitement rather than sleep in using faradic current. Hess[64] obtained drowsiness and sleep in cats by passing a direct current through certain parts of the periventricular gray. Elsewhere a team of investigators reported that thalamic injury led to "sleep" lasting in some cases for several weeks.

Sleep has also been obtained in cats by injecting 0.25 to 2.0 mg. of calcium chloride into the gray matter close to the infundibulum. Injections in other brain regions did not result in sleep. A state resembling sleep has been induced by injecting ergotamine tartrate intraventricularly, and a similar injection of small quantities of acetylcholine induced a sleeplike state in cats.

The two ways of artificially inducing sleep, by relaxation of the skeletal musculature, etc., and by the chemical and mechanical means, seem on the surface to have little in common. But as Kleitman points out, any acceptable theory of sleep must account for both types.

EXPERIMENTAL DEPRIVATION OF SLEEP

Work on sleep deprivation is more extensive than the work on production of sleep.

The first study of this nature was performed in 1896 by Patrick and Gilbert, who kept three subjects awake for 90 hours. The study was not well controlled, which may account for the rather exaggerated results in decreases in sensory acuity, reaction time, motor speed, memorizing ability, etc. These decreases were assumed to occur until another similar experi-

---

[61] Miller, M.: Changes in the Response to Electric Shock Produced by Varying Muscular Conditions, *J. Exper. Psychol., 9:* 26–44, 1926.

[62] Marinesco, G., O. Sager, and A. Kreindler: Recherches expérimentales sur le méchanisme du sommeil, *Bull. Acad. de méd., Paris, 100:* 752–756, 1928, and following papers.

[63] Ranson, S. W., H. Kabat, and H. W. Magoun: Autonomic Responses to Electrical Stimulation of Hypothalamus, Preoptic Region and Septum, *Arch. Neurol. & Psychiat., 33:* 467–477, 1934.

[64] Hess, W. R.: Stammganglien—Reizversuche, *Ber. ü. d. ges. Physiol., 42:* 554–555, 1927, and following papers.

ment was made by Robinson and Herrmann[65] 26 years later. These workers reported that performance scores "were not affected by insomnia in any marked or consistent manner." That performance scores are not markedly altered, provided the tests are brief, during deprivation of sleep, has been fairly well established by studies following Robinson and Herrmann, although some disagreement still exists.

One of the more recent studies on the effects of loss of sleep was made by Edwards[66] on 17 subjects (13 men and 4 women). Sixteen tests were used, including tapping, steadiness, static ataxia, and visual acuity. In general, no great changes were recorded. Curiously, even the tests of vision showed no definitely positive results. Blood pressure, pulse, and oral temperature were also recorded, but no significant changes were found. In most respects, the findings on the formal tests corroborated those reported in other studies. Marked effects in the performance on the A.C.E. Psychological Examination were found after 72 hours or more of wakefulness. For our purposes, the most significant results were the individual changes in behavior manifested during the vigil. Among these were loss of memory, occurrence of hallucinations, and very much changed attitudes. In some cases, subjects were unable to remember incidents of only a few minutes past. One individual "forgot" a ride in an automobile which she had just taken.

To include all the many changes in behavior that Edwards reported would require considerable space. It is sufficient to say that the subjects' behavior included "delusional statements," loss of feeling in fingertips, inability to discriminate between hot and cold water in bathing, periods of euphoria and depression, depersonalization, seeing double, "holding book upside down," etc.

Fatigue was reported in only a few cases. It is important to note in this connection that the subjects were eager to perform the experiment. In fact, the investigation was made at their request. This would account for the absence of fatigue for a considerable time during the first part of the 100-hour vigil. Even after considerable impairment and disorganization occurred, a lack of fatigue might have been expected in some instances. This was the case in other conditions, such as anoxia.

This study is one of the best demonstrations that assaults on the individual which would ordinarily be expected to induce fatigue need not do so. The mere deprivation of rest, etc., although resulting in extreme disorganization (hallucination, etc.), does not necessarily induce fatigue.

[65] Robinson, E. S., and S. O. Herrmann: Effects of Loss of Sleep, *J. Exper. Psychol.,* 5: 19–32, 1932.

[66] Edwards, A. S.: Effects of Loss of One Hundred Hours of Sleep, *Am. J. Psychol.,* 54: 80–91, 1941.

Studies of this sort should be repeated, but planned so as to test the ideas of conflict and frustration in relation to fatigue.

Other important effects of sleep deprivation, not measured by performance tests, have been reported.

Kleitman *et al.*[67] report that their subjects had to indulge in muscular exercise in order to keep awake, especially on the second night and from then on. (This has probably been the case in similar experiments, which means that the effects reported are only in part due to the sleep deprivation.) Many subjective experiences were common to most of the subjects: eyes itched and felt dry, double vision occurred during the early hours of the morning, difficulty in concentration appeared in the later stages, there was inability to sit still without falling asleep, etc. It is important to note that the diurnal rhythm was maintained. A subject, for example, might feel exceedingly tired during the early hours of the morning, but very much less tired later on in the day. Kleitman reports that after 60 to 65 hours without sleep a subject is as tired as he is likely to be.

Most laboratory tests and various physiological measures such as basal metabolism, weight, blood pressure, and pulse rate have generally been reported not significantly changed when an individual is deprived of sleep for long periods of time.

Frequently, tendencies to semidreaming and hallucination have been reported. Some subjects become quite disoriented, often making inappropriate remarks, etc.

In summary, Kleitman says that the most important effects of sleep deprivation are increased sensitivity to pain, impairment of disposition, tendency to hallucinations, and other changes of this general nature. These changes, he says, indicate "fatigue" of the higher levels of the cerebral cortex.

Another way of altering the sleep-wakefulness cycle is by the use of drugs. Most of the pharmacological research has been done with hypnotics in the treatment of insomnia.

Renner[68] names three types of hypnotics: (1) rapid action of short duration, with no detectable aftereffects (*e.g.,* Alendrin, voulutal, diogenal); (2) rapid action of longer duration and intensity (*e.g.,* hedonal, paraldehyde, acetal); (3) slow action of medium duration and intensity and with detectable aftereffects (*e.g.,* chloralamide, luminal, tetronal).

It is interesting to note that Renner states that "most hypnotics do not produce sleep in the daytime when given in doses that are effective at night."

[67] Kleitman *et al., op. cit.*

[68] Renner, A.: "Schlafmittel-therapie," Julius Springer, Berlin, 1925. Pp. 125.

Pick[69] observed that certain drugs which normally induce wakefulness may induce sleep when used in the treatment of insomnia.

Administration of hypnotic drugs usually reduces the motility during sleep of both normal and psychopathic individuals. Page[70] reports that the motility of manic patients was reduced 35 per cent when they were given a therapeutic dose of amytal, whereas that of normal individuals was reduced only 14 per cent.

In recent years, the literature has included a number of studies on the effect of benzedrine sulfate, taken by mouth. It has been used successfully in the treatment of hypersomnias of various kinds.

Benzedrine sulfate has been employed in studies of prolonged wakefulness. Kleitman reports that he was able to stay awake for 8 days and nights while taking 10 to 30 mg. per night, whereas, without the aid of the drug, he was able to remain awake only 5 days and nights. When benzedrine was used, he and his subjects felt much more alert even after long periods of sleep deprivation.

SEMISLEEP AND STATES RESEMBLING SLEEP

The distinction between being asleep and being awake is actually a rather arbitrary one. The transition stages between full awakeness and deep sleep are of special interest.

Onset of sleep. As has already been implied, there is no one moment when sleep has been reached. Rather, threshold irritability is gradually raised over a variable period of time, during which stimuli of gradually increasing intensity are necessary.

The onset of sleep is sometimes characterized by a "drifting-off" sensation. Davis and others[71] made encephalographic records of their subjects as they experienced drifting off. They were able to detect no moment when sleep began. According to Blake and colleagues,[72] the beginning of "real sleep" is characterized by alpha-delta waves. They felt they were able to narrow down the possible interval during which an arbitrarily chosen degree of sleep was actually reached.

Eyes are a good indicator of sleepiness or approaching sleep. The eyelids tend to close, perhaps involuntarily, or the open eye has a glassy, dull

[69] Pick, E. P.: Pharmakologie des vegetativen Nervensystems, *Deutsche Ztschr. f. Nervenh., 106:* 238–268; 304–319, 1928.

[70] Page, J. D.: An Experimental Study of the Day and Night Motility of Normal and Psychotic Individuals, *Arch. Psychol., 28:* 1–39, 1935–1936.

[71] Davis, H., P. A. Davis, A. L. Loomis, E. N. Harvey, and G. Hobart: Human Brain Potentials during the Onset of Sleep, *J. Neurophysiol., 1:* 24–38, 1938.

[72] Blake, H., R. W. Gerard, and N. Kleitman: Factors Influencing Brain Potentials during Sleep, *J. Neurophysiol., 2:* 48–60, 1939.

appearance. Fixation becomes poor, and if the eyes remain open, the individual may experience double vision. Eye movements are much altered and slowed down.[73]

Semisleep states are sometimes referred to as "hypnogogic" states. Perhaps the term would be better restricted to semisleep states of longer duration than usual, or to semisleep states in which the subject is acutely aware of various phenomena that we are about to mention. Slight[74] says that hypnogogic phenomena, "although of the same nature as the dream, are intimately linked up and often blended with the so-called conscious or waking thoughts of the moment, and are easily accessible for introspection." He classifies hypnogogic states into three types: (1) those in which "mind and body states" give rise to symbolic imagery; (2) those which occur while falling asleep; (3) those in which "objective stimuli" give rise to the dream imagery.

The hypnogogic state may be seen as a partial disconnection from the surroundings—less than that which occurs during sleep itself. The semisleeper may be more sensitive and responsive to certain types of stimuli than to others, but his awareness of these events will lack connectedness. Many have observed that visual imagery tends to dominate the hypnogogic state.

Like sleep, the hypnogogic state is not clear cut, nor can a definite moment be named when it is said to occur. The individual may actually alternate between being asleep and being alert enough to be somewhat self-critical. Thinking is dreamlike, circular, and rich in imagery. Matters of small importance in the waking state may loom large and intense. The hypnogogic state is likely to have an emotional tone, either pleasant or unpleasant. Mild worry is perhaps the most frequently experienced type.

Awakening. When awaking is not spontaneous, it is very likely to be sudden (as in the use of an alarm clock) and to produce a feeling of disorientation. Studies of spontaneous, gradual awakening are very scarce because of the practical difficulty in the experimenter's being at hand at the appropriate time. Most of the observations have been made when a subject awakened from a short nap, or when automatic records of certain types were feasible.

Upon awakening, tonic activity of the muscles begins to increase. Whether or not the subject feels sleepy or tired when he awakes, his per-

[73] Miles, W. R.: Eye-movements during Profound Sleepiness, *Proc. Ninth Int. Cong. Psychol.*, 308–309, 1929.

[74] Slight, D.: "Hypnogogic Phenomena, *J. Abnorm. & Social Psychol., 19:* 274–282, 1924–1925.

formance is at a rather low ebb. Omwake[75] tested body sway while standing, hand steadiness, and number checking before sleep and after 2, 4, 6, and 8 hours of sleep. The performance of her five subjects was best during the test period before sleep, and worst after 2 hours of sleep. Performance became progressively better after 4, 6, and 8 hours of sleep, but did not reach the level attained before sleep.

The degree to which the subject feels sleepy on awakening varies greatly from individual to individual. It also varies in one individual from time to time, but it seems to be characteristic of certain people nearly always to awake well rested, and of others to awake fatigued.[76] Kleitman relates this to individual differences in the diurnal temperature rhythm and associated performance curves. Which is to say, some individuals may be sleeping during the wrong segment of the 24-hour period. Although an excellent observation, it is probably only a partial explanation.

If sleep is assumed to be a state in which there is minimal connection with the surroundings, the transition stages between sleeping and awaking assume a position of great importance. During sleep, the individual has been temporarily somewhat relieved of conflicts generated during the day, on awakening feels he must return to many of these.

It has already been stated that during the semisleep states the waking evaluations of the individual may be much distorted. A small worry, for example, may assume great magnitude. Since, as the individual is awaking he estimates whether or not he feels rested, it is little wonder that he frequently misinterprets his own bodily feelings. Obviously sleep does not remedy all fatigue. Before the muscles have acquired proper tonus, the individual feels tired, especially if he has an aversion to the day ahead of him.

Individual differences in feeling rested or fatigued on awakening, although no doubt dependent upon a number of factors, probably largely mirror the individual's attitude toward the day that lies ahead, and as such are indicative of his general adjustment to his activity obligations, rather than on whether he had a good night's sleep.

Hibernation. As is well known, certain animals, both vertebrate and invertebrate, go into a long seasonal stupor which in some respects resembles sleep. Both states are characterized by relative immobility, lowered metabolic rate and body temperature, decreased reactivity, and loss of connection with the surroundings. The similarities between hibernation and sleep are apparently fairly superficial, and there are those who

[75] Omwake, K. T.: Effect of Varying Periods of Sleep on Nervous Stability, *J. Appl. Psychol., 16:* 623–632, 1932.

[76] Kleitman, Mullin, Cooperman, and Titelbaum, *op. cit.*

believe that there is little to indicate that ordinary sleep and hibernation can be attributed to a common set of conditions.

When external conditions include cold weather and lack of food, some mammals revert to a poikilothermal state. Some authors think seasonal variations found in man are a result of hibernating ancestors. No real hibernation states have been induced in man, however.

Certain authors believe that hibernation is due to seasonal variation in endocrine function. Comparative studies of sleep and hibernation have centered around irritability. Many of the conclusions drawn from these studies have stated that the low irritability which accompanies hibernation is a direct function of the low external temperature and that this is one characteristic which definitely distinguishes hibernation from sleep.

Hypnosis.   Hypnosis is another condition that resembles sleep in some respects. Charcot describes the first phase of hypnosis as a lethargic state like real sleep except for neuromuscular hyperexcitability. Forel characterized the first phase of the hypnotic state as sleepiness.

Comparative physiological measures show that on the whole the hypnotic state resembles the waking state. Tendon reflexes have been found to be undiminished in hypnosis. Loomis, Harvey, and Hobart[77] and Blake and Gerard[78] took encephalographic records during hypnosis which resembled wakefulness rather than sleep. Basal metabolic rate appears to follow the waking pattern, but a rise in electrical skin resistance as is found in sleep has been reported. Studies that have been done on respiration and circulation are contradictory. Some work has been performed on animal "hypnosis," but this is very likely not the same as hypnosis in man.

Earlier, certain writers believed that sleep and hypnosis are part of the same process. Some postulate a common mechanism for both. Pavlov[79] held that sleep is a generalized inhibition and that hypnosis is a specific inhibition. Others also believe that both states are the result of cortical inhibition. On the other hand, Bass[80] can find just about no relation between sleep and hypnosis.

[77] Loomis, A. L., E. N. Harvey, and G. Hobart: Electrical Potentials of the Human Brain, *J. Exper. Psychol., 19:* 249–279, 1936.

Loomis, A. L., E. N. Harvey, and G. Hobart: Further Observations on Potential Rhythms of Cerebral Cortex during Sleep, *Science, 82:* 198–200, 1935.

Loomis, A. L., E. N. Harvey, and G. Hobart: Brain Potentials during Hypnosis, *Science, 83:* 239–241, 1936.

[78] Blake, H., and R. W. Gerard: Brain Potentials during Sleep, *Am. J. Physiol., 119:* 692–703, 1937.

[79] Pavlov, I. P.: The Identity of Inhibition with Sleep and Hypnosis, *Scient. Monthly, 17:* 603–608, 1923.

[80] Bass, M. G.: Differentiation of the Hypnotic Trance from Normal Sleep, *J. Exper. Psychol., 14:* 382–399, 1931.

In summarizing what is known about sleep, little can be derived from purely metabolic data to account for the necessity of sleep as a recuperative process. While it is evident that processes are slowed down during sleep and balances between them provide for maximum restoration, it is not apparent why the waking state is necessarily one that cannot be continuously maintained.

If, however, one surveys the facts of neuromuscular organization, plausible reasons for the necessity of a sleep-waking cycle present themselves. The nervous system is composed of so great a number of parts, the activity of which may cluster in so many ways, that limitless numbers of patterns of over-all activity may be expected of it. Whether observed activity speeds up, slows down, or changes in other ways is not to be taken as an indication of what is happening to the parts as tissue elements (impairment). Rather it is to be seen as an expression of the functional interrelations of the parts. The character of the central nervous system is such as to require periodic occasions that provide for resolution of interrelational tangles.

We have already pointed out that conflicts on the various levels of human organization are inevitable and that these conflicts are bound to influence the alignments of the individual. If the conflicts are intense and prolonged, the individual experiences untoward results of various sorts. The changes in alignment necessary to relieve these unpleasant symptoms may be brought about, or partially brought about, in a number of ways. Sleep, in providing a large degree of unconsciousness and muscular relaxation, is frequently the most effective of these. At times it is the only really effective way of providing relief, and after a sufficient lapse of time without it, sleep becomes inevitable. The detachment provided by sleep allows a minimum of new influences to come to bear on the individual. *It would seem that the primary function of sleep is to provide for various sorts of realignment that cannot occur while the organism is in the midst of high levels of activity.*

Chapter XIV

LONG-TERM CHANGES IN THE INDIVIDUAL

It is well known that the individual undergoes changes over periods of time which significantly affect his ability to meet various demands put upon him. The changes in which we are interested, being functional, exist in terms of what the individual is able or unable to do under a given set of demands. Some changes can be traced to particular activities that have been carried on, whereas others seem to occur regardless of these. Changes of the former kind can often be readily produced and controlled, but we know little that can be done to alter the rates and directions of the latter type. A recognition that the individual is subject to change is at least as important as a consideration of his state at any given moment. Examination of the various long-term changes is a means whereby functions under study from other standpoints can be made more intelligible.

We shall consider five ways of regarding change. The first is through the concept of *training,* or the developing of greater ease in meeting certain demands through activity. The second is through *acclimatization,* or the acquiring of better adjustments to extreme conditions such as intense light, heat, or humidity. Since the individual is never fully inactive, the intensity and character of activity must be considered in the process of acclimatization. The third way of regarding change is through *tolerance,* the name given to progressive adjustments to the repeated or prolonged presence of a foreign chemical in the body. Tolerance is generally thought of as the ability to be less affected by a drug, regardless of whether the original effect was desirable or undesirable.

The fourth way of regarding change is through *learning,* or the progressive adjustments to enduring or repeated aspects of the environment. In the present chapter, this way of regarding change will be considered primarily in terms of the conditioning of organic responses. It will be seen that training, acclimatization, and tolerance, as well as conditioning and many other processes, are actually forms of learning when it is broadly defined. The various distinctions are made primarily for the purpose of analysis. By taking learning as one of the ways of regarding change, it is possible to consider features over and above those included in the concepts of training, acclimatization, and tolerance. Since progress in learning must be measured in terms of efficiency, *i.e.*, by some criterion of perfection, learning, for our purpose, will refer to the change in ability to perform when the reference is some achievement goal. The *excellence* of achievement is emphasized in considering learning, whereas the *cost* of achievement is central when change is viewed through the concept of training.

The fifth way of viewing change is through *aging*. Recently, with the increase of life expectancy in this country, the problem of aging has become a matter of increasing interest. The study of aging has been given the name of "gerontology."

TRAINING

We have defined training as the development of greater ease in meeting certain conditions or demands, through activity, and have stated that the cost of achievement is emphasized when change is viewed from this point of view. It should be noted that the term "training" has often been used to refer to any instruction, practice, or guidance intended to develop some specific ability, habit, or even attitude. Although training has been given these several connotations, it seems appropriate to limit our discussion to the development of fitness for muscular performance.

Muscle. A number of changes occur in muscle tissue as a result of exercise repeated over extended periods of time. Muscle girth increases, but the fiber length, number of nuclei, and size and number of fibrils remain unchanged. Since no new fibers appear to develop and only the sarcoplasm increases in the original ones, the increased girth seems to be the result of the hypertrophy of individual fibers.

Muscle strength and endurance also increase. Holck,[1] over a period of $4\frac{1}{2}$ years, measured the change in endurance in his forearm on a Mosso type ergograph. By the end of this time, he had multiplied his initial endurance fivefold. Another investigator found a better than eightfold increase in a 50-day training period of the arms. The same author reported a two-thirds drop in the capacity of his legs, 2 months following cessation of training.

Siebert,[2] using rats exercised in revolving drums, found that the hypertrophy of their leg muscles was determined by the rate of work rather than by its total amount. Using a medium speed, which produced slight size increases, he found that a stationary state was eventually reached. Exercise, no matter how long continued, did not produce further hypertrophy for

[1] Holck, H. G. O.: "Diet and Efficiency," University of Chicago Monograph in Medicine, University of Chicago Press, Chicago, 1929. Pp. 72.

[2] Siebert, W. W.: Untersuchungen über Hypertrophie des Skeletmuskels, *Ztschr. f. klin. Med., 109:* 350–359, 1928.

that given speed of the drum. Siebert compared the results of isometric and isotonic leg contractions in frogs and found that the isometric contractions were on the average 13 per cent more effective in producing hypertrophy.

Various investigators have found that the percentage of glycogen is higher in trained than in untrained muscles. Proctor and Best,[3] however, were ably to carry the training period to a point at which the exercised and unexercised muscles again became similar in their amount of glycogen. In dogs the differential in amounts of glycogen was found to develop and then disappear in the course of 3 weeks. From this the authors conclude that an additional glycogen supply in muscle is not an essential characteristic of the trained state. Leese and coworkers[4] from an entirely different set of conditions obtained results that point in the same direction. They found no consistent relation between the amount of glycogen in the muscles of starving rats and their work capacity.

A marked augmentation in the amount of phosphocreatin has been found in chronically exercised muscle. But this condition seems to disappear soon after active training ceases.

Some evidence that an increased acid-buffering capacity develops in trained muscles was found by Proctor and Best.[5]

Although, in general, heart weight varies with body musculature, it is uncertain whether training actually increases heart size. On this point, investigators are divided into three groups: (1) those who maintain that the heart sizes of athletes and heavy workers lie within the normal limits of the population who are of the given size and age; (2) those who hold that, whereas the heart shadows of athletes are larger than those of other similarly built persons who exercise only leisurely, this is due primarily to the personal stress and excitement involved and tends to subside after a number of weeks following active sports participation; and (3) those who believe that genuine hypertrophy develops from exertion.

Observations were made at the Boston Marathon in 1923 upon 67 runners prior to the 25-mile race and upon 20 runners just after the race.[6] All the men had had the usual training involved in 5 to 15 years of the sport. One of the results reported was a temporary decrease in heart size follow-

[3] Proctor, H. A., and C. H. Best: Changes in Muscle Glycogen Accompanying Physical Training, *Am. J. Physiol.*, *100:* 506–510, 1932.

[4] Leese, C. E., H. M. Hines, and D. P. Jordan: The Effect of Fasting upon the Activity of Skeletal Muscle, *Am. J. Physiol.*, *100:* 241–245, 1932.

[5] Proctor and Best, *op. cit.*

[6] Gordon, B., S. A. Levine, and A. Wilmaers: Observations on a Group of Marathon Runners (with Special Reference to the Circulation), *Arch. Int. Med.*, *33:* 425–434, 1924.

ing the race, this reduction disappearing in about 24 hours. Heart size determined by x-ray indicated no enlargement in Marathon runners.

The vascular system. Training may have an effect on pulse rate. It is generally admitted that the resting pulse rates of trained athletes are low. Knehr, Dill, and Neufeld[7] found a reduction in rate when the same individuals were examined before and after training. Although this reduction in pulse rate is reported by a number of investigators, certain authors have found no significant changes in *basal* heart rate with training.[8]

Systolic pressure remaining the same, or rising slightly as the subject stands up from reclining, is customarily taken as a sign of fitness. Certain "fitness" tests, such as Schneider's, utilize this feature. Systolic pressure has sometimes been found to fall as the upright position is assumed. In a group of "unfit" women a progressive decline in blood pressure was found during a 15-minute period of quiet standing.[9]

Blood-pressure changes during exercise are different in trained and untrained individuals. In the trained, systolic pressure rises more readily and much higher than in the untrained.[10] The diastolic pressure is greatly augmented, and the product of pulse rate times pulse pressure is greatly increased.

Bock and colleagues[11] found that a marked increase in systolic pressure did not appear in highly trained runners until a work equivalent of 200 cc. of oxygen was performed. Untrained subjects manifested considerable systolic increase with much smaller loads. The findings were interpreted to mean that a different elastic response characterized the various subjects and that this was quite significant in systolic pressure.

Changes in the differential count of the leucocytes occur with training. Relative lymphocytosis has been reported by Herxheimer,[12] and various other investigators have confirmed this finding. There is apparently a re-

[7] Knehr, C. A., D. B. Dill, and W. Neufeld: Training and Its Effects on Man at Rest and at Work, *Am. J. Physiol., 136:* 148–156, 1942.

[8] Gemill, C., W. Booth, and B. Pocock: Muscular Training. I. The Physiological Effect of Daily Repetition of the Same Amount of Light Muscular Work, *Am. J. Physiol., 92:* 253–270, 1930.

[9] Turner, A. H.: The Adjustment of Heart Rate and Arterial Pressure in Healthy Young Women during Prolonged Standing, *Am. J. Physiol., 81:* 197–214, 1927.

Turner, A. H.: Personal Character of the Prolonged Standing Circulatory Reaction and Factors Influencing It, *Am. J. Physiol., 87:* 667–679, 1929.

[10] Dawson, P. M.: Effect of Physical Training and Practice on the Pulse Rate and Blood Pressures during Activity and during Rest, with a Note on Certain Acute Infections and on the Distress Resulting from Exercise, *Am. J. Physiol., 50:* 443–479, 1920.

[11] Bock, A. V., C. Vancaulaert, D. B. Dill, A. Fölling, and L. M. Hurxthal: Studies in Muscular Activity. III, *J. Physiol., 66:* 136–161, 1928.

[12] Herxheimer, H.: Zur Physiologie des Trainings, *Ztschr. f. klin. Med., 98:* 484–523, 1924.

duction in the number of neutrophiles, more particularly of the older seg-
mented forms. This leftwise shift in the blood picture was described by
Egoroff[13] as an acute effect of exertion. Thörner[14] found lymphocytosis
most highly developed in his Marathon runners and concluded that it was
evidence of fitness. He considers it an exhibition of parasympathetic tone.
Lymphocytosis has been found to disappear with 2 to 4 weeks of rest.

Blood platelets have been reported to increase during training. Schneider and Havens,[15] however, found them to decrease after a period of training, and then to increase above normal in number. It would seem that
some types of training may not induce increase, while other kinds and
durations do, the outcome being determined by length and severity of
exercise, as well as by a number of other factors.

Alkali reserve has also been reported by a number of authors to be increased with training. It seems possible that this increase may reach a limit
and a reversal set in. According to the findings of Rehberg and Wisseman,[16]
a secondary reduction in alkali reserve resulted after continued training
of soldiers in heavy exercise. These authors spoke of this as "overtraining."
The trained state is said to exhibit no increase in alkali reserve with the
subject at rest.[17] The amount of reduction in alkali reserve after a standard
amount of exercise bears an inverse relation to the "athletic" state.

Apparently the resting blood-sugar level is uninfluenced by training,
although less fluctuation in level occurs during vigorous exercise. Initial
hyperglycemia and terminal hypoglycemia tend to be eliminated.

Respiration and metabolism.   Steinhaus[18] cites a number of contradictory studies bearing on changes in vital capacity of the lungs with training.
He points out that an increase in vital capacity is found only among
novices and that no increase occurs in highly trained individuals. Some
workers even suggest that "staleness"[19] or overtraining is first indicated by
a reduction in vital capacity.

13 Egoroff, A.: Die Veränderung des Blutbildes während der Muskelarbeit bei Ge-
sunden (Die myogene Leukocytose), *Ztschr. f. klin. Med., 100:* 485–497, 1924.

14 Thörner, W.: Über die Zellemente des Blutes im Trainingszustand. Untersuchung
an Olympiakämpfern in Amsterdam, *Arbeitsphysiol., 2:* 116–128, 1930.

15 Schneider, E. C., and L. C. Havens: Changes in the Blood after Muscular Activity
and During Training, *Am. J. Physiol., 36:* 239–259, 1915.

16 Rehberg, M., and N. Wisseman: Die Alkalireserve im Blutplasma bei der militä-
rischen Ausbildung und nach sportlichen Leistungen, *Ztschr. f. d. ges. exp. Med., 55:*
641–648, 1927.

17 Parade, G. W., and H. Otto: Alkalireserve und Leistung, *Ztschr. f. klin. Med., 137:*
7–28, 1939.

18 Steinhaus, A. H.: Chronic Effects of Exercise, *Physiol. Revs., 13:* 103–147, 1933.

19 Staleness and overtraining are by no means necessarily synonymous. There are
several possible ways of viewing each, and the relation of the two follows in acordance
with such views. It is not certain that "staleness" is a physiological affair exclusively.
It may rather be defined in personal terms.

Training apparently does not tend to increase the minute volume of resting respiration. Steinhaus[20] states that the level of basal metabolism is unchanged if certain collateral features of training are ruled out. When reduced basal metabolism has been found in trained athletes, it has, for example, been attributed to an increased ability to relax. Several authors suggest that this may have developed from an increased "muscle awareness." Raised metabolism found after training has been attributed to certain artifactual conditions, such as the effects of muscle soreness, or the use of invalid standard values.

In measuring work costs the amount of mechanical work is considered in relation to the oxygen consumption (over and above the basal rate) during work until full recovery. When appropriate units are used, the resulting measure is known as the net mechanical efficiency. Training seems to improve net mechanical efficiency, and there is some evidence that this is brought about by improvement in coordination. A poorly coordinated individual consumes more oxygen than the well-coordinated individual, since he is literally doing more physiological work. By improving coordination, practice decreases the necessary amount of physiological work.

Certain experimental findings show that with training there is no shift in the relative amounts of the kinds of fuel used. The working respiratory quotient in trained persons, however, tends to be lower than in untrained.

Experiments conducted by the Scientific and Industrial Research Department[21] in England showed that physical work was made easier for unfit men by breathing oxygenated air, although no difference in ease of work was obtained in fit men. When the results were plotted against the exhaled carbon dioxide for both conditions, certain differences between fit and unfit men in breathing air and oxygen were noted. When the individual was quite fit, the two curves coincided up to the maximum. When the individual was unfit, they tended to diverge as work increased. Fitness varied inversely with the divergence of the two curves.

Coordination and efficiency. Steinhaus states that undoubtedly the greatest and most permanent changes induced by training occur in the nervous system. Improved coordinations and less expensive ways of doing things seem to be the outcome of practice. The increased mechanical efficiency resulting from training was already mentioned. The reduced work involved in achieving ends demanded by specific tasks has also been measured in another way. Fenn[22] analyzed the movements of athletes by the

[20] Steinhaus, *op. cit.*

[21] Briggs, H.: Physical Exertion, Fitness, and Breathing, *J. Physiol., 54:* 292–312, 1920.

[22] Fenn, W. O.: Work against Gravity and Work Due to Velocity Changes in Running, *Am. J. Physiol., 93:* 433–462, 1930.

use of a slow-motion film. Using the same technique, Jokl[23] showed that poor or untrained runners raise and lower their centers of gravity with each step much more than do good runners. It was also shown that hurdlers raise their center of gravity but little in negotiating the hurdles.

The well-trained runner's stride is greater, his limbs move more efficiently, his trunk is inclined more forward and reciprocates less, and his own movements assist forward body movement better than is the case in the untrained runner.

Steinhaus[24] states that in the opinion of Orbeli a large factor in the trained state is the existence of a number of conditioned reflexes involving adjustments through the autonomic nervous system. In other words, training reorganizes the nervous functions of the individual so as to utilize the resources of the supporting organs more efficiently. Organization of the functioning units of the nervous system is commonly taken for granted to account for the unique achievements that are called intellectual, or even those of precision and timing of fine movements. But the importance of organization tends initially to be overlooked in the search for an explanation of endurance and other muscular achievements.

ACCLIMATIZATION

It has long been believed that individuals subjected to altered external conditions undergo certain changes. Initial unfavorable responses, both physiological and personal, tend to give way to more favorable adjustments as exposure to these conditions is continued. This adaptation is known as acclimatization, especially when it refers to the physical conditions of temperature, humidity, sunlight, air motion, altitude, etc., constituting what we speak of as weather and climate.

Acclimatization has been observed in the behavior of groups and in the behavior of individuals. A study of the fates of groups in various surroundings permits some deduction in regard to the individual. The study of groups, however, by-passes the study of individuals in them in various ways. The results of group studies are often no more than evaluations of achievements of one group relative to those of another, or notations that one group survives and another perishes in a given locale. It has been found that some types of climate have supported high forms of civilization, whereas others have not. Such findings suggest that man, regardless of race, may be pushed toward high activity and constructive behavior by one set of climatic conditions and, by another set, toward lethargy and an easy-

---

[23] Jokl, E.: Beiträge zur Physiologie des Laufens und Hürdenlaufens, *Arbeitsphysiol.*, *1:* 296–305, 1929.

[24] Steinhaus, *op. cit.*

going life. Huntington's work[25] is an outstanding example of delineation of the effect of climate on human achievement as expressed by what groups are able to do. The relation between climate and human activity has also been noted by Wheeler.[26]

Acclimatization in the individual has been little studied. The indirection of comparing natives and foreigners, or residents and visitors, in given geographical regions has predominated such work as there is. Individuals, or even groups, have rarely if ever been followed through their introduction and adjustments to new climatic situations. Many studies fail in evaluating the personalistic aspects present in the situation, and few, if any, have been devoted to these aspects.

Meteorological surroundings may be roughly divided into *latitude* and *altitude* climates,[27] each possessing certain features and variables of its own.[28] Adjustment to these two extreme types of climate undoubtedly requires both bodily changes and changes in various features of work.

Sundstroem,[29] in his review of studies on effects of tropical climates, attempts to draw comparisons, in about 24 categories, between native and white populations. Each of these pertains to the broad matters of metabolism, body regulations, and growth.

Latitude climates. According to the many sources cited by Sundstroem in his review, body temperature is not definitely lower in the native population than in the white population of the tropics. It has been presumed that individuals well acclimated to the tropics might have developed a faster means of losing excess heat by radiation and conduction. He cites a study showing that Europeans lost on the average 16 per cent more heat by evaporation than natives and about 14 per cent less by conduction. Results are conflicting on the question of the relative supply of sweat glands in the two populations. Basal metabolism does not seem to be different in tropical and white peoples.

Ratio of skin surface to body volume is another factor that has been studied. The prevalence of "weedier" body shape in the natives and the supposed tendency of the whites to become thin are taken as evidence for the significance of this ratio for adjustment.

[25] Huntington, E.: "Civilization and Climate," Yale University Press, New Haven, 1915. Pp. 333. Also 1924 edition with Tower.

[26] Wheeler, R. H.: The Problem of World Climate, *Am. Meteorol. Soc. Bull., 21:* 46–58, 1940.

[27] When altitude is not far above sea level, climate is largely dependent upon latitude. When increasing altitude begins to predominate in determining the characteristics of the climate, it is labeled altitude climate.

[28] Sundstroem, E. S.: The Physiological Effects of Tropical Climate, *Physiol. Rev., 7:* 320–362, 1927.

[29] Sundstroem, *op. cit.*

Sundstroem points out that in hot surroundings heat and water regulations are closely interrelated and that inadequate heat regulation through nonevaporative channels may be compensated for in water regulation. A shift in the partition of water in the body has been observed. Young et al.[30] report a slightly higher concentration of the blood in the tropics. Sundstroem found the same thing[31] and also reports that the blood chlorides are retained in a hot climate. The shift is limited to the plasma, while it is shown that the corpuscular elements of the blood retain some water. Sundstroem believes that the other body cells share this feature. It has been shown that blood dilution occurs just before and during the outbreak of sweat in hot and moist climates.[32]

Fair agreement exists that urine in the tropics corresponds with accepted standards aside from greater concentration. Blood-sugar levels seem to be lower in the tropics than in cooler climates. Nonprotein nitrogen rises at least during the most trying tropical seasons, with a fairly equal distribution of its components. Sundstroem[33] states that a reduction of acid-soluble and lipoid phosphorus in the blood was found in the white population of the Queensland tropics. This he found also among experimental rats in the same territory and in rats subjected to hot artificial habitats. He concludes that it is one of the most significant effects of hot climate.

The blood of tropical peoples appears to have a normal red count in spite of the sallow appearance of their skin. Some investigations even point toward stimulation of erythropoietic organs in the tropics.[33] White count is usually either normal or slightly subnormal. Some studies have found it to be high, but this is possibly due to the existence of intestinal and other parasites.[34] A shift to the left in the Arneth Index has been found, which indicates the effect of the tropics on the polymorphonuclear leucocytes. Apparently blood pressure is at first lowered by subjection to tropical climates and later tends to return to normal or even higher levels upon acclimatization. Some reports deny any effect on blood pressure, and others state that it remains low. It might well be expected that several patterns of adjustment

[30] Young, W. J., A. Breinl, J. J. Harris, and W. A. Osborne: Effect of Exercise and Humid Heat upon Pulse Rate, Blood Pressure, Temperature, and Blood Concentration, *Proc. Roy. Soc., London, B 91:* 111–126, 1919.

[31] Sundstroem, E. S.: Contributions to Tropical Physiology; with Special Reference to the Adaptation of the White Man to the Climate of North Queensland, *University of California Pub. Physiol., 6:* 1–216, 1926.

[32] Barbour, H. G., M. H. Dawson, and I. Neuwirth: Water, Salt, and Lipoid Accumulation in the Serum as a Preliminary to Sweating, *Am. J. Physiol., 74:* 204–223, 1925.

[33] Sundstroem, *op. cit.*

[34] Sundstroem, E. S.: The Physiological Effects of Tropical Climates, *Physiol. Rev., 7:* 320–362, 1927.

are possible. Sundstroem[35] states such an opinion in discussing the possible effects of tropical climates on the nervous system. He says that, in general, discrepancies of findings might well be resolved if it were possible to put each of them into the total picture where it belongs. Some individuals would seem to take the middle course of equalizing the load imposed by the trying climate, while others would deviate from this in various ways by throwing greater loads on specific mechanisms among those available.

Climatic adjustments to the concomitants of altitude. In altitude climates as contrasted with many latitude climates, the individual encounters the problem of insufficiency of a basic fuel constituent—oxygen. Biochemically and physiologically the individual is brought face to face with limiting conditions that immediately imperil life. The changes that occur are those which are provided for by basic physiology, and adjustments are called for which the individual as a person can little control in an intelligent way. Just what does take place has been the object of inquiry of a number of workers.

Barcroft and colleagues[36] state three principal factors that are positively involved in acclimatization to altitude: (1) an increase in total pulmonary ventilation, which usually raises the alveolar oxygen pressure 10 or 12 mm.; (2) a rise in the oxygen dissociation curve, so that for a given oxygen pressure the hemoglobin will take up more oxygen; and (3) a rise in the number of red corpuscles and thus in the quantity of hemoglobin.

The increase in ventilation and the oxygen dissociation curve both raise the point of oxygen dissociation for oxygen equilibrium between arterial blood and alveolar air and lessen the difference between equilibrium and the saturation of the arterial blood with oxygen. The authors believe that the role of red blood cells is secondary. They also believe that, owing to the finding that the pressures of oxygen in the blood and in the alveolar air were nearly alike, the passage of oxygen through the lungs to the blood occurs by the process of diffusion.

Haldane[37] and his colleagues have also studied the changes produced by subjection to high altitudes. The chief difference between their conclusions and those of the Barcroft group is that they do not believe diffusion will account for the oxygen transfer. Haldane and his colleagues believe that the lungs secrete oxygen into the blood just as, for instance, the kidneys secrete materials into the blood and urine. They found that the

35 Sundstroem, *op. cit.*

36 Barcroft, J., C. A. Binger, A. V. Bock, J. H. Daggart, H. S. Forbes, J. C. Harrop, and A. C. Redfield: Observations upon the Effect of High Altitudes on the Physiological Processes of the Human Body, Carried out in the Peruvian Andes, Chiefly at Cerro de Pasco, *Phil. Trans. Roy. Soc.,* B 211: 351–380, 1922.

37 Haldane, J. S.: Acclimatization to High Altitudes, *Physiol. Rev.,* 7: 363–384, 1927.

oxygen pressure of the blood oxygenated by the alveoli was higher than that of the alveolar air, after several days' exposure to altitude conditions. This change was considered an essential and immediate aspect of acclimatization. The anoxemia that occurs rapidly in "unfit" individuals appears to be due to a lack of oxygen secretion in such persons.

Douglas and Haldane[38] state that during exertion the blood flow does not increase so rapidly as does the general metabolism. The oxygen pressure of the mixed venous blood (with a large fraction of blood from the muscles) is then much lower than it is when the individual is at rest. Although lung ventilation increases nearly in proportion to body metabolism, oxygen pressure may drop much lower than it does under resting conditions in the less well-ventilated alveoli. Active secretion is believed to compensate and thus prevent the otherwise untoward consequences. Douglas and Haldane believed the excitant for this secretion was some substance arising mainly in the active tissues.

Haggard and Henderson,[39] referring to the fact that forced breathing induces a state of acute alkalosis, concluded that the heightened breathing in oxygen want must also result in such a state. Haldane *et al.* found that during initial subjection to altitude, *i.e.,* during "mountain sickness," both the renal excretion of acid and the formation of ammonia were diminished. The kidneys thus play a part in the process of acclimatization by gradually overcoming the alkalosis that results from increased breathing.

Conclusions. In virtually all the numerous studies on acclimatization the human being has been considered as solely a physiological system, sensitive to various physical factors. Investigations in this field have been done as group studies, and not as observations of *individuals* subjected to particular sets of conditions for long periods of time. While such studies have disclosed a few physiological differences between natives and foreigners, as two classes of individuals, for example, these have been fewer than anticipated. Such studies in failing to take the person as a whole as a reference, or even to take selected personal factors into account, have thrown little light on the process of acclimatization as an over-all change in the individual. If it were recognized in the planning of research, as it is in the common-sense outlook, that acclimatization is more than a sum of physiological changes, an adequate accounting for the differences in effectiveness between individuals in various extreme climates would result.

[38] Douglas, C. G., and J. S. Haldane: The Regulation of the General Circulation Rate in Man, *J. Physiol., 56:* 69–100, 1922.

[39] Haggard, H. W., and Y. Henderson: Hemato-respiratory Functions (and following papers in the series), *J. Biol. Chem., 39:* 163–201, 1919.

TOLERANCE

Although, in the introduction to this chapter, we defined tolerance as the progressive adjustment to the repeated or prolonged presence of a foreign chemical in the body, the term frequently carries a much broader connotation.

To tolerate a drug is to be little affected by it: the less the effect, the greater the tolerance. Tolerance may be congenital or acquired. Congenital tolerance is made meaningful only by an implied comparison between individuals, whereas tolerance by acquisition is meaningful in terms of changes in the individual himself. Only acquired tolerance will be considered in this section.

While it is well known that tolerance may be acquired, so that enormously greater amounts of some substances become no more effective than small doses were initially, the basis for this shift is little known. It is usually supposed that delayed or retarded absorption, greater ability to destroy the substances by oxidation, etc., are responsible.

Tolerance is to be distinguished from immunity, another term that is used in connection with the organism's reaction to foreign bodies or chemicals within it. The acquisition of immunity to toxins, bacteria, or any protein material involves the formation of specific antibodies in the blood. Presumably no such antibodies are formed to nonprotein substances.[40] Gunn points out that "immunity" has been retained in most quarters to refer to the reactions with regard to foreign proteins, and "tolerance" to nonprotein substances. He warns that the distinction has two dangers: (1) the implication that the processes by which adjustments are made to nonprotein substances are not included when foreign proteins are involved, (2) the fact that the distinction does not apply to congenital immunity. There is no doubt that such immunity both to foreign protein and nonprotein substances is the expression of an insusceptibility of the cells themselves to the action of the substance.

For example, it has been thought that tolerance for alcohol is acquired by a systemic change involving an acceleration in the rate of alcohol metabolism and a decreased rate of absorption into the blood stream. Newman and Cutting,[41] administering alcohol to dogs by injection, found that the rate of alcohol metabolism was not increased in addicted animals. They

[40] Gunn, J. A.: Cellular Immunity: Congenital and Acquired Tolerance to Nonprotein Substances, *Physiol. Rev., 3:* 41–74, 1923.

[41] Newman, H. W., and W. C. Cutting: Alcohol Injected Intravenously: Effect of Habituation on Rate of Metabolism, *J. Pharmacol., 55:* 82–89, 1935.

Newman, H. W., and W. C. Cutting: Alcohol Injected Intravenously: Further Observations on the Effect of Habituation on Rate of Metabolism, *J. Pharmacol., 57:* 388–393, 1936.

found no evidence that tolerance could be explained by differences in the rate of absorption from the alimentary tract and suggested that some sort of tissue tolerance must develop. Newman and Card[42] studied the effects of 7 months' lapse in the administration of alcohol in dogs that were previously habituated. This length of time was sufficient for the complete loss of tolerance as measured by a nine-point scale of overt behavior.

So far, the kind of information needed to bring the process of tolerance into proper relation with fatigue and other personal stances is lacking.

CONDITIONING OF ORGANIC RESPONSES

In general, conditioning can be defined as the process of altering stimulus-response relations through repeated temporal association of two formerly isolated stimuli or stimulus complexes. The kind of learning that involves changes in organic adjustments is very significant for the problem of fatigue. Such changes are *conditioned*. In everyday life the conditioning that occurs is often left to chance combinations of circumstances. For this reason many of the fundamental characteristics of the individual are not commonly viewed as learned. This is true especially of the modes of organic adjustment. Conditioning is frequently overlooked as the basis for many phenomena that come to attention in other connotations.

The conditioning process accounts for the "unpredictableness" of certain functional stances and explains how various apparently unrelated organic processes may cooperate as parts of a total reaction to a given situation. Since directed conditioning might be used in changing certain unfortunate alignments, it is our intention in this section to describe conditioning.

Autonomic processes. Autonomic reactions are not limited to adjustments to so-called "physical" demands. For example, shifts in blood pressure are required as much in fear or danger as they are in adjusting to the gravitational factors in changing posture. Autonomic adjustments in all types of situations can be viewed only in terms of the organism's over-all stance which always involves categories other than the physiological.

Although the individual in infancy is capable of certain organic orientations, a large proportion of these are quite rudimentary. Only by the process of change or learning does he arrive at the extremely intricate patterns of adjustment that we find in the adult.

Experimental conditioning. Conditioning has been studied in the laboratory where rigid controls are employed. It is the name given to the form of learning in which an initially ineffective event or condition comes to "substitute" for another in eliciting a response. The conditioning pro-

[42] Newman, H. W., and J. Card: Duration of Acquired Tolerance to Ethyl Alcohol, *J. Pharmacol.*, 59: 249–252, 1937.

cedure consists simply in determining the adequate stimulus for a given response and presenting it in close temporal connection with some other event such as a sound, a visual signal, or a tactile pressure. After the initially adequate stimulus is presented with the arbitrarily selected one a number of times, the originally adequate stimulus can be omitted and the individual will respond to the substitute alone. At this point the individual is said to have become *conditioned.* The substituted stimulus is called the *conditioned stimulus* and the response to it, the *conditioned response.*

The work of Menzies[43] illustrates conditioning autonomic responses in the laboratory. He conducted five experiments. The aim of experiment 1 was to discover whether vasoconstriction[44] could be conditioned to an auditory stimulus. The natural stimulus used for vasoconstriction was ice water. The procedure consisted in sounding a buzzer 2 seconds before immersing the individual's hand in the water. Both the immersion and the sound were continued for about 1 minute. Suitable recording devices registered the change in the volume of the hand (vasoconstriction). When the sound was terminated, the individual's hand was dipped in warm water in preparation for the next conditioning trial. After 9 to 20 trials, a definite amount of vasoconstriction was found to have been established to the sound alone.

In experiment 2, an attempt was made to establish a conditioned vasomotor response to a verbal stimulus and to compare this with a nonverbal stimulus in effectiveness. As in the first experiment, the original stimulus was ice water. The verbal stimulus was a nonsense word, "prochaska," which was whispered by the subject before his hand was immersed. The sound of a buzzer, the nonverbal stimulus, was presented alternately with the verbal stimulus. The results indicated that conditioning was somewhat more effective for the verbal stimulus. It should be noted, however, that the conditioning was very probably to the larger situation and not merely to the specific word whispered.

In experiment 3, an attempt was made to condition both vasoconstriction and vasodilatation to the verbal and nonverbal stimuli used in the previous experiment. The results showed that it was possible to condition both vasoconstrictor and vasodilator responses to different stimuli in the same person. In this experiment, as well as in the previous one, some time elapsed after the "practice" series before the effect became marked. When

[43] Menzies, R.: Conditioned Vasomotor Responses in Human Subjects, *J. Psychol., 4:* 75-120, 1937.

[44] Vasoconstriction is the contraction of the blood vessels of a body part. Superficially, this may be evidenced by paling of the skin, but more essentially it is represented by reduced volume of that body part. Through this change, vasoconstriction may be instrumentally measured in the laboratory.

the response was tested at the end of a period of several days, the effect was more pronounced than it was immediately following the repetition series.

Experiment 4 was planned to test the effectiveness of three *movements* and *postures* as conditioned initiators of vasoconstriction. In this experiment as before, the initially adequate stimulus was ice water. For the three subjects, respectively, substitutions were (1) "stimulation" from the forward movement and posture of the arm, (2) closing the fist, and (3) backward movement and posture of the head. In these cases, presumably both tactile and proprioceptive "stimulation" were the essentials to be tested. Although the responses in the control or practice tests were those of vasodilatation, all three substitutions eventually resulted in development of vasoconstriction.

In experiment 4, as in 3, latent conditioning was manifested and the conditioned responses persisted for a number of days. Such a finding puts conditioning into temporal terms significant for everyday circumstances. Had the conditioning disappeared quickly, it would have only academic interest. At home, office, school, and factory, where stereotyped postures are the rule, we should expect to deal only with persistent effects. *The fact that vascular changes can become conditioned to movement and posture is a very important consideration in our everyday lives.*

Experiment 5 of Menzies had two parts: (1) the testing of the effectiveness of a visual stimulus for vasomotor conditioning, and (2) the attempt to discover whether simply thinking about a visual situation would be effective in such conditioning.

In part 1 the original stimulus was again ice water and the visual stimulus was a configuration of two blue crosses. In all of the four subjects, definite conditioning was produced in 25 to 20 trials. In one, the conditioned effect was retained over a 92-day interval without intervening practice, whereas in the other three the results were more unstable.

In part 2 the same four subjects were used, and the substitute "stimulus" was thinking of the visual pattern used in part 1. Instead of presenting the two blue crosses, the experimenter said, "Recall the pattern of light as well as you can." In one subject this situation was found to be fully as effective as the previous one in inducing vasoconstriction. Menzies concluded that at least in some individuals imagining the conditioned stimulus is sufficient to elicit a vasomotor response.

At least in some of Menzies' experiments the "substitute" was not merely the conditioned stimulus, but rather the total situation. What the subject had originally been instructed to do and what he did during each conditioning trial played a crucial role. As has been indicated, it is hardly permissible to speak of the word that the subject whispered in experiment 3 as more than a small part of the substitute for the cold water that originally produced vasoconstriction. The act of whispering was involved in the outcome, although ignored in the interpretation of the results.

Conditioning was successful in the experiments in which movements and postures were taken as the conditioned "stimuli." This fact indicates that what the individual *does* is involved. The final experiments, in which the individual was instructed to think about the visual stimuli (blue crosses) that had previously been used as conditioning stimuli, showed that the acts need not be all of the same type to be effective. Conditioning may well be a much more pervasive affair than generally supposed.

Conditioning in everyday life. The further the situation recedes from the rigid formality of conditioning experiments, the more significant to everyday life the process becomes. It seems safe to assume that rigid experimental conditions are by no means necessary for the successful shifting of relations between various behavior components and external situations. Conditioning then is occurring at all times and in a very complex manner. The further we penetrate into how this "substitution" takes place, the more apparent the intimacy of the relations among the individual's thoughts, personal alignments, and the discernible systemic manifestations become. For one of the most complete reviews of cases revealing the personal nature of bodily changes, the reader is referred to Dunbar's "Emotions and Bodily Changes."[45]

It remains for us to sketch a few situations that will serve to connect conditioning and fatigue in everyday life.

For every individual there are certain situations in which he develops discomfort very quickly. These situations may be concerned with unpleasant tasks in which definite duties are to be performed, or they may be situations in which the confrontment involves scarcely more than maintenance of posture and appearing courteous. Little positive "work" need be involved for difficulty to arise in meeting whatever the demands may be. In any case the readiness with which fatigue develops in a situation similar to one in which it has occurred before is one indication of its *learned* character.

The demand for maintenance of posture in continued standing is an example of a situation that may involve considerable discomfort and actual inadequacy. Standing requires stronger heart beat and higher blood pressure than does sitting or reclining. Systemic inadequacies may not result in acute discomfort during the first few moments of standing, but with prolonged standing they become increasingly crucial. If the past circumstances that called for an individual's prolonged standing involved

[45] Dunbar, H. F.: "Emotions and Bodily Changes," Columbia University Press, New York, 1935. Pp. 595.

unpleasant social aspects, these inadequacies are particularly likely to develop.

Being forced to stand, the individual fidgets and shifts position in progressive uneasiness. He feels he cannot stand any longer and may anticipate fainting. He is extremely fatigued. After a few experiences of this sort, he is likely to become tired whenever he *anticipates* meeting similar demands. The whole set of changes in the individual up to the point of becoming fatigued at the mere thought of prolonged standing is conditioned. When a situation evokes aversion, it heightens the physiological, as well as the personal, aspects of avoiding it or retreating from it. Through conditioning, small differences tend to lead to further inadequacies. Although extreme cases are not common, many individuals show lesser degrees of distortion. Progressive changes may eventuate in relatively fixed and thus readily elicited modes of acting.

In the discussion just given, the attempt has been to show that conditioning as a form of learning pertains to organic behavior as well as overt. Conditioning is actually a process of shifting behavior so as to constitute new stances of the whole individual toward the environmental situations he encounters in everyday life.

AGING

Human life is limited in span. Both its limits and the progressive changes known as the process of aging are the object of present-day interest and study. At present, there are two main groupings of interest, gerontology and geriatrics. The former is the study of aging in all its aspects; the latter is the clinical study and treatment of the difficulties and diseases of old age. Gerontology as a science is just beginning, and we have little information in this field with which to document our inquiries. We can point out only the general direction in which the relations among aging, fatigue, and impairment may be sought.

With the increase in expectancy of life, individuals of 60 and over are constituting a greater and greater fraction of the total population. The problem of aging is assuming more and more importance owing to the increasing number of older people. In the decade of 1930–1940, the U. S. Census indicated a 35 per cent increase in numbers of individuals over 65, associated with only a 7 per cent increase in total population. In 1940, there were 9 million persons in the United States 65 years old or over.[46] By 1980, at least 15 per cent of the total population will constitute individ-

[46] Stieglitz, E. J.: Pertinent Problems of Geriatric Medicine, *Ann. Int. Med., 18:* 89–95, 1943.

uals having reached or passed 65.[47] Over 40 per cent of the population will be older than 45 years of age.[48]

It is well known that in aging, physiological changes occur which do not constitute disease. These changes are manifested in a lessened ability to do muscular and intellectual work. Robinson[49] states that the most distressing symptoms of old age are mental, although not all of them need be looked upon as "pathological." He does not believe that the entire responsibility for senile psychoses should be sought in structural change.

While many characteristics of behavior are premised upon inevitable changes that might be taken as a manifestation of organic aging, some of the characteristics studied are results of living in a social world. The effects of meeting conflicts on all levels over long periods of time accumulate and become progressively obvious as the individual grows older.

The histologist inventories the individual's tissues, the educational psychologist attempts to measure his overt abilities, whereas the physician seeks to remedy or in some cases prevent the breakdowns that are peculiar to the later age periods. In studying aging no one yet has adequately taken account of the individual's purposes and his accumulated experiences. For our purposes, the consideration of aging takes on the form of dealing with the relations among the individual's changing abilities, his accumulated experiences, and his abiding or changing purposes.

The problem of aging is an example of the genetic approach to behavior, and the genetic approach is not the only one. It is not easy, if at all possible, to distinguish clearly between phenomena which may be attributed to aging and those which may be better understood in other terms. In fact, in many cases, it is profitable to avoid making this distinction.

Tissue changes in aging. Histological and physiological changes that occur during life are basic to the formulation of a concept of aging. Cowdry[50] points out that certain body cells are replaced thousands of times during the human individual's lifetime, while others are replaced much less often. Some are never replaced. Among the latter are heart-muscle cells, nerve cells, and those of voluntary muscles. Some tissue replacement may be inadequate. In the case of white connective tissue, old fibers may be retained, tending to "clog" functional processes.

The body is provided with an excess of both replaceable and nonreplaceable cells. Although information is still lacking as to the extent of this surplus, there is evidence of a progressive decrease in functional cells of

47 Bortz, E. L. Geriatrics—New Light on Old Folks, *Clinics, 1:* 386–405, 1942.

48 Stieglitz, E. J.: The Potentialities of Preventative Geriatrics, *N. England J. Med., 225:* 247–254, 1941.

49 Robinson, G. W.: Psychiatric Geriatrics, *J.A.M.A., 116:* 2139–2141, 1941.

50 Cowdry, E. V.: Factors in Ageing, *Scient. Monthly, 56:* 370–374, 1943.

the nervous and muscular systems. For example, a gradual decline in the number of myelinated fibers in the eighth and ninth dorsal and ventral roots of the spinal cord was found in individuals from the fourth to the eighth decades of life.[51] Frayed cells and atypical cells due to degeneration are often found in older adults. The decrease in ganglion cells from the fifth decade onward amounts to almost one-third. Taste buds and olfactory fibers also noticeably decrease.

Aging involves a shift in the distribution of mineral salts, as for example, calcium. Texture and pigmentation of skin and hair also undergo changes as life progresses. Among the manifestations of physiological changes that occur with age are the following:[52] graying of hair; increasing pallor of skin from decrease in capillary beds; decrease in or loss of deep tendon reflexes; atrophy of thyroid gland, liver, kidneys, lymphoid tissues, etc.; the development of a kind of emphysema with concomitant reduction in vital capacity; osteoporosis of the long bones and large flat bones.

Other changes. Aging also is reflected in a decrease in the adaptability of the nervous and cardiovascular systems. Perception also becomes less acute, and responsiveness is diminished. There may be discrepancies between enthusiasm and the ability to perform. Aging usually involves a tendency to recall pleasant events and to forget pain. The older individual is able to endure more severe physiological inroads made upon him by feeling less pain than the young. He may become more mellow and shift from personally centered activities to interest in others, especially the young. He may become less exacting in demands.

Vision and hearing are at their best in the late teens.[53] At 50, hearing abilities have declined to a point at which ordinary conversation is often affected. Visual efficiency is 10 to 20 per cent below that at the age of 40. Reaction time, a standardized measure of the quickness of certain reactions, is at its best (shortest) in the first half of the third decade of life. So-called immediate memory is best at the same stage in life. This is also true of so-called new learning. If vocabulary is taken as an example of the manifestation of "old learning," decline is very slow to occur.

Intelligence-test scores reach their peak between the ages of 13 and 16. At 55 years of age the average test scores are somewhat lower.[54] As soon as

[51] Gardner, E. D.: Decrease in Human Neurons with Age, *Anat. Rec., 77:* 529–536, 1940.

Corbin, K. B., and E. D. Gardner: Decrease in the Number of Myelinated Fibres in Human Spinal Roots with Age, *Anat. Rec., 68:* 63–74, 1937.

[52] Piersol, G. M.: Medical Considerations of Some Geriatric Problems, *Arch. Ophth., 29:* 26–35, 1943.

[53] Lawton, G.: Mental Decline and Its Retardation, *Scient. Monthly, 58:* 313–317, 1944.

[54] *Ibid.*

these tests are broken into their components, aging tested in the separate categories proceeds at distinctly different rates.

Accomplishments appear to reach their peak in the fifth and sixth decades. Dorland[55] found that the mean age at which various leaders produced their masterpieces were as follows: naturalists and jurists, 58; historians, 57; satirists and humorists, 56; astronomers, mathematicians, and philosophers, 54; physicians, surgeons, and statesmen, 52; reformers and essayists, 51; artists and clergy, 50; actors and composers, 48; explorers and military men, 47; novelists, 46; inventors, poets, dramatists and playwriters, 44; physicists, 41.

Lehman[56] studied the average annual publications per person in the various age levels as a percentage of individual's maximum. This he did for men in geology, psychology, educational theory, mathematics, economic and political science, practical inventions, and chemistry, productions of grand operas, short stories, poems sung as hymns, and hymn tunes. "Superior contributions" were plotted in one set of curves, and contributions of "lesser merit" in one or more other sets. In almost all cases the maximum was found in the range between 32 and 45 years of age for both quantity and quality. However, there is no strict relation between the two, and the graphs for the "superior contributions" tend to "peak" more sharply and at a slightly lower age level. It would appear, in most cases, that productivity by the time the common "retirement age" (65) is reached is down to the level of a beginner in his early twenties both in "superior contributions" and in the "lesser" ones.

J. T. Landis,[57] using "retrospective interviews" given by 450 subjects, attempted to determine the period of life they considered to be the happiest. Seven per cent of the group were unable to decide. Half of the group designated the period between 25 and 45 as the happiest. Twenty per cent judged the years between 15 and 25. Eighteen per cent chose childhood, and only 5 per cent picked middle and old age. One-third of the married subjects, in contrast with two-thirds of the single, chose childhood as the happiest. The married subjects usually chose the period between 25 and 45. In another study,[58] 49 per cent chose the 25- to 45-year period as the happiest.

[55] Dorland, as reported by Lawton.

[56] Lehman, H. C.: Man's Most Creative Years, *Scient. Monthly, 58:* 384–393, 1944.

[57] Landis, J. T.: What Is the Happiest Period in Life? *School and Society, 55:* 643–645, 1942.

[58] Morgan, M.: The Attitudes and Adjustments of Recipients of Old Age Assistance in Upstate and Metropolitan New York, *Arch. Psychol.,* No. 214, 1937.

One of the best accounts of a variety of problems of aging is given in the recent book edited by Kaplan.[59]

The individual's awareness of aging has been investigated.[60] When subjects were asked about their first realization of growing old, "physical" symptoms were found to be twice as abundant as "mental" ones. Miles[61] has shown that common physiological functions do show decline before the mental.

The first symptoms were found to be deterioration of locomotor apparatus, nervous troubles, sense-organ impairment, deterioration in hair, skin, etc., greater tendency to fatigue, and greater need for sleep.

The average age of becoming aware of being old was found by Jones to be about 49 years, although the range extended from 18 years to 82 years.

Conflicts tend to increase with age until maturity. They develop gradually as the individual comes up against increasingly difficult problems. Ordinarily, conflicts do not arise suddenly.[62] When the personality is well formed, the threat a conflict may mean to personality integration is greater than it is in the immature where personality integration is still loose.

Although it is generally held that conflicts increase with age, it is by no means true that conflicts are nonexistent in early childhood or even in infancy. It is rather that the conflicts of adults are more complex and more far reaching in their effects than those of the immature individual. According to Sherman, a conflict may arise as "a result of an unsatisfied need or desire which the person regards as requisite for his well-being." This by no means exempts the very young child, although it is not often likely that he is aware enough of his need himself to regard it as requisite. Consequently, although conflict occurs, it is likely to be of a rather transient nature. But if the same conflict situation is often repeated, the effects will become increasingly far reaching.

As the individual passes through life, not only the opportunities but also the difficulties and the frustrations change. Each period carries with it its own occasions in which futilities may develop. We should expect the individual to become increasingly set in ways of doing things and in thinking. If by unfortunate conditioning the individual builds up more and more stereotyped aversions to situations he is bound to get into, old age closes in with considerable cruelty. But if his stances have become stereo-

[59] Kaplan, O. J.: "Mental Disorders in Later Life," Stanford University Press, Stanford University, Calif., 1945. Pp. 436.

[60] Jones, W. L.: Personality and Age, *Nature, London, 136:* 779–782, 1935.

[61] Miles, W. R.: Psychological Aspects of Ageing, Chap. 28 in "Problems of Ageing," ed. by E. V. Cowdry, Williams & Wilkins Company, Baltimore, 1942.

[62] Sherman, M.: "Mental Conflicts and Personality," Longmans, Green and Company, New York, 1938. Pp. 319.

typed in the opposite direction, he can transcend much that from the observer's standpoint might be considered very trying. In certain cases, habits may be decidedly favorable. Certain life goals might be achieved and a more easygoing attitude adopted.

In dealing with fatigue we are dealing with aspiration, personal integration, and the collision of the individual with his surroundings. Gerontology needs to delineate a number of the more typical life patterns. The changes that occur in successive decades of life should be investigated. If it could be shown that new combinations of aspiration, physical fitness, mental alertness, enthusiasm, social sensibility, etc., emerge from decade to decade, it would be expected that fatigue would be aroused by different situations as the individual grows older. In the process of penetrating into the actual mainsprings of action, techniques for discovering the determining conditions for fatigue would be found.

Chapter XV

"MENTAL FATIGUE"

IT IS quite common for some fatigue to be thought of as mental. The reason for our devoting space to this subject lies in the attempt to discuss fatigue from the familiar and customary standpoints, rather than in the belief that it is profitable to think of *kinds* of fatigue. When kinds of fatigue are implied, the mode of classification pertains either to the situations in which fatigue arises, or to the way or place fatigue operates within the individual. "Mental" fatigue, when imputed to be the result of intense central nervous activity, is an example of the second type of classification. Mental fatigue has also been classified in terms of the task at hand. This is the case when Bills[1] defines it as the result of such work as adding digits, as contrasted with the results of weight lifting, which is called "muscular" fatigue.

Older attempts at distinguishing between mental and muscular are illustrated by devices of Thorndike[2] and of Watson,[3] for example. Thorndike wished to designate the "connection" processes in the nervous system as mental and the processes of the sense organs and muscles as nonmental. Watson tried to keep all considerations "objective" by dividing action into the overt and the implicit. He assumed that all action involves at least incipient muscle activity. Granting a kind of distinction between what is gross and what is incipient does not, however, provide two categories, one of which is "mental." Those who seize upon the overt-implicit dichotomy for contrasting mental and muscular fatigue turn out to be making nothing more than an issue of the fineness of measurement.

Dodge,[4] many years ago, discussed the problem of *mental work* and attempted to justify it as a concept. In that day (1913), resistance against such an idea was prevalent in this country, although various European writers were less reluctant to use the term "work" in connection with mental activity. He pointed out that, despite this resistance, terms which

[1] Bills, A. G.: Fatigue in Mental Work, *Physiol. Rev., 17:* 436–453, 1937.

[2] Thorndike, E. L.: The Curve of Work, *Psychol. Rev., 19:* 165–194, 1912.

[3] Watson, J. B.: "Psychology from the Standpoint of a Behaviorist," 2d ed., J. B. Lippincott Company, Philadelphia, 1924. Pp. 448.

[4] Dodge, R.: Mental Work. A Study in Psychodynamics, *Psychol. Rev., 20:* 1–42, 1913.

he believed to be synonymous to work were being used. These were mental operation, mental elaboration, etc. For him mental fatigue could mean nothing unless mental processes were taken to follow the second law of thermodynamics.

Dodge brought to attention the two general attitudes toward the word, *viz.*, work as the physicist uses it, and work as opposed to play. The distinction between *work* and *play* exists in the psychological realm and not in the physiological or the physical. Work experientially defined involves *effort*, action against resistance, the disagreeable, etc. When Dodge stated that "mental operations" were equivalent to mental work, he was ignoring this. It is apparent that Dodge was seeking a way to measure mental operations in the same terms as muscular exercise. This could be done only in the sense that all that an individual does involves physiology and thus some expenditure of energy. Attempts to measure the energy cost of mental work show that the cost of mental operations is trivial. Consideration of cost has little bearing on the problem of fatigue. Those who persist in searching for energy costs to explain the feelings of lassitude, weariness, aversion, and exhaustion in doing intellectual tasks are on the wrong track. Many of those who continue to use drop in efficiency to identify "fatigue" will admit that the amount of energy spent does not seem to account for the end result.

Since fatigue is experiential, and since "experiential" and "mental" are common synonyms, all fatigue is mental and the term no longer differentiates between kinds of fatigue.

Lack of subjective distinction between "kinds" of fatigue. Many of those who distinguish between mental and muscular fatigue use subjective elements present in both to support the differentiation. If we examine their descriptions, we find them to be mostly those of localized bodily sensations which differ from one activity to another. Bodily feelings from doing arithmetic without pencil and paper are different from those following a game of football. Bodily feelings differ in so many details that it is not surprising that much has been said in delineating these differences. Although those who make the "mental-muscular" dichotomy assume that an attitudinal factor is a part of the subjective description of fatigue, they are not able to bring out, as would logically be required, that the essential attitude in the two cases is different. Since they cannot use attitude as a differential, they have failed to disinguish between the supposed two kinds of fatigue.

Bills[5] gives a description of bodily feelings arising from the two contrasting kinds of pursuits, intellectual (mental) and muscular. He points out

[5] Bills, A. G.: "The Psychology of Efficiency," Harper & Brothers, New York, 1943. Pp. 361.

that in physical exertion aches and pains of the gross musculature arise. Soreness develops. A feeling of powerlessness to move, awareness of heaviness of body and limb, and a sensation of lassitude or even limpness eventuate. A feeling of muscular relaxation and an awareness that thinking is done with effort make up the individual's experience of his own condition.

On the other hand, when mental pursuits have been continued for some time, the small muscles of the face, head, and neck region, including the eyes, become uncomfortable. Restlessness instead of listlessness develops. This signifies a feeling of tension rather than relaxation. It is supposed that sensory thresholds may be lowered, and emotional irritability develops. A sense of impotence ensues which is not the kind imputed to the results of physical exertion. There is also some implication in Bills's description that physical fatigue is pleasant and that mental fatigue is either unpleasant or undetectable. Bills says that in physical fatigue sleep is easily induced, whereas in mental fatigue restlessness and even sleeplessness are common.

When this description is examined, it will be found that bodily feelings form the exclusive material. It will be noted that nothing is said about the individual's attitude toward his previous activity or toward further exertion. Statements about aversion and personal distaste for activity are absent, and self-assessments in ability to be active are at the minimum. Hence the possible common denominator, that of attitude, which would have been the same in the two situations if they both represented fatigue, was left out.

As an illustration of a further extension of the idea that subjective symptoms are not all of one pattern, there is the recent article of Ryan.[6] He states that fatigue is of a highly varied character and proceeds to classify kinds of fatigue-producing situations, giving the effects produced by each of them. He points out seven different types of fatigue, arising in (1) dromal tasks, involving vigorous muscular exercise; (2) steady grinds; (3) postural restrictions, such as in typewriting; (4) repetitive local tasks, exemplified by ergographic performance; (5) prolonged sensory adjustment, as in reading, etc.; (6) emotional predicaments; and (7) problem-solving situations, as in working mathematical problems. For each of these situations he suggested certain types of outcomes. These are somewhat different in the several classes and are supposed to signify different kinds of fatigue. Thus instead of the gross division of subjective elements into only two kinds to support the dichotomy of mental fatigue and muscular fatigue, as Bills did, Ryan has proceeded to a seven-part classification which might follow the same kind of reasoning. Were fatigue a personalistic concept for Ryan, he might have seen that its essentials are the stance the

6 Ryan, T. A.: Varieties of Fatigue, *Am. J. Psychol.,* 57: 565–569, 1944.

individual takes. Fatigue is an identifiable experience from occasion to occasion. If fatigue had to be identified in its *details* from occasion to occasion, many more than Ryan's seven situations would have to be included. Not even a great number of classes would take care of the variations in detail that are actually encountered in everyday life, and no definition of fatigue could be made.

All but the most transient situations in which the individual finds himself involve a discernible pattern. The individual forms a conception of his place in the situation. This involves a conception of what is required of him. His attitude with regard to his ability is in turn based on past experience, bodily feelings, the time required, the kind of activity, and what is to be gained by the activity. Organic reactions develop, many of which are conditioned. These stereotyped organic reactions may roughly represent moblization for activity or retreat from it. Feelings of tension or lassitude develop and may represent, among other things, readiness to do the thing conceived of, or anticipatory fatigue. In this the individual is pictured as first experiencing realization of demand, secondly reacting either by acceptance or by rejection. This is shown in situations in which need for activity is merely anticipated and pertains as well to assessments in the midst of activity. Bodily sensations become a part of this stance, although their exact nature or location is irrelevant to the presence or absence of the fatigue.

The stance of the individual in fatigue remains the same regardless of the particular cluster of sensational elements; therefore kinds of fatigue cannot be deduced from them. Just so long as the attempt to define fatigue rests on enumerations of items, confusion will exist. Workers will still continue to invent kinds of fatigue.

Conventional mental fatigue. Bills[7] suggests that there are four kinds of mental fatigue. These permit of four ways in which estimates can be made of the state of an individual as he progresses with a task. One is to measure what is done during successive equal periods of time, assuming that the individual continues to try equally hard as time goes on and that output is limited only by capacity. He believes the validity of this procedure could be taken for granted if the external incentive is constant, so that lack of interest is not mistaken for fatigue. Since lack of interest is an aspect of fatigue, it could scarcely be ruled out. A second method is to measure metabolic rate, while a third is to note and record all external signs of nervous tension. These would be excessive muscle tonus, squirming, fidgeting, reduced emotional control, and the like. He says that this is

[7] Bills, A. G.: "The Psychology of Efficiency," Harper & Brothers, New York, 1943. Pp. 361.

a very inaccurate method, but might be useful as a supplement. The fourth method is to ask the individual himself for reports on his own feelings as work progresses.

The methods recognizing the four kinds of mental fatigue Bills calls, respectively, the objective method, the organic method, the by-product method, and the subjective method.

The objective method assumes that fatigue is a diminished capacity for work, as evidenced by the decrement in output. Bills says that originally this reduced capacity was presumed to be general. It is not evident that diminished capacity in the particular task under measurement disadvantageously affects all other things that the "fatigued" person might attempt to do. It is not certain that fatigue from a few hours of working arithmetical problems could be amply tested by the individual's achievement in some subsequent physical exercise. As Bills points out, this assumption of the generality or all-pervasiveness of fatigue produced by a specific task led to the interpolated task method, a procedure in which periodically a worker on a prolonged task is tested on a short task of a second type. It was presumed that, as the individual becomes tired from the first type of task, he would show a lessened ability to do the second type of thing. Successive reductions in the ability to do the second task are used to construct a fatigue curve. This has not worked out too well in practice, so that now even those who have a *work* concept of fatigue recognize that fatigue does not seem to be so general as first thought. The interpolated task method has been largely replaced by the continuous task method which measures the work decrement in the task itself.

It would appear that the methods outlined by Bills measure the following four aspects of the task situation: (1) productivity; (2) the amount of energy used; (3) the display of lost motion, or release of uselessly distributed tension, etc.; and (4) the individual's attitude toward the task, the feeling of relative comfort or discomfort, the amount of aversion and desire to quit.

Energy consumption in mental work. Various workers have investigated the energy consumption during the performance of tasks taken to be examples of mental work and have compared them with some "resting state." One of the well-known studies of this sort was that of Benedict and Benedict,[8] in which it was found that adding digits without the use of paper and pencil requires only 3 to 4 per cent more energy than is required at rest. This of course was the energy involved in whatever bodily movements, extra muscular tension, etc., occurred under test conditions

[8] Benedict, F. G., and C. G. Benedict: Mental Effort in Relation to Gaseous Exchange, Heart Rate, and Mechanics of Respiration, Carnegie Inst. of Washington *Pub.* 446, 1933. Pp. 83.

as contrasted with "rest." The authors conclude that if solely the energy used in the central nervous system were included the amount would be negligible. Goldstein[9] investigated the biochemistry of the blood during mental work with varying amounts of overt physical activity and under conditions of "no work." Six determinations, including those of organic phosphorus, cholesterol, sugar, chlorides, calcium, and creatinine, were made. The mental work with overt components was cancellation and the taking of the CAVD Intelligence Test, Levels M-Q. Three hours of cancellation and 3 hours used in taking this intelligence test produced about the same changes, *viz.*, an increase in organic phosphorus, cholesterol, and creatinine, and a decrease in blood sugar. Changes in the same direction took place when individuals in a control group performed overt physical work.

However, Goldstein was able to conclude that, when the overt muscular constituent of mental activity is reduced to a minimum, biochemical means fail to indicate that mental activity changes the character of metabolism from that in the resting state. He further concludes that the explanation of fatigue following mental effort must be attributed to brain activity. He suggests that intense activity of brain tissue cannot be measured by present methods, since it comprises so little of the total tissue mass involved in body metabolism.

These two studies are sufficient to indicate the general expectations with regard to correlating experiential factors with energy measurements. Fatigue, as such, was studied in neither, but "mental operations" were used as test material. Since the experiments were tests to determine to what extent expenditure of physical energy is involved in mental processes, they were considered experiments on mental fatigue. They should be interpreted as indicating that to expect a direct energy basis for fatigue is quite futile.

The distinction between work and play, as a significant classification, may turn out to be a more fruitful frame in which to use the term work. Work implies the experience of effort, distaste, etc. The relation of fatigue and work is much more meaningful in this reference than in a frame that attempts to draw psychophysical parallels.

Refractory period used as a factor in explanations of fatigue. Numerous writers have introduced certain facts regarding the behavior of the single nerve fiber to help explain various phenomena of work decrement, changes in gross physiological function, mental fatigue, etc. A few examples will suffice to indicate the customary trend. The premise generally used

[9] Goldstein, H.: A Biochemical Study of the Metabolism of Mental Work, *Arch. Psychol., N. Y.,* No. 164, 1934.

is that repetitive stimulation of an isolated nerve fiber prolongs its refractory phase. Although such a lengthening does occur, it results only under some conditions, and those who use this fact seldom seem to take this adequately into account.

Dodge,[10] after stating that Vervorn proved relative refractory phase identical to fatigue, went on to enumerate many phenomena in everyday life which he took to be examples of this. His reasoning here seems to rest only on the most remote analogy. The kind of phenomena he recited were those in which the individual tended to resist or dislike repetition (of jokes, etc.). The interval until a recurrence of an event was tolerated or enjoyed was spoken of as refractoriness, as if a direct expression of simple refractoriness in nerve. He attempted to use "refractoriness" not only as an explanation for, but also as a synonym of aversion. He also employed it to explain one's ability to tolerate repetition. Throughout, as was already emphasized, there was no concrete delineation of how these gross features of human behavior were dependent upon the highly particular property of nerve known as refractoriness.

The attitude of Dodge is somewhat curious when we examine his objections to relating work decrement to "true" fatigue. He stated a number of reasons why the mental work decrements treated as mental fatigue could not likely be attributed to true fatigue processes in nervous tissue. The reasons are as follows: (1) Nervous tissue *in the body* has been found very resistant to fatigue and exhaustion under usual conditions. (2) Normal psychophysiological rhythms are excluded in the customary explanations of mental-work decrement. (3) In mental-fatigue experiments, the repetition of the same stimulus is avoided, not allowing for a just comparison with nerve-muscle fatigue experiments. (Literal repetition is absurd in mental work. For example, as he points out, the experimenter never requires that the subject repeatedly get the product of 2 times 2. Hence literal repetition is never attained, and we do not know how nearly it is even approached.) (4) Work decrement and fatigue cannot be identified on account of the operation of incidental inhibitions. Supposedly every mental process arouses widespread associated reverberations, showing up as serial associative recall, operating to confuse the work at hand as a kind of associative rivalry. Associations likewise more or less direct inhibition.

Robinson and Bills[11] also resort to Vervorn's emphasis on refractoriness of living tissue as one of the most general of biological principles. They attempted to relate this principle to the fact that homogeneous material

10 Dodge, R.: The Laws of Relative Fatigue, *Psychol. Rev., 24:* 89–113, 1917.

11 Robinson, E. S., and A. G. Bills: Two Factors in the Work Decrement, *J. Exper. Psychol., 9:* 415–443, 1926.

very often results in more work decrement than varied material. Bills[12] later introduces cumulative refractoriness to account for "blocking." Barmack[13] speaks of refractory nerves as fatigued nerves.

Mental activity and the musculature in the production of fatigue. More significant than the amount of energy consumed in mental activity is the effect of intellectualization on the musculature. Some connection between thinking and muscle tone and movement is not a new conception. It was talked about many years ago and demonstrated by such devices as the planchette or ouija board and from observing incipient movements by plumbline and other simple laboratory improvisations. James in his "Principles" speaks of "dynamogeny" and points out the connection between thought and muscle activity. Such observations seem to have fared the fate of many others—left by most workers and theorists alike to gather dust as museum pieces.

For many years, Jacobson[14] has been interested in the matter of muscle tonus and relaxation in their relation to personal comfort and health. Not content alone with the success he has had in dealing with patients by teaching relaxation of skeletal musculature, he has pursued his studies in the laboratory to disclose the concrete relation between mentation (imagination, etc.) and muscle tension. Jacobson has shown that imagining moving a bodily member, such as flexing the forearm, institutes action potentials in that member large enough to be detected, amplified, and recorded, whereas the visualization of movement in other members does not induce detectable activity at the original recording site.

Recollection[15] of previous acts also served to induce measurable potentials in the members involved in them. After it was found that patterns of activity could be recorded from specific eye movements,[16] such as up, down, to the right, and to the left, which were distinguishable from winks, frowns, etc., tests showed that incipient potentials characteristic of definite eye movements were set up during visual recollection and imagination. A

[12] Bills, A. G.: Blocking: A New Principle of Mental Fatigue, *Am. J. Psychol., 43:* 230–245, 1931.

[13] Barmack, J. E.: Boredom and Other Factors in the Physiology of Mental Effort, *Arch. Psychol., N. Y.,* No. 218, 1937. Pp. 83.

[14] Jacobson, E.: Electrical Measurements of Neuromuscular States during Mental Activities. I. Imagination of Movement Involving Skeletal Muscles, *Am. J. Physiol., 91:* 567–608, 1930.

[15] Jacobson, E.: Electrical Measurements of Neuromuscular States during Mental Activities. II. Imagination and Recollection of Various Muscular Acts, *Am. J. Physiol., 94:* 22–34, 1930.

[16] Jacobson, E.: Electrical Measurements of Neuromuscular States during Mental Activities. III. Visual Imagination and Recollection, *Am. J. Physiol., 95:* 695–702, 1930.

trained subject, when asked to relax, could do so and reported the absence of imagination and recollection during the state of relaxation.

These experiments, along with others like them, enable us to speak of the engagement of the whole neuromusculature of the body in the act of thinking. This, in connection with the fact that prolonged thinking could be expected to give rise to accumulation of tensions, etc., gives ground for expecting considerable bodily effect from thinking, or to look upon thinking as a bodily act.

Freeman[17] has concerned himself with the problems of the relation of experiential activity to muscular tension, using not only the findings from his own studies but also from others, notably Jacobson's, in relaxation; Johnson's, in sleep, etc. As a result, he stated his working hypothesis, which is about as follows: (1) The cortical centers primarily underlying mental activity possess relatively high thresholds of excitation. These centers, since involved in more than one activity, vary in their thresholds, depending upon the activity in question. For example, such centers might function in perception more easily than in memory. (2) When the thresholds are lowered, cortical centers are activated by otherwise inadequate "stimuli" during the working state. (3) The threshold reduction in 2 is accomplished by irradiation or excitation from lower neural levels, especially those having to do with muscular contraction. (4) Cortical activity is sustained and reinforced by a continuous flow of proprioceptive impulses. When such a flow drops below a certain minimum, cortical elements are unable to respond to external events of a moderate physical intensity. (5) Central-nervous economy is such that muscular contraction not only supports experiential processes, but contributes toward the determination of which processes will occur. (6) Beyond a certain intensity, muscular contraction through its consequences can become an inhibitor of neural integration needed for certain precise tasks. (7) The regulation of muscular tension is for the most part self-induced. Habituation to a task diminishes its amount, whereas "relative fatigue" enhances it.

Nonrepetition factors in mental fatigue. Robinson[18] reported that three variables in addition to repetition itself influence the amount of mental work done. These she calls "connectedness," "associative value," and "comprehensibility," each producing its distinguishable effect. Decrement in mental work is inversely related to connectedness, whether decrement is measured in speed or in accuracy. More decrement results from very high and very low than from moderate degrees of associative value.

[17] Freeman, G. L.: Mental Activity and the Muscular Processes, *Psychol. Rev., 38:* 428–449, 1931.

[18] Robinson, M. F.: The Work Decrement as Affected by Three Kinds of Meaningfulness, *J. Exper. Psychol., 22:* 124–149, 1938.

Decrement is inversely related to comprehensibility. With discrete items, mental work is carried on with low efficiency and considerable decrement. In contrast to this, with connected materials, mental work is carried on with high efficiency and with slight or no decrement, particularly if the materials have a high degree of "comprehensibility."

To test "connectedness," a story was chosen and broken into sentences in scrambled order and into scrambled sentences. These two arrangements were meant to represent degrees of disconnectedness. "Associative value" was tested in several ways, including the use of three groups of monosyllables written in code. In order to obtain evidence of their relative associative value, the three groups of monosyllables were given to junior college students prior to use in the experiment. The test itself consisted in the use of a number code, in which the digits were translated into letters to make words. Comprehensibility was tested by selected paragraphs in which the words were written in code.

Feeling tone and mental fatigue. A typical investigation of mental fatigue[19] was that on the loss in work output developing in four tasks, *viz.*, addition, sentence completion, taking intelligence tests, and judging compositions. Subjective reports were taken every 20 minutes during a 5½-hour work period. Seven degrees of feeling tone, from "extremely good" to "extremely tired," were used for the subjective scale. Plots showed that feeling tone declined continuously from the outset in all the tasks, whereas output was maintained in two, fell in one, and rose in the other. The highest degree of correspondence came in the fact that those individuals reporting the greatest change in feeling tone tended to show the greatest loss in output. In other ways, no relation was obvious. The fact that what one individual called "extremely tired" possibly compared with what another designated as "moderately tired" precluded simple interpretation.

One person quits possibly when he is not extremely tired, or another one shows greater decrement in work output when he is moderately tired than a third individual does when extremely tired. To some, this would seem to be not only disappointing, but also a reason for abandoning the use of any subjective measure at all.

Blocking in mental function. A phenomenon called "blocking" has often been observed in the course of so-called mental performance. A subject may pause for an unusual length of time before giving a response, or may interject an interval of no response in the middle of a response series. If asked to describe his experiences, the subject may report that he

[19] Poffenberger, A. T.: The Effects of Continuous Work upon Output and Feelings, *J. Appl. Psychol., 12:* 459–467, 1928.

underwent a "blank period" when nothing seemed to occur and no progress was made toward a response. The term blocking has been used to label both the pause in performance and the experience associated with it.

Blocking has frequently been attributed to fatigue, or even taken as an example of fatigue. Since fatigue in these cases has included both what we would call impairment and physiological disorganization, the pause in performance has been imputed to something physiological. Those who have used blocking as an example of fatigue have done so under a definition of fatigue which excludes the personal or subjective.

Blocking may occur preceding the response to a single stimulus situation, or in the midst of responses to a series of stimuli. Since it is easier to demonstrate and measure blocking in the second case, a series of responses have most often been chosen for the study of blocking in psychological experiments. From the methods used, more limited definitions of blocking are possible.

Bills[20] in 1931 reported the results of his study on blocking in a series of "mental" tasks. He arbitrarily defined a block "for the sake of uniformity" as "a pause in the responses equivalent to the time of two or more average responses." The use of such a definition, he states, made an adjustment of the criterion relative to the speed of the subject possible.

The mental tasks chosen by Bills were (1) alternate addition and subtraction, (2) reversible perspective, (3) color naming, (4) giving opposites, and (5) making substitutions. These tasks were chosen not only because they were considered mental, but also because each was homogeneous in nature and involved simple, frequent, and easily recordable responses.

Bills found that blocks occupying the time taken for two to six responses occurred on the average at about three per minute, although there was decided individual difference in frequency. He also found that practice on each of the tasks diminished both the duration and frequency of the blocks. Fatigue tended to increase the duration and frequency of blocks. A fatigued subject showed a greater irregularity in the succession of responses but no decrease in the number of responses per minute for periods as long as 1 hour. The responses between actual blocks did not occur at a uniform rate, but tended to bunch toward the mid-period. Bills observed that fatigue exaggerated the bunching. Individuals giving a rapid series of responses tended to have fewer and shorter blocks than did others. As a final result, Bills reports that errors were consistently found in con-

20 Bills, A. G.: Blocking: A New Principle of Mental Fatigue, *Am. J. Psychol.,* *43:* 230–245, 1931.

junction with blocks, which suggested to him that the basis for the errors lies in a recurrent poor neural functioning disclosed by the blocks themselves.

Bills suggested that blocking might well be expected from the cumulative refractory period reported by Forbes and Rice.[21] Barmack[22] poses five objections to Bills's use of refractoriness to explain blocking. (1) There is a discrepancy between the temporal magnitude of prolonged refractoriness and the length of an average mental block. In this connection, Barmack furthermore states that Bills misinterpreted the finding of Forbes and Rice, in which diminished response of nerves stimulated at high frequencies was taken to be due to accumulated refractoriness. (2) Repetitive stimulation of nerve groups is more likely to affect the synapses between elements than the participating elements themselves. (3) The refractory-phase theory raises puzzling theoretical problems. (4) Certain facts would suggest that motivation is a contributory component in the occurrence of mental blocks. (5) The refractory-phase theory fails to account for well-known shifts in feeling tone commonly characterizing extended repetitive work.

Barmack offers his own explanation of mental blocks. In his view, they are motivated changes of attention away from work and act as an "anti-hypnotic" and a natural means of retreating from an unpleasant task.

Bills tested the blocking rhythm for relation to the Traube-Hering wave, and to breathing rate, but could find no relation. Bills believes that the blocks explain why work decrement was not found as expected in many studies of mental activity. He believes the blocks offered rest periods to maintain average efficiency despite the changes produced by fatigue in the nervous system.

It is interesting to note that the injection of pauses[23] obliterated blocks, when the pauses were of the proper size and distribution. Bills's method was first to find the average number of blocks per minute and their average duration for each person when performing at his greatest automatic speed in form and color naming. The exposure apparatus was made to present colors or forms at the speed just determined and to introduce pauses equal to the average block frequencies. As a result, blocks almost completely disappeared. From this, Bills concluded that the artificial pauses fulfilled the same function as he attributed to the natural ones, viz., that of rest. Since "rest periods" were introduced, no blocks needed to occur.

The results that Bills obtained do not necessarily indicate that the

[21] Forbes, A., and L. H. Rice: Fatigue in Peripheral Nerve, *Am. J. Physiol., 90:* 119–145, 1929.
[22] Barmack, *op. cit.*
[23] Bills, A. G.: Fatigue, Oscillation and Blocks, *J. Exper. Psychol., 18:* 562–573, 1935.

blocking periods are rest periods. We must recognize first of all that the relation of nervous activity to overt activity is not so simple as is sometimes thought. Blocking may only be a symptom of rhythmic change in the *way* the nervous system acts, and not a sign of periodic *action* and *rest*.[24] In fact the term blocking signifies action rather than rest. In order for a result to be blocked, a kind of activity must exist as an interference. The collateral symptoms surrounding the performance tested suggest that the individual is not necessarily inactive but rather in a "clinch" at the moments of blocking. Blocking would seem to represent a type of momentarily unfruitful organization of activity.

Blocking and rate of work are related. For example, Bills and Shapin[25] showed that fatigue, as evidenced by frequency and duration of blocks and frequency of errors, increased progressively as higher and higher speeds of response (color naming) were required. A point of breakdown was reached at about 130 vocal responses per minute and 110 manual responses per minute. When the very high rates are imposed by the task, almost continued blocking, or random naming without relevance to the stimuli, occurs.

Results also differ when "paced" performance is compared with "unpaced." Paced performance provides for greater speed, at least throughout short periods. In longer periods, less fatigue (same criteria as above) developed in paced performance than in unpaced. This was taken by Bills and Shapin to suggest that decrement in unpaced performance accrued from a deterioration in the regulatory mechanisms usually spoken of as volitional control, and not in those "stimulus-response" processes which seemed well able to continue to function. They also pointed out that they were not able to tell to what degree the benefit of pacing came from the regularity of the imposed rhythm and what was due to the effect of the external excitement itself.

The relation of loss of sleep and blocking was studied by Warren and Clark.[26] Each of four persons was tested at 10-hour intervals. In color naming and in addition and subtraction, increase in the number of blocks reached a maximum after 48 hours of wakefulness, while the average time of response remained almost constant. Blocks in tapping showed no significant change in frequency during loss of sleep.

[24] Bartley, S. H.: The Relation between Cortical Response to Visual Stimulation and Changes in the Alpha Rhythm, *J. Exper. Psychol.*, 27: 624–639, 1940.

[25] Bills, A. G., and M. J. Shapin: Mental Fatigue under Automatically Controlled Rates of Work, *J. Gen. Psychol.*, 15: 335–347, 1936.

[26] Warren, N., and B. Clark: Blocking in Mental and Motor Tasks during a 65 Hour Vigil, *Psychol. Bull.*, 33: 814–815, 1936.

Bills[27] reports a resemblance between the results of fatigue (continuous work) and those produced by anoxemia. One-hour sessions, in which the oxygen content varied from 12 to 9 per cent, were used to produce anoxemia. Certain frequency and duration features of blocking were taken as indications of fatigue.

In 1935, Bills[28] came to the conclusion that certain of his findings on blocking could be described in terms of two oscillation rates in the nervous system. Thirty-five persons were employed at color naming and form naming for periods of 30 minutes. Continuous responding was required in each test period. Two types of response, vocal and manual, were used, the latter consisting in pressing appropriate keys. The data were put through three kinds of graphical analysis: (1) frequency polygons for each duration of reaction, (2) frequency polygons for each interblock interval, and (3) graphs showing successive interblock intervals plotted against their duration.

The first kind of analysis disclosed two discrete modes, one of normal reaction times, the other of blocks, practically devoid of overlap. The second analysis revealed whether length of interval between blocks was typical or varied in chance fashion. Periodicity in block occurrence, if present, should appear in a high frequency of occurrence of some interblock interval and cluster about this as a mode. If more than a single modal interval existed, more than one periodicity would be evident. The third kind of analysis was used to determine any possible tendency for long interblock intervals to recur periodically.

From the data, Bills came to the conclusion that there are at least two periodicities involved and that these represent *amount* rather than *time* (rate) rhythms. Although he speaks of amount in terms of energy, it is possible to think of the amount in terms of number of processes occurring and that these constitute not so much an *amount* as a pattern of performance, which by virtue of its nature runs into a tangle and has to work into free action again. It is difficult to think of energy, as such, acting as the limiting factor. Two individuals, for example, are not to be distinguished so markedly by the relative *amounts* of energy consumed as by the patterns in which the energy is structured.

The fact that the administration of extra oxygen induces some recovery from "mental fatigue" indicates that some impairment is probably induced by tasks of the sort tested. Bills[29] reported that breathing pure oxy-

[27] Bills, A. G.: A Comparative Study of Mental Fatigue and Anoxemia, *Psychol. Bull., 33:* 814, 1936.

[28] Bills, A. G.: Fatigue, Oscillation and Blocks, *J. Exper. Psychol., 18:* 562–573, 1935.

[29] Bills, A. G.: The Role of Oxygen in Recovery from Mental Fatigue, *Psychol. Bull., 34:* 729, 1937.

gen caused some recovery in performance. He found, however, that the best combination was 50 per cent pure oxygen, 3 per cent carbon dioxide, and 47 per cent air, in his color-naming experiments.

Distraction.   In the course of experimentation on mental activity, the term "distraction" arose as a label for the effect of certain factors that were introduced to influence performance. As ordinarily defined, distracting is the process of diverting and confusing. Distraction redirects attention in any one of a number of ways. The problem of what is required to induce distraction has been long unsolved. In the history of the application of the term, it was considered that some external event, some feature of the surroundings, was responsible.

A distraction method was originally proposed for studying the degree of attention. But since no satisfactory distractors were ever arrived at, the method was doomed to failure. Distraction methods were next used in reaction-time experiments in which performance rather than attention was the primary interest. Here the results from the use of the method were so highly divergent that it was eventually abandoned, only to be taken up later in other fields. Unfortunately in work on mental efficiency, the whole concept of distraction was accepted rather uncritically and used loosely in interpreting performance. The basic theoretical considerations involved in the concept of distraction have, throughout the course of its use, received all too little attention. Certainly no set relation between any external event and the behavior of the organism, whether considered from the overt standpoint or from the experiential, can exist. Consequently, seizing upon any external event as a distractor is unjustified.

Certain investigators have given recognition to the fact that the relation between stimulus and output is not fixed. In 1932, Dulsky[30] suggested that a distractor be defined as a stimulus having a detrimental influence on efficiency of performance. Such a definition makes "distractor" a mere label for a certain external influence which, in a given instance, appeared to reduce efficiency. It has no end product like distraction, and is thus no more than a taxonomic device, but as such it does do away with the frequently encountered distractor which does not distract. Definitions of this sort are of little theoretical value to biology or psychology, since they deliberately omit all reference to the organism.

The unraveling of the distraction process involves some of the same difficulties inherent in dealing with concepts of fatigue, pain, joy, boredom, etc. Terms of this sort must be defined from the vantage point of the individual. It should be recognized that terms like distraction all imply an organism *acting*. The first problem in each case is not to make a con-

30 Dulsky, S. G.: What Is a Distractor? *Psychol. Rev., 39:* 590–592, 1932.

nection between the physical world and the behavior of the organism, but to understand the ways in which the organism can behave.

Various effects of distractors on performance have been reported in the literature. So-called distraction has not always been found to interfere with performance but is frequently said to have no effect on or even to improve it. Some writers[31] have concluded that distraction, in bettering performance, is a spur to attention.

Hovey[32] attempted to discover the effects of "general distraction on the higher thought processes" by administering a mental test to a group of college students under standard and under "severe general distraction" conditions. He concludes as follows: (1) The higher mental processes are little impeded by distraction. (2) Intelligence is unrelated to distraction susceptibility. (3) There are no individual differences in susceptibility to distraction. (4) A true measure of intelligence is less well approximated under standard than under distraction conditions.

Tinker[33] administered an intelligence test to 56 college students, under standard conditions and under conditions where two bells rang intermittently. His results were as follows: (1) Average performance was not hindered. (2) The better students were more hindered than the poorer students. (3) There was less dispersion under distraction conditions.

Some time ago, Dockeray,[34] as a result of his experiments on sound discrimination where auditory stimuli and electric shock served as distractors, claimed there were marked individual differences in the ability to resist distractions and fatigue.

Certain workers have noted the importance of the observer's attitude. Cassel and Dallenbach,[35] in a study of the effect of auditory distraction, found that the simple sensory reaction was (1) inhibited, (2) lengthened, or (3) facilitated, depending upon the attitude of the observer. More recently, Baker,[36] adopting Dulsky's definition of a distractor, studied

[31] Tanner, A., and K. Anderson: Simultaneous Sense Stimulations, *Psychol. Rev., 3:* 378–383, 1896.

Tinker, M. A.: A Study of the Relation of Distracted Motor Performance to Performance in an Intelligence Test, *Am. J. Psychol., 33:* 578–583, 1922.

[32] Hovey, H. B.: Effects of General Distraction on the Higher Thought Processes, *Am. J. Psychol., 40:* 585–591, 1928.

[33] Tinker, M. A.: Intelligence in an Intelligence Test with an Auditory Distractor, *Am. J. Psychol., 36:* 467–468, 1925.

[34] Dockeray, F. C.: Attention, Distraction, and Fatigue, *J. Comp. Physiol., 2:* 331–370, 1922.

[35] Cassel, E. E., and K. M. Dallenbach: The Effect of Auditory Distraction upon the Sensory Reaction, *Am. J. Psychol., 29:* 129–143, 1918.

[36] Baker, K. H.: Pre-experimental Set in Distraction Experiments, *J. Gen. Psychol., 16:* 471–488, 1937.

the effects of "preexperimental set" in distraction experiments. He concluded that attitude is an important factor in determining performance in a distraction experiment. He obtained equivocal results with a group of subjects who did not have a "prepared" attitude. Baker includes in his paper some good criticism of the work that has been done on distraction. Perhaps the greatest fault, he says, lies in the fact that the subject is aware of the nature of the experiment. He points out also that experimenters have failed to distinguish between "simple distraction of attention and 'startle.'" Baker also recognizes the fallacy in interpreting the findings as results of a particular stimulus (distractor). He notes a number of additional factors that may serve as sources of distraction. One of the purposes of his study was to demonstrate the importance of one of these uncontrolled variables, the subject's attitude toward the specific task at hand.

Morgan,[37] a number of years ago, studied the effect of distractions on response to visually exposed material in a room free of uncontrolled disturbances. The task material was sufficiently varied so that the individual was unable to memorize it. Reaction times of responses and the pressure of the fingers on the keys were recorded. Breathing records were also taken. Distractions consisted in such sudden sounds as those of an 8-in. gong 8 ft. behind the subject and bell mechanisms whose clappers struck against a resonance box, a metal beam running the length of the room, and the subjects' tables. Phonograph records of vocal solos, orchestra pieces, and vocal dialogues were also used.

Morgan's findings were as follows: (1) The first effect of noise was to slow down the rate of work. (2) After the initial retardation, work rate tended to increase and even to exceed the original. (3) Additional effort was used to overcome the effects of the sounds, as evidenced by extra pressure on the keys. This persisted quite uniformly throughout the distraction period. (4) Articulation (speech) was used to compensate for the noise, so that finally the extent to which this device was employed was a better measure of the effect of the noises than the time record. (5) In cases in which quantitative comparisons were possible, changes in the apparent expenditure of effort were much greater than fluctuations in rate of doing work. As conditions varied, the individual tended to compensate by changes in amount of effort used, keeping rate constant. (6) Finally, any objective or imaginal change in the "resistance" offered against the preservation of particular alignment induced overt behavior changes taken to be indicative of increased energy output.

Morgan's findings support the idea that the individual resists those in-

[37] Morgan, J. J. B.: The Overcoming of Distraction and Other Resistances, *Arch. Psychol., N. Y., 35:* 1–84, 1916.

fluences which tend to interfere with the maintenance of a set or alignment toward a task. Part of this resistance flows into useful channels and part into wasteful ones. Muscular tonus is heightened, part of which is effective in the maintenance of the set, while part may represent overaction. It may induce consequences that eventually thwart the maintenance of the set needed to continue the work. Distractions come to involve musculature in an unmaintainable pattern. Consequently, becoming cognizant of the change, the individual experiences a letdown, and this becomes a part of the fatigue picture.

Frequently after continuous occupation with an intellectual task, an individual becomes more distractible, *i.e.,* more sensitive to a variety of influences foreign to the activity in progress. To attribute this change to fatigue or impairment is quite customary, whereas to assign it to principles inherent in activity itself is quite unusual. Frequent observations of what are apparently repetitive items of activity have possibly masked the features of constant change.

Boredom. Although in everyday use "boredom" refers to the feelings of the individual, while "monotony" refers to the individual's estimate of his surroundings, these terms are often used interchangeably, particularly in industrial studies. Naïvely, one might assume that monotony results in boredom, yet phrases such as "feelings of monotony" are not uncommonly encountered in the literature. Fatigue is sometimes confused with boredom and monotony, making the situation even more troublesome.

Barmack[38] wishes to distinguish between *feelings* of monotony or boredom and an *attitude* of boredom. The former are said to be the appreciation of dullness, sleepiness, and "pseudo-fatigue" coming from depressed or otherwise inadequate vital activity. Depressed activity, he says, may be caused, in part, by an attitude of boredom or decreased effectiveness of some motive. Barmack defines an attitude of boredom as a state in which inadequate motivation and inclination to get away from a situation conflict with inclination to continue. He states that the inclination to get away from the present situation results because the individual feels physiologically inadequate, or because physiological adequacy is maintained with considerable effort, or because discomforts are more intensely sensed. How "inadequate motivation" and the inclination to continue oppose each other is not made clear.

Barmack states that the physiological feature of the situation arises out of the functional relationship of what he designates as "primary" and

[38] Barmack, J. E.: Boredom and Other Factors in the Physiology of Mental Effort, *Arch. Psychol., N. Y.,* No. 218, 1937. Pp. 83.

"accessory" organs. The primary organs are such structures as muscles, nervous system, and receptors. The accessory include endocrine glands and the alimentary, vascular, and respiratory systems. In adequate functioning, the activity of the accessory organs must meet the needs of the primary. For example, respiration must meet the demands of the muscles, or else muscular activity must decrease. Feelings of fatigue are said to be associated with insufficient or depressed accessory activity, whereas euphoria arises in connection with accessory activity above the primary organ demands. The relation of the activities of the two classes of organ to each other is said to be the basis for the feelings evoked.

Various other concepts of boredom exist. One of the older ideas was that proffered by Münsterberg, who held that boredom is a type of revolt against uniformity.

Others[39] have utilized the term in connection with the factor of distraction. Dissatisfaction is set up by the condition that necessitates increased effort to compensate for distractions. Spontaneous alignment with the task gives way to a kind of behavior whose conscious component is the feeling of effort. Action that is required by the task may be replaced periodically by spontaneous types of activity.

McDowall and Wells[40] have made observations on the relation between the attitude they label boredom and the vasomotor adjustments involved. Those situations, which usually call for vascular adjustments, fail to evoke them when personal interest and enthusiasm are lacking. Situations that evoke certain vascular adjustments to begin with do not maintain them when interest flags. Fatigue, as an assumed direct result of prolonged activity, is not responsible for the outcome in such cases. Rather, the feelings that arise are associated with the disappearance of the specific bodily adjustments.

They state that "feelings of monotony" and relaxation of vascular adjustment (to meet the needs of posture, exertion, etc.) go hand in hand. As the situation continues, the feelings of boredom increase from the sense of bodily inadequacy that arises out of the vascular failure. If feelings and bodily changes go practically hand in hand, then when the individual is disinterested in certain situations he could be expected to make only slight and therefore inadequate bodily adjustments. Disinterest may accumulate from occasion to occasion, until the individual becomes unable to do what he seemed originally well capable of doing. In athletics, for

[39] Poffenberger, A. T.: "Principles of Applied Psychology," D. Appleton-Century Company, Inc., New York, 1942. Pp. 655.

[40] McDowall, R. J. S., and H. M. Wells: The Physiology of Monotony, *Brit. Med. J.*, *1:* 414–415, 1927.

example, there is a condition called *staleness,* and the authors apply their concepts to account for it.

According to this view, monotony is a state in which the experience comes from the individual's unwitting assessment of his own inadequacy. This in turn seems to be transmuted to the task or other object of attention, becoming a quality of it. Thus we might deduce that if the same failure of bodily adjustment accrued in highly varied work it would not be the quality of sameness that would be held responsible, but rather the quality of tediousness. The important role of bodily components of the organism, which is usually overlooked, is emphasized by McDowall and Wells. Their view is in contrast to those which depend solely on the characteristics of the task to explain boredom and monotony.

Various other views regarding boredom have been expressed. Wyatt, Fraser, and Stock[41] lay boredom to improper motivation, and Winkler[42] to those moments when tasks at hand are occupying only a part of one's attention.

In many of the cases in which the attempt is made to account for boredom, it turns out that the very thing to be explained is employed as the "cause." The factors used to explain boredom are those existing only after boredom has developed, and thus boredom is a necessary condition for the factors mentioned. This applies very well to Winkler's explanation. It must be recognized that what is needed is not so much a direct causal explanation, as a description of the full group of concomitants in the case, representing the organism's characteristics at the moment.

Bills[43] avoids the terms boredom and monotony. Instead, in dealing with the characteristics of fatiguing work, he employs the terms continuity, sameness, conflict, unfamiliarity, satiation, and meaninglessness. Sameness, which might be a synonym of monotonousness, is said to be a quality of those tasks which involve repeating either one or more operations over and over again. Bills discusses satiation and meaninglessness together, since he believes that they are probably two terms relating to the same thing. He alludes to the claim of that German school of psychology which holds that individuals always respond to meaningful wholes, and not to their parts. Tensions exist during the attempt to complete a task, and action stops when the objective has been accomplished. Satiation is said to arise when a unit of work is completed and is then a term used to label "closure."

[41] Wyatt, S., J. A. Fraser, and F. G. L. Stock: The Effects of Monotony on Work, Industrial Fatigue Research Board, Rept. 56, 1929.

[42] Winkler, H.: Die Monotonie der Arbeit, *Z. angew. Psychol., 20:* 46–88, 1922.

[43] Bills, A. G.: "The Psychology of Efficiency," Harper & Brothers, New York, 1932. Pp. 361.

Moore[44] attempts to differentiate between fatigue and boredom. He lists four general groupings of contrasts between the two, and from these it is apparent that, for the most part, he identifies fatigue with what we call impairment and boredom with what we call fatigue. The fact that this does not represent a mere shift of terms needs emphasis. The following table will illustrate the general trends of his differentiation. This list reveals a tacit distinction between mental and physiological, or mind and body.

Fatigue	*Boredom*
Physiological depletion	Mental dullness
Diminished capacity for work	Diminished interest
Conscious inability	Feeling of incapacity (Possible lack of physiological basis)
Gradual work decrement	Irregularity of rate of work
Rate drop during work day	Same during day
Task beyond capacity of worker due to exhaustive character of work	Feels capacity beyond demands of task; consciousness of uniformity or monotony of work; temperamental incapacity
Derived from expenditure of "considerable proportion" of energy	Derived from feeling inferior or superior to job—thus compensating
Measurable	Subjective—defies measurement
Definite physiological accompaniments	Mental and emotional accompaniments
Urge for rest	Urge for change

Boredom, monotony, and fatigue, when properly used, are surely not synonymous terms. Monotony, indeed, does not belong in biological or psychological classifications directly descriptive of the organism, but is rather a term to label the individual's perception of his surroundings. As often used, monotony refers either to boredom or to some supposedly intrinsic property of a situation external to the individual. In the latter connection it has been used in adjective form, *e.g.*, a monotonous sound, and in noun form, monotony, to label a mere abstraction. The former use is direct and pertains to perception; the latter is less direct and pertains to ideation.

[44] Moore, H.: "Psychology for Business and Industry," McGraw-Hill Book Company, Inc., New York, 1939. Pp. 527.

If it is recognized that monotony is an imputed property of the surroundings, it cannot at the same time be used to label an attitude toward the surroundings. Furthermore, if all properties of the surroundings are man-made (imputed) rather than intrinsic, then monotony can imply no fixed relation between situation and experience. What is monotonous for one may not be for another. Monotony, while it pertains to perception, does not represent a personal stance and is not a personal term. Consequently, it may at this point be eliminated from our discussion.

The problem of distinguishing between boredom and fatigue is a more difficult one. Part of this difficulty lies in the use of language. The identical experience might be described by one person as boredom, by another as fatigue. Further difficulty lies in that nature of human functioning and behavior. The fluidity of such functioning makes rigid lines of demarcation between similar patterns impossible.

Both boredom and fatigue are stances taken by the individual to situations that he confronts. The general character of these two stances is negative and somewhat passive, as opposed to more positive and active stances such as euphoria or a "feeling of well-being." In a broad biological framework, boredom and fatigue might be said to belong to a larger stance whose main characteristics are negativity and passivity. Of the two terms, fatigue is clearly the more inclusive, and while it might be maintained that boredom is a part of the general fatigue stance, the reverse proposition would be rather ridiculous. Certainly boredom and fatigue may well exist in the same person at the same time. It is difficult to be sure whether either can exist without some small amount of the other.

Boredom or ennui is generally characterized by such terms as dissatisfaction, satiety, disinterest, and irksomeness. The general terms describing fatigue are aversion, lassitude, weariness, impotence, and inability.

In boredom the unpleasant feelings are thought to arise from the surroundings. Fatigue, on the other hand, is felt to be more intimately a part of the person. Its emphasis is on the individual's bodily or personal state rather than on external factors. Fatigue is more circumscribing. The bored individual is likely to feel that he will automatically overcome his unpleasant feelings when he escapes the external situation. On the other hand, the fatigued person, so long as he is fatigued, feels aversion to facing any situation, since he believes that his unpleasant feelings arise within himself, as a result of his own incapabilities. Fatigue is taken to be less transient than boredom. The fatigued individual is likely to take his condition more seriously than does the bored one, because he anticipates no immediate escape from the fatigue.

Chapter XVI

PERSONAL FACTORS IN THE WORK SITUATION

IN THE PREVIOUS chapter on industrial fatigue the physical conditions involved in daily work were discussed. Such items as hours of work, rest periods, lighting, ventilation, and posture were dealt with one by one, with work output as the criterion by which the individual was gauged. Since industry is concerned primarily with work output, it might seem that such studies rightly cover the full scope of industry's concerns. It must be recognized, however, that the consideration of such matters constitutes but one possible way of dealing with the fatigue problem. And if it is admitted that fatigue bears more broadly upon the worker and work situation than can be measured in gross studies on work output, then other possible ways of dealing with fatigue are also pertinent to industry.

Every treatise on industrial psychology seems to contain a sizable section on "morale" of the worker. Whereas many admit that conflicts lower morale and thus decrease work output, the subjective factors are treated fairly separately from those bearing on fatigue or on work conditions. Discussions of fatigue and of morale have little in common, although there is some recognition that a person with low morale and poor motivation tires more easily.

In the previous chapter, the necessity of recognizing the personal factors already came to light. It was apparent in nearly all the studies that were discussed. This chapter will first present and discuss an example of the type of study that demonstrates the importance of individual alignments. Following this the fatigue problem from the point of view of the worker himself will be discussed. His attitude toward his job situation, what he expects to obtain from work, and how he expects to be treated will be included. A theoretical discussion of what jobs essentially require of the individual will follow.

THE HAWTHORNE STUDY

In recent years, industry has been forced to recognize that personal alignment factors have an influence on the quantity and quality of the work done. The results of studies that supposedly were to deal with the effects of changed external conditions could be interpreted only as dealing with more personal changes. The measure of work output that was obtained was in some cases obviously due more to psychological changes in the workers than it was a result of altered physical conditions. For this reason, studies that were originally aimed at external conditions of work provide part of our evidence for the great significance of the personal factors in the work situation.

The prime example of a study that indicates changes in the workers' alignments as measured by work output is one performed at the Hawthorne plant of the Western Electric Company in collaboration with the National Research Council.[1] A part of this study will be described in some detail, and certain of the conclusions discussed.

The original aim of the Hawthorne study was to determine the relation of the intensity of illumination to changes in work output. The results of the initial experiments, which were simply contrived, revealed no obvious relationship between work output and illumination. It was concluded that the lack of apparent relationship was due to a failure to control other variables, notably psychological variables, which were also effective in determining work output. Unfortunately, although psychological variables were conceded to be present, their importance was underestimated. The personal factors were taken to be disturbing influences rather than an integral part of the work situation. The effort was made to eliminate them from the experiment, rather than to study them directly. It was thought that the psychological variables would eventually become ineffective in a setup where a few workers were isolated and prevailed upon to cooperate in the study. The hope was that any changes in work output would then be the direct result of the changes that were introduced in the external conditions. By now the management had lost interest in the illumination studies and had turned to the effect of hours of work, rest periods, etc., on efficiency as measured by work output.

In line with this, six girls, whose job consisted of assembling telephone relays, were chosen as average workers for the study. These operators worked in a small test room, and a careful record was kept of their work output. Periodical physical examinations were given the subjects. A number of other records were kept, including a log of hour-by-hour events in the test room. A "test-room observer," always present in the room, kept the log, arranged the work, and maintained a cooperative spirit among the operators. The girls were instructed not to hurry, but to work at a com-

[1] Committee on Work in Industry of the National Research Council, "Fatigue of Workers—Its Relation to Industrial Production," pp. 56–99, Reinhold Publishing Corporation, New York, 1941. Pp. 165.

fortable pace. At the beginning and at intervals during the experiment, the girls were invited to participate in conferences on the experiment which were held in the superintendent's office. Their reactions to all suggested changes were encouraged.

The first part of the experiment, which lasted over a year, was divided into a number of "experimental periods" each lasting several weeks. A variety of changes in the work conditions were introduced. Among these were rest periods of different lengths and frequencies, work stopping half an hour and an hour earlier, a 5-day week, etc. A number of control periods were also used.

The results of this experiment were striking. Regardless of what the changes in the external conditions were, the work-output curve showed in general a slow, steady rise throughout the course of the year. In each experimental period, the work output was higher than in the preceding one.[2] Obviously some factor other than the changed working conditions was operating. The efficiency of the workers was so affected by the personal factors that any effects of the working conditions themselves were almost totally masked. The statements of the subjects themselves corroborate such an interpretation. All the physical changes that were introduced had a favorable *social* significance. Each girl by her own report felt freer in in her work and working relationships and enjoyed working in the test room. The entire industrial situation had become changed.

It had been hoped that the systematic changes that were introduced in the working situation would throw some light on fatigue in workers. Had the study been specifically directed on fatigue as an experience, more definite insight could have been gained. As it was, the results merely showed that work output was not closely related to the changes in conditions that were introduced. The fact that work output rose steadily, regardless of altered conditions, gave the investigators little chance to observe fatigue. Although no literal subjective reports were given, it seems reasonable to assume that the girls felt consistently less tired in the test room than they had previously in the regular shop. From this it might be concluded that when fatigue develops it must arise from something in accordance with the outlook of the individual.

WHAT WORKERS EXPECT IN THEIR JOBS

Any work situation is a *personal* one. All human life is personal, and it cannot be too strongly emphasized that the work situation and its consequent output has a personal character. The worker cannot depersonalize himself, nor can he be depersonalized by standardized arrangements pertaining to him. Before fatigue can be fully understood and measures taken

[2] The experiment was continued for a number of years. During the latter part, the work-output curve continued to ascend until it was maintained at a high plateau.

RELATIVE IMPORTANCE OF 28 FACTORS TO THE NONSELLING EMPLOYEES OF A LARGE
MERCHANDIZING ORGANIZATION*

Factors	Rank
Receiving help necessary to get results expected by management	1
Being encouraged to offer suggestions and try out better methods	2
Being able to find out whether work is improving	3
Reasonable certainty of being able to get fair hearing and square deal in case of grievance	4
Certainty of promotions going to best qualified employees	5
Encouragement to seek advice in case of real problems	6
Being given information about important plans and results which concern the individual's work	7
Being given reasons for changes which are ordered in work	8
Not being actually hampered in work by superior	9
Not getting contradictory or conflicting orders	10
Being given to understand completely the results which are expected in a job	11
Pay—*assurance of increases when deserved*	12
Being invited to offer suggestions when new plans are being considered	13
Feeling that the superior understands all about the difficulties of the individual's job	14
Being given to understand completely the general methods which the superior wants followed	15
Complete definition of duties	16
Not being responsible to too many superiors	17
Knowledge of other jobs in the organization which the individual feels capable of handling and would prefer	18
Knowledge of other jobs preferred, even at same pay	19
Red tape in the organization, preventing best work	20
Pay—*compared to that of other jobs of equal importance in the organization*	21
Pay—*compared to that of similar work in other organizations*	22
Treatment when being employed	23
Knowledge of lines of promotion	24
Value of Mutual Benefit Association	25
Being permitted to make important decisions in work	26
Regularity of amount of work	27
Service of Medical Department	28

* Reprinted by permission, from J. Tiffin, "Industrial Psychology," p. 315, Prentice-Hall, Inc. New York.

for its alleviation, some idea of what workers want and what they wish to avoid must be obtained.

If the daily job situation contains many elements that are distinctly distasteful to the worker and that he wishes to avoid but feels he cannot, it is not surprising that he becomes unfit for his task. The attention and energy used to resolve major or constantly recurring conflicts cannot be used for useful work. The personal organization required of the individual for bracing himself against unpleasant features of the work situation is an entirely different one from that required for full application to the task. The failure to realize the full *personal* nature of the work situation may be a remnant of a time when work was seen as something that accrued from a moral imperative rather than from a set of psychological conditions.

Various attempts have been made to find out the rank order value of different personal items that enter into a common work situation.

The chart on page 327 is an example of the results of one study that was made on the non-sales force of a large mercantile concern.[3]

The order of the items in the list denotes the order of importance for most of the employees. It will be seen that wage is not the initial consideration. The worker wants those conditions to exist which will expedite production. Those items which have to do with fair play are very high on the list, as are also those features which represent freedom from inconsistency and contradiction. The highest rankings are given to those items which when analyzed indicate an absence of conflicts and contradictions.

PERCENTAGE OF UNION AND NONUNION EMPLOYEES WHO CONSIDERED THE LISTED ITEMS AS "MOST IMPORTANT" AMONG FACTORS RELATED TO THEIR JOBS *

Item	Per cent of union employees checking item as "most important"	Rank of item	Per cent of nonunion employees checking item as "most important"	Rank of item
1. Employee stock subscription..............	5	11.5	2	13.5
2. Voice or share in management..............	13	9.5	6	11.0
3. Fair adjustment of grievances..............	80	1.0	24	7.0
4. Chance of promotion.....	28	6.0	47	3.0
5. Steady employment......	65	2.0	93	1.0
6. Medical and dental service	0	13.5	6	11.0
7. Safety.................	57	3.0	21	9.0
8. Amount of pay..........	49	4.5	51	2.0
9. Working conditions......	49	4.5	45	4.0
10. Hours of work..........	13	9.5	23	8.0
11. Type of man in charge...	18	7.5	38	5.0
12. Methods of pay.........	0	13.5	2	13.5
13. Insurance systems and pensions..............	18	7.5	36	6.0
14. Chance to show initiative.	5	11.5	6	11.0

* Reprinted by permission, from J. Tiffin, "Industrial Psychology," p. 316, Prentice-Hall, Inc. New York.

[3] Houser, J. D.: "What People Want from Business," McGraw-Hill Book Company, Inc., New York, 1938. Pp. 250.

It is not at all certain that human beings really know what they want as clearly and accurately as it is often assumed. Tiffin[4] points out that many individuals do not know what is required to make their jobs satisfactory.

Hersey[5] found a somewhat different line-up of values in his study of union vs. nonunion workers, as indicated in the table on page 328.

This table indicates that among the nonunion employees steady employment rated highest while among union men fair adjustment of grievances counted most.

Somewhat more generalized items were ranked in another study.[6] Of these, steady work was given first place, as is shown in the following table.

RANKING OF TEN ITEMS IN ORDER OF IMPORTANCE BY
325 FACTORY WORKERS*

Factor	Rank
Steady work	1
Comfortable working conditions	2
Good working companions	3
Good boss	4
Opportunity for advancement	5
High pay	6
Opportunity to use your ideas	7
Opportunity to learn a job	8
Good hours	9
Easy work	10

* Reprinted by permission, from J. Tiffin, "Industrial Psychology," p. 316, Prentice-Hall, Inc. New York.

Further considerations of the matter of attitude toward working conditions and morale is to be found in such works as Tiffin,[7] Viteles,[8] Burtt,[9] and Poffenberger.[10]

CLASSIFICATION OF WORK EFFECTS:
WHAT DO JOBS REQUIRE OF THE INDIVIDUAL?

Work can be classified in terms of the specific performance (skill) and intelligence required to accomplish it, or else in terms of the processes brought about in the individual. These include motivation, aversion, etc.

4 Tiffin, J.: "Industrial Psychology," Prentice-Hall, Inc., New York, 1942. Pp. 386.

5 Hersey, R. B.: Psychology of Workers, *Personnel J.*, *14:* 291–296, 1936.

6 Wyatt, S., J. N. Langdon, and F. G. L. Stock: Fatigue and Boredom in Repetitive Work, Industrial Health Research Board, Rept. 77, 1937.

7 Tiffin, *op. cit.*

8 Viteles, M. S.: "Industrial Psychology," W. W. Norton & Company, Inc., New York, 1932. Pp. 652.

9 Burtt, H. E.: "Psychology and Industrial Efficiency," D. Appleton and Company, Inc., New York, 1929. Pp. 395.

10 Poffenberger, A. T.: "Principles of Applied Psychology," D. Appleton-Century Company, Inc., New York, 1942. Pp. 655.

No job is fully defined in terms of a single factor, but if the relation of fatigue to the several kinds of processes is determined, the procedure ought to yield a comprehensive understanding of fatigue. Accordingly, a listing of the possible kinds of crucial demands found in the workaday world is given below. To the degree that these demands are aptly described, we have a list of the possible kinds of situations individuals are called upon to face, not in terms of specific work operations, but in terms of what the situation and doing of the work mean to the workers.

Kinds of work[11] in terms of their effects and requirements are as follows.

1. Expenditure of large amounts of physical energy
2. Maintenance of pace, either slower or faster than natural for the individual
3. Physical discomfort
4. Unfavorable postures
5. Maintained mental clarity
6. Excessive demands on vision with the disclosure of visual deficiencies
7. Constantly maintained cheerfulness and courtesy in dealing with people (the public, etc.)
8. The influencing of others
9. Ability to speak and act in public
10. Creative thinking
11. Resolution of difficulties incident upon confrontment with incompetent help or administration

In these 11 items it may be seen that the crucial difficulty may lie in the situation as a whole, or in a deficiency of the worker himself. Judgment as to which of these features dominates is often difficult. In any case, the consciousness of trouble arises within the worker, and it is his description of what he experiences in the work situation that challenges our attention. Although it has been most common for the outward aspects of the situation to be dealt with exclusively, it is our aim to deal with the worker as a purposive organism.

1. *Work that requires the expenditure of considerable physical energy, such as lifting, carrying, shoveling, etc., usually called manual labor.* Unlike many other kinds of work, this type involves human limitations growing out of exhaustion of energy supplies. All individuals, regardless of strength and endurance, eventually reach a state of impairment during the course of such work. This looms especially large in considering the state of the individual who performs manual labor.

---

[11] *Monotonous work* will be discussed separately at the end of this chapter.

In connection with the discussion of results of actual physical exertion, two kinds of fatigue are often believed possible. The one is said to be a pleasurable state, and the other an unpleasant and undesirable state. This implies that some fatigue is desirable. It is certainly true that on some occasions following exertion an individual may feel comfortable and satisfied with his bodily feelings, and on other occasions dissatisfaction, discomfort, nausea, and many other untoward symptoms may occur. Although these two kinds of end results do occur, they need not both be called fatigue.

For example, one might choose two days in any worker's life, during which he was doing about the same kind and amount of manual labor as far as the outward results were concerned, but which turned out very differently from the worker's standpoint. We shall say that on the first day he developed the pleasurable fatigue that was mentioned above, and on the second he became miserably tired. On the first day he worked along quietly. No confusion, hurry, or contradictions occurred. On the second, in the very same job, various distressing situations arose. He was required to do some work over again that had been done before, and he discovered that his efforts were not being greatly appreciated. On both days, enough work was done to induce such bodily sensations as a feeling of heaviness in the arms and legs, etc. At the end of the first day, the individual admitted to himself that he had done a good day's work and had accomplished as much or more than could be expected of any man. At the end of the second day, he realized he was "tired," but, although his feelings contained components of bodily sensations similar to those which occurred on the first day, the pattern as a whole was much different. The feeling of weight and inertia in body and limb was much greater and took on a different significance. The feelings were now unpleasant and signified to the worker that he was far more greatly impaired than on the previous occasion.

According to our view, the individual was definitely fatigued on the second day, but on the first day he was not. It is obvious that the second work situation had induced the individual to behave in a different way from the first one. The work had not only required physical exertion, but also forced him to take a different attitude toward it. Conflicting impulses involving questions of whether to hurry, to slow down, to take one course or its opposite, etc., were induced, and all this was reflected in muscle tone and function. There was less orderliness in muscle movement. Instead of a uniform flow of energy and exertion, various kinds of wastefulness of effort ensued. A degree of disorganization was set up which was reflected in bodily feelings continuing after work had ceased.

To understand the difference on the two days, we must try to isolate

muscular states and feelings from the total situation. Although it is difficult and artificial to separate them, the attempt does enable us to gain
conviction that the sheer muscular end product of exertion is not necessarily unpleasant. To be unpleasant it must be a constituent of an over-all
attitude characterized by conflict and aversion. If the work went well and
very little inefficiency and conflict developed during its course, a pleasant
state may have ensued. The reason this pleasant state has been called a
feeling of tiredness is that it is known to have grown out of exertion. The
bodily feelings resulting from exertion, *i.e.,* the feelings of relaxation, etc.,
in themselves can be quite pleasurable provided that one is not bestirred
to return to activity. If the individual with the "good tiredness" can look
forward to an evening of relaxation, he continues to feel serene. Just so
long as no demands are made upon him, all is well. But if he contemplates
returning to work, his feelings will change to the unpleasant ones of fatigue; or if he has to write a letter (or do some other task that does not
require any great physical energy), he immediately feels unable and un-
willing. The individual suddenly realizes he is very tired and honestly
feels incapable of summoning the necessary "energy" to do what is asked
of him. Having felt so well in a situation without demands, the individual
will be made to feel extremely fatigued if called upon to work, or even
to contemplate work. "Good tiredness," then, exists only when little or
no demands are made upon the individual. In fact, the experience is not
tiredness at all. It should be clear from this that *no statement about fatigue
can be made without regard to what is being asked of the individual at the
moment.*

The subtle interplay of the demands of the task and the state of the individual is demonstrated here. Even when bodily exercise has been great
enough to cause considerable need for recuperation, the bodily feelings
arising at the time do not have an intrinsic character because they are also
dependent upon attitudes. In turn, the long-term attitudes built up by the
worker are partly dependent upon how his work is viewed in connection
with his bodily feelings. The end results of considerable exertion may be
pleasant, if the exertion factor is not a part of an unpleasant and conflict-
provoking general situation.

The task for the management of industry in jobs requiring the expenditure of considerable amounts of energy is not only that of easing the
physical exertion. Workers should be free from conflicts in the jobs and
taught to develop fortunate attitudes toward their bodily sensations and
physiological states.

2. *Work whose pace is the crucial aspect.* There are various kinds of
tasks in which a worker must maintain rapid bodily motion, or keep pace
with moving machinery, or with other workers. None of the movements

involved is in itself difficult, but it must happen at specified instants in order to be successful. Up to a certain point, practice develops skill and timing becomes more precise. The task is not only made easier with practice, but also certain performances that are initially out of the question can finally be expected. Considerable conflict in attempted movements is eradicated, and the energy expenditure is reduced to a minimum. Even so, the task requires the maintenance of a high degree of alertness if it is to remain in the category we have specified.

Although skill has been developed, activity on the part of the worker does not proceed equally smoothly at all times. There are momentary tendencies to lag. If the pace of the machine with which the individual is working is a fixed one, and if this is somewhere near the individual's maximum, the tendencies to lag must be met with increased alertness and effort. In this unnatural hurry, mistakes and spoiled work are bound at times to result. A kind of disorganization in the neuromuscular system of the worker eventually develops. It represents the clash between inclination and requirement, and it is from this rather than from the sheer expenditure of energy that fatigue can be expected to arise.

To emphasize the fact that fatigue is a result of disorganization rather than simple exhaustion of energy stores, it may be pointed out that during the day fatigue may rapidly come and go, even though there is no obvious opportunity for recuperation according to the conventional energy concepts of physiology. New motives may enter at any instant, and the discomfort may for a time play a very subordinate role. A shift in neuromuscular organization emerges as an aspect of this total change, and for a while achievement is accelerated and fatigue becomes less.

Paced work includes certain jobs in which waiting is demanded. Slowing down a pace to an arbitrary rate requires effort and reorganization of neuromuscular patterns and thus may be just as fatiguing as hurrying. Discomfort is bound to become a component of the situation.

3. *Work in which general physical discomfort is paramount.*   The usual discomforts that enter into work in this class are inclement weather conditions (cold, heat, excessive humidity), noise, vibration, foul odors, etc. The human organism is capable of remarkable adjustments to most of these conditions if the attitude of the worker does not start out with an ingrained revolt against them. Extra compensations are frequently entailed in this kind of work. High wages are usually paid. The knowledge that the work is indispensable and thereby represents an achievement may be rewarding to the individual. Companionship with other workers undergoing the same discomfort is also a factor on the compensatory side.

If the individual is torn between the obligation to get the work done and his aversion toward the work situation, fatigue is inevitable. Aversion induces a manner of working that is less efficient, more energy consuming, and more productive of bodily discomfort. Fatigue is likely to set in early and be considerable before the end of the work day.

4. *Work requiring unfavorable postures.* In some kinds of work the feature that becomes the center of the workers' attention is the body position it requires. A number of tasks require a standing position which becomes difficult to maintain. Standing requires more of the circulatory system than sitting or reclining, and at times sufficient blood pressure in the upper parts of the body, including the brain, is not maintained. A lack of muscular tone and a feeling of lassitude and faintness are associated with this. It is possible that this kind of experience leads to a chronic dislike for the work. On the other hand, if the individual starts out with an aversion for the work, a systemic inadequacy may develop when he attempts it. Regardless of how these sequences develop, discomfort results and militates against the obligation to continue work. Genuine fatigue develops. The worker attributes it wholly to physical or physiological origins.

All individuals are not equal in the maintenance of circulatory and muscular tone under similar external conditions such as those of long periods of standing. Though this inequality can be taken for granted at any moment, it carries with it no indication of how it developed. In addition to the more usually recognized origins of inadequacy, conditioning of unfortunate systemic reactions in connection with certain postures is a possible source of inadequacy. Considerable conditioning for or against such tasks may have taken place over long periods. In any case, the amount of interest and absorption in the task at hand is bound to have a bearing upon the individual's adequacy in standing. Admitting wide personal differences at the outset, one of the crucial factors is the amount of conflict that develops during the work. It is this that determines whether or not the individual becomes tired.

5. *Work requiring routine mental alertness and clarity.* In many tasks, the crucial factor is the maintenance of mental alertness so that processes of calculation, accurate recall, etc., may be accomplished. In work of this sort, muscular activity is reduced to a minimum. In work requiring mental alertness, the factor of interest is of utmost importance. If the day begins with a lack of interest in the work, or if a lack of interest develops in the course of the day, it can easily be considered to have much to do with alertness, performance, and the development of fatigue. When fatigue occurs, it is to be assumed that the basic physiological pattern is changed. Some individuals experience a definite slump a few hours after meals, which can be overcome, for example, by resorting to something to eat or drink. It is customary to assume that food or drug elements in the

substances taken are largely responsible for the recuperation. Although they are known to have certain physiological effects, their place in the recuperation of the individual is not fully understood.

As in preceding descriptions of work effects, we are dealing with situations in which the individual measures himself in the light of his sensed ability to accomplish the task. The experiences accruing from untoward systemic changes frustrate the individual in getting his work done, with the end result—fatigue.

6. *Work that puts heavy demands upon vision and in which visual deficiencies become crucial.* Common concepts about visual defects are sometimes expressed simply in terms of "weak" or "strong" eyes, and sometimes in the more sophisticated terms of static refractive corrections supposedly required to compensate for fixed anatomical anomalies. More rarely, seeing is interpreted as a kind of manipulatory or motor skill.

Certain individuals, who see clearly enough when their eyes are allowed to move more or less spontaneously in casual seeing, cannot summon the oculomotor skill to do the close work demanded in certain professional and industrial jobs. In such work, the operations involved are determined by what is required to turn out given products, and no account is taken of what the eye is able to do.

Part of the difficulty in trying to meet the visual demands of precise work lies in the fact that the control of visual function is not wholly voluntary. Focusing and converging are carried out through the autonomic nervous system. Skill in seeing cannot be developed in the same free way in which skill in typing, etc., can. In seeing, the individual does not know how to improve, and is even unaware of just what he is doing in order to see as well as he does. As yet, very little professional knowledge has been accumulated or technical procedure developed to instruct the individual in seeing. There is as yet no adequate theory as to what occurs either physiologically or in an over-all personal way during the act of seeing.

In addition to the common failure to recognize vision as a skill, there is also a failure to recognize it as a perceptual process. What is seen and what objects are interpreted to be depend not alone on refractive conditions of the eye, but upon the fact that all vision involves an interpretive or "problem-solving" factor. Visual cues are utilized in answering fundamental questions for the organism, among which are, "what" and "where," and in some cases "when." This approach makes seeing a function of the whole personality. In the fact that seeing involves contradictions in process, a tangible explanation is found for the development of fatigue in seeing.

7. *Work requiring a constantly pleasant treatment of other persons.* Positions in which the individual must constantly face the public require

a manner of pleasantness, cheerfulness, courtesy, and patience. "Job sophistication" must play a considerable role, and a favorable attitude is probably more a product of a fortunate philosophy than it is the result of good over-all working conditions. Meeting a none-too-pleasant public cheerfully is not always an easy task, and frequently such workers are called upon to efface or conceal their own feelings. The obvious conflict involved is fertile ground for fatigue.

The personal end result, fatigue, often involves as complete a pattern of bodily sensations and muscular inadequacy as that expected from grueling physical exertion. This is another demonstration that fatigue is not primarily a result of physical energy consumption. The fact that the worker sometimes feels he is at the end of his energies should not be interpreted in physical terms but rather in terms of personal organization.

8. *Work in which negotiating with and influencing other people is primary.* The attitudes and psychological processes involved in the individuals concerned with influencing other people are not greatly different from those already mentioned. If anything, the tensions involved are greater, for the stakes may be greater. The job involves success in communication plus the maintenance of a pleasant and courteous attitude.

In conference work, the participants may be at a loss to know whether they are actually being understood. It is all too often discovered that what seemed originally plain language has become open to new interpretations in the course of time. Exasperation is typical in such a situation, and anxiety and fatigue may arise.

9. *Work requiring the ability to speak and act in public.* The public speaker must often ask himself whether he has something to communicate, and whether he knows how to communicate it. He is frequently in doubt as to whether he will please his audience, or whether he will succeed in gaining some more immediate end. This kind of work not only involves human criticism, the estimates from crowds of people, but is the bluntest of all exposure to it, and therefore evokes perhaps the most frequent and most severe self-observation of any kind of work. The individual is bound to be filled with doubts, and to offset them, attempts self-reassurance. It is obvious that considerable fatigue is likely to be a consequence of such activities. In moments of public success, the limpness and paralysis of exhaustion and doubt may be swept away, but at other times the individual's state is evidenced both in predicament of body and personal attitude.

10. *Creative thinking.* Creative thinking is not in itself particularly fatiguing, yet individuals engaged in this type of work are frequently fatigued. Frustration and difficulties of all sorts may occur in connection with communicating the ideas to others, putting ideas into action, or pro-

ducing ideas to order, etc. It might be said that in creative work the fatigue arises more from the necessity of dealing with certain other people than it does from the act of thinking itself.

11. *Resolution of difficulties incident upon confrontment with incompetent help or administration.* Regardless of the specific character of the job, its most salient feature sometimes becomes that of dealing with other persons in the organization. Of the items listed in the inventories of what workers expect of their jobs, the relations between worker and management and between worker and fellow workers loom the largest. This item, although it pertains to social relationships more or less outside the specific nature of the job itself, is mentioned here because of its great importance in nearly all job situations. We have already emphasized the fact that genuine and extreme fatigue often grows out of human relations via the inconsistencies and contradictions involved. The internal conflicts aroused in the individual from this source are apt to be of a most overpowering type.

JOB ANALYSIS

"Job analysis" arose in part as an attempt to discover what the job requires of the person. It includes the study of occupational activities and requirements by means of a variety of techniques. Unfortunately, however, the emphasis has been all too often placed on the job rather than on the individual, and the approach has been an extremely elementistic one. The practical angle of finding people who can best perform the job in order to increase production has blinded many investigators to the fact that such an aim can be adequately achieved only through the worker himself. The approach through the individual does not mean merely a simple observation of the worker at his task, but a thorough-going study in which the worker is viewed holistically, neglecting none of the personal angles that might be involved in his work situation.

Tead and Metcalf[12] define job analysis as "the scientific study and statement of all the facts about a job which reveal its content and the modifying factors which surround it." Such a definition will bear criticism on several counts, but chiefly, for our purposes, for its lack of personal reference. Taking the individual rather than the job as a starting point is essential in an understanding of fatigue and impairment. This view is seldom the one taken in job-analysis procedures.

The most extensive work has been done for employment purposes, *i.e.*, for the selection and placing of employees, and for making wage schedules.

---

[12] Tead, O., and H. C. Metcalf: "Personnel Administration, Its Principles and Practice," p. 225, McGraw-Hill Book Company, Inc., New York, 1920. Pp. 538.

Viteles[13] states that job analysis for employment purposes is restricted to determining the actual duties, working conditions, and qualification of the potential employee. Viteles points out that there is a serious neglect of these "personal requirements" in many industrial setups. Some companies make no personal specifications at all. Others limit them to such general factors as age, sex, nationality, etc. Frequently there is no attempt to specify such job requirements as intelligence or special abilities, or when traits of this sort are specified the terminology is so vague as to be nearly meaningless. In addition to the general factors, Viteles includes under personnel requirements, general and special abilities, previous experience, and physical, educational, temperamental, and character requirements.

The sources of information concerning the specific job analyzed are also frequently inadequate. No job can be sized up in what is known as an objective manner. Yet often job analyzers are content with a mere viewing of employees working on the job in question, or with studying output and turnover records, or photographic records of the movements involved in the task. Interviews and questionnaires are also popular, but, by themselves, quite inadequate. The analysis of what is required on a job can be approached only through the person who performs it. Two operations, for example, may appear "objectively" to be very similar, yet "subjectively" involve two completely different experiences. Since introspections from an inexperienced person are of little merit, questionnaires, etc., do not suffice. The job analyzer, assuming he is a trained observer, must himself perform the job and make his observations during the course of his work. A few investigators, notably Link[14] and Viteles,[15] have followed this procedure. Viteles[16] states that the secondary sources of job information can never take the place of direct contact with the work and the work situation.

A description of the various methods and procedures used in job analysis can be found in any modern text of industrial psychology. There is no need to go into further detail here regarding this rapidly growing field.

RELATION OF ACCIDENT PRONENESS AND FATIGUE

The actuality of accident proneness. Both industry and medicine recognize that a certain percentage of the total population is prone to have accidents. While these accidents occur in a variety of situations, it is from

13 Viteles, *op. cit.*

14 Link, H.: "Employment Psychology," The Macmillan Company, New York, 1919. Pp. 40.

15 Viteles, M. S.: Research in the Selection of Motormen, *J. Personnel Research, 4:* 100–115; 173–199, 1925.

16 Viteles, M. S.: "Industrial Psychology," W. W. Norton & Company, Inc., New York, 1932. Pp. 652.

the statistics of automobile accidents and industrial studies that accident proneness has come out most clearly. Accidents in general have been classified into two categories,[17] "true" and "purposeful." For example, concerns employing large numbers of truck drivers have looked into the possible causes of accidents among their employees, by taking into account weather, season, day of the week, defective equipment, experience, and speed. These studies have shown that the preponderance of all accidents occurred under ideal driving conditions. This finding would indicate that the crucial reasons for accidents lie within the drivers themselves.

It is a known fact that a relatively small number of individuals have the vast majority of all the accidents. Some studies show that statistically the number of accident-free individuals is just slightly greater than would be expected, a finding in accordance with expectations were accidents pure chance phenomena to which everybody is equally liable. In contrast to this, the high-rate group greatly exceeds the expectation on a chance basis. One study showed that accident-prone drivers were accident prone in other situations. As a test of accident proneness another industrial concern attempted to screen out accident-prone drivers and thus reduce accidents, with the result that in a few years the accident rate was reduced to about one-fifth the original.

Dunbar, who has accumulated considerable experience with accident-prone individuals, points out that these individuals tend to respond to events in their daily lives by action rather than by thought and mood. They tend to avoid externally imposed discipline and responsibility. But the situation is so subtle that the only sure way to detect the accident-prone individual as yet is through his past record.

As an example of the personal nature of accidents, it was found in one study[18] that 60 per cent of the fracture cases confessed resentment or guilt or characterized the accident as purposive. In other words, the individual tended to view the accident not as a chance, uncontrolled event, but as meaningful. Whether this meaningfulness is an interpretation after the fact, or whether the personal mechanisms participating in producing the accident really exist is a matter to receive more study. Nevertheless, the evidence points strongly in the direction of "accidental" behavior being frequently just as meaningful and purposive as "successful" or useful performance.

Limitations of using accidents as an index of fatigue. Accidents are frequently taken to be an index of fatigue. The finding that accident proneness is a peculiar syndrome of some people brings up the question

[17] Rawson, A. J.: Accident Proneness, *Psychosomatic Med., 6:* 88–94, 1944.
[18] Motor Vehicle Traffic Conditions in the United States. The Accident-prone Driver, Part 6, No. 462, The U. S. Government Printing Office, 1939.

of whether accidents may be used as any indication of fatigue or impairment. If accident proneness has no close positive or negative relation to fatigue, not all accidents can be attributed to fatigue or impairment. It is usually supposed that the normal individual has more accidents when fatigued or impaired.

Both accident proneness and fatigue are personal syndromes, characteristic ways of attempting to resolve behavior situations. Fatigue is quite universal, but accident proneness is not. Whether fatigue and accident proneness have a simple positive, negative, or a more complex relation is not at all clear at present. But until this relation is discovered, accidents should not be used as they are now, as an index of fatigue.

If it were to be found that accident proneness is of more than one kind, it might follow that one of the kinds is an end product of fatigue. In this case the individual might be said to develop a conflict and aversion to continuing work that he resolves in a "purposeful accident."

REPETITIVE WORK, MONOTONY, AND FATIGUE[19]

The term "monotony" suggests *sustained and unpleasant sameness.* Both intricate and simpler tasks can become tedious, but it is usually simple repetitious tasks that become monotonous. .Monotony is a general characteristic that may be imputed to the work at hand. It is a term used to label the individual's perception of his surroundings, and although often spoken of as belonging to the situation, can imply no fixed relation between situation and experience. Work is characterized as monotonous by an individual, and that which is monotonous for one may be quite interesting for another. Any sort of work at one time or another may become unpleasant, tedious, or monotonous. Our purpose here is not to further identify monotony, but to analyze it in order to see how it contributes to fatigue.

Work is judged tedious or monotonous when it loses its importance to the worker. The longer he must continue in spite of the attitude he has developed, the greater is his aversion. A peculiarly mobilized conflict exists between inclination and duty or external compulsion, and fatigue results.

[19] Chapter IX contains a detailed discussion of boredom. Theoretical distinctions are made among the concepts of *boredom, monotony,* and *fatigue;* and the general usages of the three terms are discussed.

Chapter XVII

VISUAL PERFORMANCE AND FATIGUE

A PRECEDING chapter was devoted to describing a number of phenomena conventionally taken to be examples of visual fatigue. The array represented considerable variety. Underneath the obvious differences one would have expected certain properties in common which could be called fatigue. The outstanding apparent common denominator, however, was the fact that in every case some sort of diminution or extinction occurred with the passage of time. Each of these visual phenomena was dealt with as a distinct function. The whole description in each case applied to local phenomena. Although investigators claimed the presence of fatigue, all that could actually be said was that the local phenomena changed. No description of the individual who experienced the phenomena was given, so the presence of fatigue could not be determined. Diminution of function is not fatigue, since fatigue is a concept to be applied only to personal experience.

Ideally, "visual fatigue" is a term that should not be used, since it tends to imply that there are specific kinds of fatigue, or that fatigue is a localized phenomenon. Our employment of the term in this chapter is necessitated by common usage. Our task here is to take into account the phenomena ordinarily dealt with under this label and to distinguish fatigue from the rest of the frustration picture. Fatigue may arise in the use of the visual apparatus, since personal frustration may develop in the course of seeing. The individual, in this case, attributes his difficulties to the use of his eyes.

Fatigue, arising in the attempt to use the eyes, where the conflicts develop through failure of visual accomplishment, either in the inability to see, or in discomfort while attempting to see, is essentially the same as fatigue arising in other conflicts. The experience of fatigue arises out of the way vision as a means to an end serves in the activity of the individual as a whole.

Whereas the previous chapter on vision was given primarily to studies based on the idea that visual processes themselves became fatigued (impaired), the present chapter proposes to describe vision as participating in personal conflict and *contributing* to fatigue.

341

It is our purpose in this chapter to look upon visual phenomena in the light of their contribution to the focal task of the individual. When phenomena are neutral or virtually irrelevant to what the individual is doing, changes in such phenomena, regardless of what sort, have nothing to do with fatigue.

Vision is the name for a mode of contact between the individual and the physical world. In studying vision, as well as the various other modes of contact (the senses), there are two reference points possible, from which all facts can be considered and all inferences made. These reference points are the physical world and the organism. These references lead immediately to two different trains of consequences in modes of observation, in logic, and in terminology.

Whether the physical world or the organism is taken as the reference, naming and defining the items involved presents a problem. *It is proper to define a stimulus as a physical item that elicits some fairly direct effect in the organism.* If this effect is taken to be but a chemical or physical affair, the stimulus may be spoken of as a physiological stimulus. If the effect is experiential, the stimulus may be called a psychological one. Thus effects define not only whether some physical item or situation is a stimulus, but also the class to which the stimulus belongs, although the stimulus in itself is always physical. Usually both psychological and physiological effects result from a single physical event. Frequently the above definition of stimulus is ignored, and any physical event that is merely supposed to affect the organism is called a stimulus. Furthermore, stimulus, as loosely defined, is not always restricted to the physical world. The organism is sometimes said to provide its own stimuli, as, for example, in ideas that evoke others, or in "centrally excited processes." It is obvious that each of these uses, notwithstanding its prevalence, not only differs from the others, but has strayed far from the strict definition.

The proper definition of stimulus, in implying that the organism may or may not be affected by a particular physical event, gives the organism, rather than the physical world, the crucial role. Other features of the conventional treatment of organism-physical world relations indicate that in the main the physical world tends to be held as the reference, neglecting the crucial role of the organism.

In effect, a stimulus frequently becomes something that does not stimulate. It may have no effect at all on the organism. As a result, it may be said that the more usual reference is neither the physical world nor the organism, but a variable point not fully one or the other. Such an unfixed reference is often unwittingly taken and is, therefore, doubly confusing. It serves to give its possessor false security, since it is always difficult for anyone else to succeed in making references explicit in such a logic.

Using the physical world as the reference leaves the theorist or investigator without a way of determining how effective physical items ought to be. There are stimuli, which by their physical intensity, etc., might be expected to be effective, but owing to the organization of the individual at the moment, they do not prove to be. Among those which are effective, the actual degree of effect is likewise left undetermined when only physical properties are considered. Furthermore, there is no way of telling what stimuli will clash with each other, or on the other hand be synergistic.

To predict the organism's behavior in terms of fixed physical quantities is commonly the main objective in dealing with relations between the organism and the physical world. This approach is so customary that it is not given up even when, nominally at least, the attempt is to learn something about the organism. Mainly for this reason, the outcomes of most attempts to study the organism directly have been disappointing.

The remedy for this confusion is a frank and full acceptance of the organism as a point of reference. This does not mean discarding the use of physical terms. It does mean that physical terms are only a part of the ultimate relating of the organism to the physical world.

It seems inescapable that the physical world is a heterogenous mass, except as the organism itself lends it a certain unity and continuity. The physiology of the organism is of such a nature that the organism is selectively sensitive to various physical factors (light, heat, moisture, etc.). It determines its own environment. The organism as a whole is always purposive. Sensitivity is never standard, but specific for a given occasion, depending upon the momentary activity of the organism. Relations between an organism and the physical world are continually evolving. Changes that may be taking place both in the organism and in the physical world contribute to this. Repetition, if there be such, can be viewed as (1) something pertaining to the organism, (2) something pertaining to the physical world, or (3) something viewed by the organism either in itself or in its environment. Repetition as pertaining to the organism occurs only when the observer takes a very superficial view. The relations between organism and the physical world to be dealt with in this chapter are environmental relations.

The functional relations between physical items and perceived items is recognized in the concept of signaling. Neither items in the physical world nor perceived items are themselves signals. A signal merely expresses the relation between the two, as determined by the functional outcome. The physical items from which the signals arise should be called stimuli. The signaling function, always, of course, occurring within the organism, may also be initiated by organic events.

GROSS ORGANISM-ENVIRONMENT RELATIONS THAT LEAD
TO FRUSTRATION

Whereas, for our purposes, the organism is totally unaffected by certain physical events, it is characteristically sensitive to other kinds. The former never form a part of the organism's environment and therefore play no part in the development of a picture of frustration; the latter may or may not, depending on a number of factors.

Some stimuli although not totally ineffective are insufficient to result in clear signals. In cases of this sort, there is no frustration unless the individual attempts to make use of such stimuli in a task.

1. The general level of illumination may be so low that "objects" are not visually discernible. Visual areas supplying slightly more light than the general field will not be seen. This may occur at general levels much above those considered as "darkness." When the levels of intensity between two adjacent areas are insufficiently different, the difference cannot be utilized to distinguish objects, etc. If the individual is trying to do something in which vision is needed for supplying guidance, the lack of "clues" will thwart him in his efforts.

Modes of visual performance vary with degrees of illumination. Trying to see in an extremely low illumination, for example, is not harmful, because the ocular mechanisms are able to follow their own organizational trends. Attempts to see at somewhat higher illuminations, however, involve the ocular mechanism in overwork and distorted action. When the illumination is strong enough to induce oculomotor adjustments, and yet too weak for adequate guidance, localized discomfort and dysfunction are most likely to form a part of the frustration picture. Fatigue, in any case, would arise from the inability of the individual to achieve his purpose.

2. Objects may be too small to be seen. The area of receptor surface involved in direct stimulation is too scant to lead to perception of the object. If objects subtend too small angles on the retina, whenever possible the observer reduces their distance from him. He either brings the objects closer or approaches them. The working distance may involve considerable convergence and accommodation of the eyes. When very close vision is required, certain incompatibilities between convergence and accommodation are likely to develop. Many individuals cannot make the necessary adjustments at all, whereas others cannot maintain them over long periods without getting into difficulty. The fatigue that results does not rest on being unable to see, but upon being unable to maintain appropriate and comfortable ocular adjustments for clear vision. Headaches, gastrointestinal disturbances, and other general difficulties may form part of the frus-

tration picture. Even though the difficulty is labeled visual, obviously the whole individual is always involved.

Visual situations of other kinds may also result in disorganization and conflict in the organism. In a visual situation, unless the individual is attempting to use his eyes for a specific purpose, neither "visual fatigue" nor any other part of a marked frustration picture is likely to develop.

3. The movement of objects may be too fast or too irregular to be adequately perceived. In ocular pursuit, control of spontaneous eye movements is required. Rapid or irregular pursuit movements may be necessary for clear visibility. The requirements being quite precise, the system must operate at its best to achieve the amount of control necessary. Contradictions in motor behavior often arise and lead to consequences in which general ocular behavior may be worse than before pursuit movements were attempted. Incompatibilities tend to become quite pervasive in their train of consequences. The difficulties thus become general aspects of the individual's experience, and one of the stances very likely to eventuate is fatigue.

4. Some visual situations call for steady fixation, a type of ocular behavior opposed to the eyes' tendency to rove. Voluntary effort is required to oppose the more or less spontaneous irregular eye movements. Rather than successfully and easily abolishing or forestalling spontaneous movements by a smooth compensation process, such voluntary intervention sets up opposing tensions and movements. The opposition to spontaneous eye movements is thus vigorous but not precise. Throughout fixation attempts, there is little or nothing to evidence an easily attained or "passive" balance between eye muscles. Although no eye movements occur at moments, spontaneous innervation eventually gets the upper hand, and this is accompanied by heightened opposition. If unsteady oppositional tensions are slightly out of phase, unavoidable movement occurs before the opposing voluntary innervation becomes effective. When this occurs, voluntary movement in the opposite direction is required to bring the eyes back to the original position. Such a process often results in "overshooting" compensations, and correction by "bracketing" sets in. One of the best setups for demonstrating the contest between spontaneous eye movements and deliberate compensatory adjustments is that in which two bright lights are used in a dark room. The lights are placed on opposite sides of the line of regard, at about 30 degrees from it. This is essentially the setup used by Bartley[1] in certain ocular experiments, in which a 5-minute steady fixation midway between two lights, without the use of a fixation point, was attempted.

[1] Bartley, S. H.: A Factor in Visual Fatigue, *Psychosomatic Med., 4:* 368–375, 1942.

5. The individual may also become fatigued when visual situations involve too much light. This light may exist either in the entire visual field or only in limited portions of it. If the general illumination is low, limited areas of the field need not supply very intense light before the individual finds them very bright. These areas are not only uncomfortable to look at, but also obscure the more poorly illuminated objects. The eye cannot adapt to these high illuminations, not because they are beyond adaptation limits, but because the eyes are not stationary. Various retinal areas are successively supplied with the image of the bright light. No single retinal area becomes sufficiently adapted for maximum effectiveness, since before adaptation can occur the area involved is moved, and the bright image lies on a new portion of the retina. The whole retina becomes light-adapted above the level effective for low illumination, because of the stray light within the eye from reflection of the image. The visual effect of the bright light, called glare, cannot be avoided when there are extreme brightness gradients in the field, or when the total light is very great. Fatigue resulting from glare is a common experience. Although it occurs most conspicuously from the headlights of oncoming vehicles at night, for example, untoward contrasts are also encountered frequently in everyday working conditions. The experience is marked when the visual field contains a great difference between the level of illumination of the working surfaces.

6. Some visual situations involve alternations in levels of illumination. When these alternations occur at certain rates, they produce the subjective effect of flicker. Flicker, to say the least, is uncomfortable. It has been shown that the pupil is able to dilate and constrict in pace with slow alternations of light and darkness. But beyond certain limits, conflict develops between the dilator and constrictor fibers. Various untoward systemic effects may be produced. It is obvious that such conditions would be the more frustrating the more precise the accomplishments attempted.

7. Some visual situations demand working with material too close to the eyes. Near vision, unlike distance vision, requires considerable convergence and accommodation. Incidental head movements require far greater accommodative changes in close work. The individual with an oculomotor mechanism taxed to its maximum in near vision is bound to discover that head movements are a problem, for they result in getting into and out of focus. His attempt to maintain proper distance and steady head and neck posture then becomes a difficult part of the task of seeing. If convergence and accommodation for "near vision" are difficult to achieve, head position is all the more crucial.

In addition to the already mentioned contrasts between near and distance vision, there may be differences in the way peripheral vision is involved in the two cases.

GEOMETRY, IMAGE FORMATION, VISUAL PERCEPTION, AND OCULOMOTOR ACTIVITY

The previous section has already described characteristics of the visual situation (organism, environment, and physical world) that lead to frustration and fatigue. The discussion dealt merely with the grosser features of vision. In the present section, we wish to analyze visual situations further.

Our first task is to indicate the character of the working relations between the organism and the physical world, so as to show how disjunction can occur. The second task is to indicate how it produces fatigue, and the third task is to convince the reader that the processes which are described do induce fatigue in everyday life.

The relations between given experiences and abstracted features of the physical world presumed to elicit them are not fixed. The relations between stimuli, taken as fixed entities, and retinal images are not simple and constant, nor are the relations between retinal images and ensuing visual experiences of a one-to-one character. From the following, it will be seen that one cannot reason from the physical world to experience.

1. When objects remain fixed in size, shape, and in *spatial relation to the eye,* the retinal image remains fixed. But when the eyes shift position, even though objects remain unchanged their retinal images change. The retinal image also changes, of course, when the object moves.

2. When objects change shape, they may or may not produce changes in the shape of retinal images, depending upon the visual angles their parts subtend at the eye. An infinity of geometrical shapes may subtend the same visual angles. Various distances and orientations of stimuli may be involved so as to result in geometric equivalence in the retinal image.

3. When retinal images remain constant, the perceptual *experiences* of objects pertaining to size, shape, etc., may or may not remain constant, depending upon the character of the total stimulation and the ongoing activity of the organism (see Figs. 56 and 57).

4. Retinal images may change in size and shape, and the experienced position and size of the object may change. On the other hand, the retinal image may change in *size* and the *experienced* object may remain fixed in size.

Although these four pairs of conditions, two pairs dealing with the stimulus and the retinal image and two with the retinal image and experiential outcome (sensation), are the result of logical analysis, they are usually neglected. Customary reasoning proceeds from the physical object directly

FIG. 56.—A reversible perspective figure in which the shift involves a change of the identity of the object.

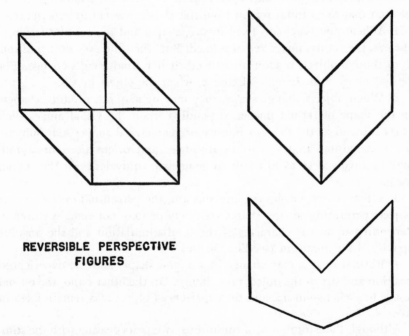

REVERSIBLE PERSPECTIVE
FIGURES

FIG. 57.—Reversible perspective figures in which the change of perspective does not involve a change of identity of the object.

to experience, or even *from the perceived object* (experimenter's), wrongly termed the stimulus, *to the experience of the observer.*

In the relations between stimulus, retinal image, and sensation, it is not only obvious that equivocality exists, but that its kind depends upon whether we are considering relations between stimulus and retinal image, retinal image and experience, or stimulus and experience.

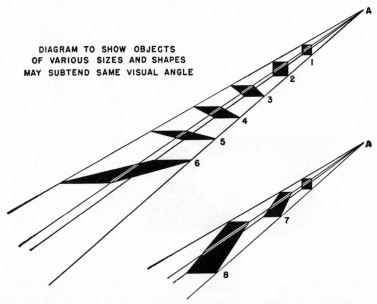

DIAGRAM TO SHOW OBJECTS
OF VARIOUS SIZES AND SHAPES
MAY SUBTEND SAME VISUAL ANGLE

Fig. 58.—An unlimited number of two-dimensional figures may subtend the same angle from a point *A*, which represents the nodal point of the eye. All two-dimensional figures which subtend the same solid visual angle as the square (1) will be seen as squares unless there are clues which would form a basis for differentiating between them.

Examples of looseness in relations between stimulus, retinal image, and sensation, as dependent upon external conditions. For purposes of the present discussion, the variability of the organism which could be expected with uniform stimulation is neglected. Figure 58 illustrates the fact that a number of plane figures subtend the same visual angles at the eye. All of them are visual equivalents to the observer unless they are part of a larger visual situation that helps differentiate between them. Each figure in the drawing becomes the equivalent of the other, depending upon two things: its distance from the eye, and its orientation with reference to the eye. Figure 59 shows how a two-dimensional figure may be the perceptual equivalent of a three-dimensional one. In daily life we are continually confronted with three-dimensional objects and have been successful in representing them in two-dimensional drawings. The complete visuo-experiential identity of a two-dimensional with a three-dimensional object is possible under limited conditions.

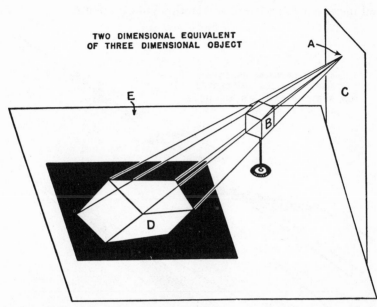

TWO DIMENSIONAL EQUIVALENT
OF THREE DIMENSIONAL OBJECT

Fig. 59.—A three-dimensional object, such as cube *B*, can be represented by a two-dimensional drawing. This so-called representation may substitute for the cube with varying degrees of success. The realism depends upon the absence of other clues in the visual field. Cube *B* may be withdrawn and *D* may be observed from the peep-hole at point *A*. Screen *C* obliterates the view of the table top and other objects which would indicate that *D* is but a drawing. If *D* is shaded to simulate *B* it may function as a perfect substitute. It will not only be seen as three-dimensional, but will be a real cube to the observer. With certain sized drawings, a marble, if it is rolled on the table across *D*, will appear to roll up th side of *D*, across the top, and down to the table as it would have to on a literal three-dimensional object.

If one views a cube from a fixed vantage point, let us say obliquely, as indicated in the diagram in Fig. 59, a figure can be drawn on a piece of paper lying on the top of a desk beyond, which will substitute for the cube. The outline of this figure is determined by points on the paper obtained by sighting past the corners of the cube. When these points are connected by lines, and when we supply additional lines within the figure to complete it, we get a figure which, when observed from other vantage points, is a representation of an elongated solid. We may call the cube object I, and the plane figure, object II. The latter can be viewed from the original vantage point after removing the cube (object I). Under these conditions, II will tend to look like I. It is possible, however, that the existence of clues from the illuminated surroundings may prevent it from looking entirely like a cube or prevent its full three-dimensional appearance. Under such conditions, one sees that it looks *like* a cube, but *knows* it is only a representation. If a peephole is supplied at the vantage point and all other objects in the field of view screened out, the object will be seen as a cube.[2] If one is careful to construct object II to reproduce light and shade that existed within object I, the identity of subjective end result is complete. One shown it will say it *is* the cube that was seen before (the actual solid cube). Thus two different "environmental" objects can be made to give rise to identical experiences.

If the surface on which object II was drawn is placed at any one of an indefinite number of angles of tilt from the horizontal plane of the table, other figures could be constructed by means of the principle described above. Each one could be made to substitute for the actual three-dimensional cube (object I). This is an illustration of one of the alternatives in item 2, *viz.*, that an infinity of geometrical shapes may produce the same retinal image. For an example, see Fig. 58.

If one changes the physical intensity of the stimulus (consequently the intensity of the retinal image), the object perceived may shift in distance. It may recede when intensity is reduced and come nearer when intensity is increased. This means that not only the shape and size but also the *intensity* of light in the retinal image may play a part in determining the location of a perceived object. This is but one case in which changes may occur when the retinal image supposedly remains fixed in size and shape (one alternative of item 3 in the above list).

The conditions we have been describing pertain to what the organism has to work upon, *viz.*, the retinal image. Inasmuch as it has been shown that two or more stimuli may produce the same retinal image, the organism is left without the means of gaining sufficiently different signals for appropriate activity. The organism left with this degree of indeterminism in what it has to work with is bound to appear capricious when the actual physical constellation is taken as the theorist's point of reference.

Examples of looseness of relation between stimulus, retinal image, and sensation, as dependent upon the organism. Discrepancy between expected and actual experiential outcomes necessarily involves the selectivity that characterizes the activity of the organism. Several illustrations will

---

[2] This is essentially the class demonstration used by Prof. Fritz Heider of Smith College.

be given. The first of these will clarify the second alternative of item 4 in the classification.

Miniature, giant, and normal-sized specimens of familiar objects such as playing cards, match boxes, or packages of cigarettes, may be presented to the observer. If a playing card, for example, is exhibited in a dark room where it is the only object illuminated, all cues surrounding it being obliterated, it will look near or far away depending not only on its actual physical distance from the observer, but also on whether it is a miniature specimen or a giant. The observer sees it its natural size and at a distance consistent with this. While the actual *distance* and the physical *size* determine the size of the retinal image, they do not directly determine the seen size of the card, for the organism uses retinal image size as if it were dealing with the retinal image of the normal object. In the case of familiar objects, it is thus possible to demonstrate a "constancy" which acts as the reference for the other phenomenal properties of the perceived object. Ames[3] speaks of these as cases involving "known size."

Shifts in relation between expected and actual experiential outcome occur notably in the case of looking at a picture of the human face. As one observes such a picture various changes in its appearance occur. For example, if a resemblance to some other person is suggested, the whole character of the face in the picture may be altered. Such a change is not one of "superimposed interpretation," but is immediately perceived. The face actually appears to be a different geometrical pattern from moment to moment.

The signal value of a given stimulus changes in keeping with the significance of the perceived object to the observer. Perception is dependent throughout upon this significance. Although we know very little about it as yet, there is clearly a relation between "significance" and all the other features of the perception which may be abstracted by the observer. Certain objects appear threatening, attractive, etc., their geometry varying accordingly.

It is well known that the organism is constantly using objects around it as means to an end. It would seem that the matter of relevancy would necessarily influence the character of so basic a feature of behavior as sensation. A study of whether or not sensation can be altered in line with the organism's over-all activity would demonstrate the truth of this assumption. The principle that sensation varies in line with the individual's orientation is masked in everyday affairs, for it is not often that strong reasons exist for a *single* alignment. The dependence of the character of

---

[3] "Known size" operates in the many demonstrations which are used at the Dartmouth Eye Institute in elucidating a point of view that takes the organism as a reference in sensation theory.

sensation upon the individual's "purposes, needs," etc., could be studied by experiments set up to measure the sensation that emerges under a single predominant alignment.

Proshansky and Murphy[4] have performed experiments that bear on this subject. In a pretraining period, the observers reported their estimations of length of lines and weights of lifted objects. In the training period, observations but no reports were required. As the longer lines were presented, monetary rewards were given, and as the shorter were presented, punishment was applied in the form of loss of money. As the intermediate lines were shown, sometimes reward and sometimes punishment was given. This same technique applied to weights. In the posttraining period, new sets of estimations were obtained. The results of this last period showed that lines were seen as longer and the weights were felt as heavier than before. The subjects were unaware of the purpose of the experiment and of the differences in their pre- and post-training results. The shift was simply a change in the sensed lengths of lines and weights of objects. It demonstrates that the immediate awareness of objects is dependent upon the individual's alignment. The authors spoke of these shifts as a demonstration of autistic tendencies in accordance with need satisfaction. To overlook the possibility that these reactions are *sensory* fails to do justice to the phenomena studied. The term "autism," as defined, falls into the general class of delusions and "wishful thinking" and for this reason hardly seems appropriate.

This experiment and one later,[5] in which ambiguous (ambivalent) figures were seen one way or the other in line with need, indicate that perceptions are subject to change. The outcomes, instead of being fixed, can be expected to vary because they depend upon the individual and his alignment at the given moment.

Personal organization is always expressed in visual performance. Customarily, however, quality of some selected aspect of performance, rather than matters of personal alignment, is the main consideration in experiments on so-called fatigue. A laboratory technique for illustration here is the use of adjustable optical devices, which the observer manipulates to "correct" for the perceived inequality in distance between two strings seen through a reduction screen. The amount of "correction" shown in the final reading in each trial is taken as the measure of lack of precision. Considerable variability in precision may be manifested in a series of trials. If precision becomes less and less, fatigue is customarily imputed.

[4] Proshansky, H., and G. Murphy: The Effects of Reward and Punishment upon Perception, *J. Psychol.*, *13:* 295–305, 1942.

[5] Schafer, R., and G. Murphy: The Role of Autism in a Visual Figureground Relationship, *J. Exper. Psychol.*, *32:* 335–343, 1943.

Rather than precision, the nature of the performance from the observer's standpoint is important for us to consider here. The salient feature of the performance to the observer is the oscillation of the positional appearance of the two strings, since this involves difficulty in arriving at a stable judgment. The performance may be difficult owing to the lack of sureness that is associated with most of the seen positions. When maximum precision is important to the observer, the instability of the seen positions of the strings is distressing. In the course of his performance, the observer exercises some degree of self-evaluation which, under conditions like these, usually becomes unfavorable. The individual soon begins to lose interest, and fatigue develops. Such a personal outcome need have no relation to the excellence of the measured aspect of performance, for as was said, in such situations the observer is uninformed of the measured results.

Uniocular-binocular incompatibilities in seeing. The fundamental distinctions between uniocular and binocular vision have been partly recognized for a long time. More recently, these distinctions have become progressively clearer. Some of the features involved are now seen as oppositely functioning items in the production of the net visual outcome.

The individual is able to use stimuli impinging on one eye to perceive spatial relations of objects and to identify the objects themselves. When the individual uses both eyes, not only is each eye receiving stimulation that alone would serve to signal the position of objects, but the difference in the stimulation in the two eyes and the postures they must assume provide additional signals.

The size and shape differences of the images of the two eyes change as the eyes shift their orientation to spatial objects, and these disparities are important in giving objects position in phenomenal space. The participation of innervations from the extrinsic ocular muscles is not certain.

There is some suggestion that the different end results when uniocular and binocular processes for positioning objects operate alone lead to actual conflict when the two processes are involved at one time. There are as yet no descriptive terms for the nature of this conflict. But the fact that pictures of three-dimensional objects appear to have a greater depth when viewed with one eye than with two, is an example of one of the kinds of evidence for the existence of this conflict.

The opposition between uniocular and binocular factors in distance perception may be illustrated also by the following:

Let two like ribbons or rods be suspended from the ceiling, equally illuminated and viewed through an aperture, as shown in Fig. 60. When equidistant they will appear equidistant, barring ocular defects, etc. Let one ribbon be exchanged for a wider or narrower one. If the new ribbon is narrower it may appear farther away than its mate; if wider it may appear nearer. According to strict binocular vision the two should still appear equidistant from the observer, for the geometric relation of the two ribbons from the eyes has not been changed. If the ribbons continue to be seen as equidistant, it can be said that binocular vision is dominating. If the two ribbons are seen in the position that their relative widths would indicate in terms of relative distance, then uniocular vision is functioning with equality of width as a reference. If a distance somewhere between

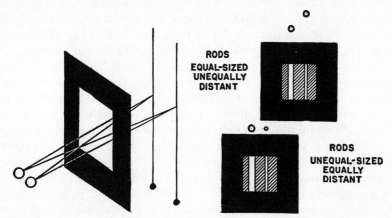

RODS
EQUAL-SIZED
UNEQUALLY
DISTANT

RODS
UNEQUAL-SIZED
EQUALLY
DISTANT

Fig. 60.—The effects of viewing two vertical rods, strings or ribbons. On the basis of binocular function two unequally sized rods are seen equally distant and different in diameter. With only uniocular vision functioning the unequally sized rods are seen unequally distant owing to the difference in the visual angles subtended. This inequality of distance can be calculated mathematically. By many persons the rods are seen not where they would be expected to be under the two conditions just mentioned: they are seen as unequally distant, but the rod seen farther away is not so distant as would be predicted by its lesser visual angle.

these two extremes is judged, then it may be said that a compromise has occurred. We have already described an example in which the seen position of two strings is not stable. Although the instability of such objects may arise from insufficient information obtainable through use of a single eye, it is possible that the use of two eyes may not always stabilize the object's seen position, but introduce another basis for difficulty.

This description of a fundamental difference between uniocular and binocular vision has served to point out a basis for potential conflict. The extent to which personal conflict results depends upon the particular role which the two are playing at the moment, and this in turn depends upon the task. If precise localization of objects in the visual field is being attempted, and the successful achievement is extremely important to the individual, the task may become difficult. Failure to achieve ready perceptual resolution is accompanied by the experience of effort. If prolonged attempts are required, aversion toward the task develops, and this is expressed in weariness and fatigue.

THE MOTOR FACTORS OF VISION

Vision inescapably includes certain motor performances that adjust the eyes to the proper focus, point the two eyes toward a single object, and perform exploratory, manipulative, and pursuit functions. The failure of the eyes to accomplish any one of these functions either impoverishes the accomplishments of the individual, or makes certain of them completely impossible. While the disorganization of the individual, growing out of a number of origins among which may be tissue impairment, leads to oculomotor difficulties not specifically related to the over-all trouble, the specific nature of oculomotor trouble may be sought in the character of personal organization. An extreme example of this would be hysterical blindness. In cases in which the nature of the oculomotor difficulty cannot be traced directly, it can at least be said that the oculomotor inadequacy is a potential thwart to the individual. To the degree and in the manner that it succeeds in being a thwart, frustration is bound to arise. The peculiar thing about oculomotor thwarts is that they cannot be well understood by the individual, and little can be done about them except to oppose them indiscriminately. The more vigorous the opposition, the greater the discomfort, the more futile the situation becomes to the individual. Fatigue finally arises from the opposition.

The oculomotor mechanism. There are three groups of ocular muscles: the pupillary, the extrinsic, and the accommodative. The first group provides for adjusting the amount of light entering the eye and secondarily for sharpening focus in near vision. The second group provides for eye movements and the proper pointing of the two eyes, and the third group for adjusting the lens. These muscles must cooperate for effective behavior of the individual, and it is to failures in such cooperation that considerable of the individual's visual trouble may be attributed.

It must be recognized from the start that the control of these muscle systems is mostly involuntary, although the extrinsic muscles can be used to move the eyes partly at will. When vision is thought of as a skill, the fact that the mechanisms are partly or wholly involuntary has a particular significance. Since their activity cannot be modified wittingly, the training of increased skill, or the eradication of certain kinds of behavioral defects are an indirect and much more difficult task.

The three groups operate on the same broad principle, that of reciprocal innervation. This common denominator in all three muscle groups is provided for by the pairing of fibers—an obvious feature in the pupil, and in the opposing extrinsic eye muscles, but only more recently believed to be the case in the ciliary body.[6] By means of pairing, some degree of reciprocity between the contraction of one member of the pair and the relaxation elongation of the other is structurally provided for. The *actual* degree of functional reciprocity under varying conditions is what we are primarily interested in as we deal with the concrete physiological features of seeing.

Essential differences between the three groups of ocular muscles must, however, be pointed out. The ciliary body and the pupillary muscles are autonomically innervated, whereas the extrinsic muscles of the eyeball are controlled by somatic innervation. A difference is thus introduced in behavioral character between the pupillary and ciliary on the one hand and the extrinsic on the other. The former are less facile and flexible, although all three must work well together for precise, quantitative, and simultaneous adjustments.

On account of the partial and indirect control over ocular adjustments, the individual never knows what he does in order to see. He who is unfortunate enough to make inappropriate muscular adjustments for seeing does not know what he is doing wrong. And so, although correction would require learning, direct instruction as to how to move the eyes or to focus them could not be helpful. The proper training is to be gained indirectly through exercises devised in the laboratory or clinic.

Oculomotor difficulties that come to the attention of the clinician do not all exist under oculomotor labels. A certain class that involves accommodation-convergence relations in which improper accommodation is the center of attention is spoken of as *refractive*. These difficulties are generally dealt with as if optical. Only some difficulties are specifically labeled those of *muscle imbalance*. In a broad sense, improper muscle functioning is at the basis of all purely functional difficulties.

"Muscle imbalance" exists in two forms, "manifest imbalance" such as seen in squint or *heterotropia,* and "latent imbalance" which is called *heterophoria.* The concept of phoria is made clear in the section that follows.

The concept of phoria and ocular muscle imbalance. In the process of understanding ocular behavior and visual fatigue, *phoria,* with its alleged causes, has a prominent place in clinical practice. Since the eyes are moved in their orbits by a group of muscles so arranged that they can by appro-

---

[6] Morgan, M. W., Jr.: The Nervous Control of Accommodation, *Am. J. Optom., Arch. Am. Acad. Optom., 21:* 87–93, 1944.

priate amounts of contraction and elongation put torque on the eye, the concept of *perfect muscle balance* has been taken as a natural starting point. In such a state, the muscles would act efficiently. The opposing members of the group do not pull vigorously against each other, but just enough tension is exerted so that the eye is held in the proper position.

It is commonly believed that although some pairs of eyes converge and move so as to maintain single vision under a wide range of conditions they lack proper balance. It is presumed that the muscular performance necessary for single vision is achieved only under compensatory tensions or under the temporary dominance of one nervous center (the fusion center, for example) over another.

Since it is supposed that in all individuals the needed convergent movements of daily life are achieved only under domination of the *fusion* centers in the brain, the question of balance may be investigated by setting up conditions under which "fusion" cannot be expected to operate. Let it be so arranged that the two eyes are independently confronted with objects or patterns so different that they need not become fixed parts of a new visual object (Maddox rod test). Under such conditions, the axes of the two eyes may remain pointed in the same direction as before, or they may take up any one of various new positions. In ordinary parlance the eyes take up "positions of rest," and if these are different from the positions assumed when fusion of the two independently presented objects occurs, then a *phoria* exists. The domination of a fusion center is thus presumed to be superimposed, masking the more nearly "intrinsic" behavior of the muscles.

It is obvious that the "compulsion" for two designs presented independently to the eyes, to fuse into a single pattern, is relative. A number of tests varying in the amount of "stimulus to fusion" have been used. Some compulsion for fusion is not entirely absent in most of them. A second way of measuring phoria is to cover one eye while having the observer fixate with the other. In this test, the tendency for fusion during occlusion is obviated, for only uniocular vision is involved. The occluder is quickly withdrawn, and the presence or absence of eye movement, as fusion occurs, is observed. If movement occurs, the prism power necessary for obliterating it is the measure of the phoria.

Phorias are credited with inducing many kinds of discomfort and other untoward results, including headaches, eyestrain, and ocular fatigue. On this account and because of the relation of the concept of phoria to the general problem of muscle innervation and behavior, the subject is pertinent in the discussion of muscular disharmony and of fatigue.

It is highly probable that what can be done about phorias is partly dependent upon the nature of what induced them. Beacher[7] states that *anomalies of refraction* play a considerable role in the production of horizontal muscular imbalance—exophoria and esophoria. He states that in uncorrected hyperopia the individual tries to overcome his difficulty by adding accommodation. A tendency to converge occurs with accommodation. The result is that although convergence would pull the eyes inward the fusion center pulls the eyes back into the needed position for single vision at the required distance. This means that there is a tendency of the eyes to turn inward even though they do not do so—esophoria.

Unfavorable consequences in muscle behavior also may arise from myopia. The tendency in this condition is to minimize accommodation. In doing so, convergence is necessarily minimized also. Near work that requires considerable convergence will induce it only by compensating for the tendency not to accommodate sufficiently. Hence conflicting tendencies in innervation are believed to be involved.

Besides these refractive origins of heterophoria, it is also supposed that there may be anomalous attachment of the eye muscles. Attachment at an unusual point on the globe would supposedly require the muscle to perform additional work. Likewise improper length of one or more of the muscles will produce anomalous functioning as a result of the need for extra innervation for excessive contraction, etc. Anomalous location of the macula is also considered to be a reason why certain of the extrinsic muscles will have to do excessive work.

Since phorias are usually measured in stationary situations, the possible difficulties of the patient called upon to move his eyes in certain ways at certain speeds in active situations is not tested. Thus what we know of difficulties in active situations comes primarily from the patient's own description of his discomfort, etc.

The most usual discussions of phoria fail in making a clear separation between what is muscular and what is innervational. Muscles act only under innervation, and therefore what occurs can be attributed to innervation. Since in phoria conditions proper action of the several extrinsic muscles *can* take place, this should form the rational starting point. If innervation were always appropriate, all would be well. To say that a given muscle pulls too hard and forces its antagonist to oppose it energetically should imply incorrect innervation, but not necessarily anything about the intrinsic nature of the muscles.

The foregoing remarks have indicated that oculomotor behavior is subject to internal inconsistencies so as not only to induce local discomfort,

---

[7] Beacher, L. L.: "Ocular Refraction and Diagnosis," L. Lester Beacher, Brooklyn, N. Y., 1931. Pp. 286.

but also to thwart the individual in the accomplishment of his everyday activities.

Oculomotor behavior and central organization. There are two extreme viewpoints regarding the dynamics of oculomotor behavior. One is that oculomotor adjustments are rigidly reflexive;[8] the other view regards them as learned. The second view does not deny the reflex character of oculomotor performance, but does involve a different concept of reflex.[9]

If oculomotor behavior is considered reflexive in the first sense, its development and activity are to be left to chance. Difficulties may only be remedied by procedures such as surgery and the application of lenses. These remedies leave the essential organization of the system unchanged and are merely superimposed "corrections." If oculomotor behavior is considered a learned performance, training is required from the very beginning to ensure that the performance meet all the demands that we know will be put upon it. The development and activity involved are subject to guidance.

The evidence that seeing is a learned task has been rapidly accumulating in the past few years in reading clinics, in special studies on school children, and in studies on the differences between good and poor adult readers. Individuals with poorly developed ability to read may improve to a very marked degree later in life, which is contrary to expectations were the oculomotor abilities examples of rigid mechanico-reflexes.

The problem faced in considering the role of ocular adjustments in vision reduces itself to whether or not the intrinsic properties of peripheral mechanisms limit the expression of the adaptive flexibility of the system as a whole. It is only when such limitations can be shown to occur that the behavior of the periphery is crucial. If stereotypy in overt performance does develop, it may arise either from peripheral limitation or from central organization. It is important to distinguish which source is primary in a given case.

That central organization underlies the intellectual aspect of reading ability is to be granted. That it is also involved in the determination of eye movements in reading is brought out by some of the findings of Anderson[10] and others. It was found that the eye movements of good readers are more flexible than those of poor readers. Differences in oculomotor behavior in good and poor readers are shown to be greatest when the individuals are instructed to read to get only the "general idea." Good readers

---

[8] This term is often used to preclude learning entirely, and at best it emphasizes development along largely voluntarily unmodifiable lines.

[9] Reflex behavior is learned, since its development may be directed by modification of conditions, many of which are voluntary on the part of the individual.

[10] Anderson, I. H.: Studies in the Eye Movements of Good and Poor Readers, *Psychol. Monogr., 48:* 1–35, 1936–1937.

then make their most regular eye movements, their fewest regressions, use their shortest fixational pauses, and read their fastest. In such cases, the eye-movement irregularities of poor readers are great, though exceeded by those when such individuals are called upon to read for detailed study purposes. A closer approach toward stereotypy is evidenced in the poor readers.

A study[11] in which good, unselected, and poor readers were compared in oral and silent reading also is pertinent here. The difference between eye movements in oral and silent reading was greatest for good readers. In silent reading, poor readers exhibited a behavioral mode characteristic of oral reading. Since oral reading is the genetic predecessor of silent reading, the similarity between silent and oral reading in poor readers suggests the prominence of the earlier functions. In contrast to this, good readers have become sufficiently divorced from habits of oral reading to provide for more highly differentiated intellectual functions to operate in their silent reading. The study emphasizes the common elements in silent and oral reading, particularly among poor readers. This, as a whole, seems to be a demonstration that certain functional features of early learning are retained in such a way as to preclude further refinement in procedure. Although the concrete evidences of stereotypy exist only in the form of particular kinds of eye movements, and the employment of incipient oral movements, etc., the whole neural organization of poor readers may have also remained in an early stage of development.

The fact that the whole neural organization is involved in visual problems is illustrated by the individual who finds himself suddenly unable to perform a task which at other times is well within the limits of successful achievement. One task of this sort involves the use of rapid searching movements, as in hunting for a lost item on a table cluttered with small objects, or in searching for a specific card in a game of double solitaire.[12]

In this situation the individual feels unable to move his eyes freely and comfortably, as the task requires. He experiences specific ocular tensions, his eyes seeming to "pull" in unwonted directions. The individual experiences a feeling of exasperation in which the localized discomfort and the inability to perform seem causal.

If we analyze the situation further, what is often initially taken as a visual difficulty is seen as part of a personal situation. This is best illustrated by the fact that ocular difficulty is never uniform and is often highly variable, even over a period of 15 or 20 minutes. It may grow worse under

11 Anderson, I. H., and D. E. Swanson: Common Factors in Eye Movements in Silent and Oral Reading, *Psychol. Monogr.*, *48:* 16–69, 1936–1937.

12 It will be noted that the items are large enough to be well above the threshold of resolution, so visual acuity as such is not involved.

defeat and improve in success. The inability to maintain skeletal posture often intrudes as a more pervasive symptom of the picture of functional inadequacy. This postural difficulty follows much the same ups and downs as the ocular, in relation to success and failure in the task at hand.

Thus to the extent that it can be shown that the nature of visual behavior at any specific moment is an expression of the state and organization of the individual as a whole, it can be seen that oculomotor behavior may, in itself, be an expression of a general disorganization arising from thwarts that have little to do with vision. Conversely, the lack of visual accomplishment, in being a thwart to the individual, can be unfavorably reflected in diverse ways, leading to fatigue, which as we have shown is always a kind of state of the individual as a whole. What is detected and expressed as a localized peripheral phenomenon is determined centrally. On the other hand, what is so detected by the individual himself may become a conscious factor in the further development of trouble. It is, as it were, something that the individual *utilizes* in one way or another.

It must further be emphasized that in confronting the physical world the individual may employ ineffective modes of oculomotor adjustment dependent upon factors already described in the early part of the chapter. All action is selective—a kind of choosing. When these choices lead to ineffective activity, further ineffective activity often develops. The developments that are ineffective as corrective adjustments are sometimes merely diffuse releases of energy.[13]

---

[13] For the general principles involved and for examples in peripheral muscle, the reader is referred to the chapter on Organization in Neuromuscular Activity.

Chapter XVIII

CONFLICT AND FRUSTRATION

CONFLICT

THE ASSERTION that fatigue arises from conflict evokes the question of what conflict is and how it eventuates in fatigue.

A review of the literature in psychology shows that the term "conflict" has been used in a great variety of ways in describing human behavior. Notwithstanding, crucial relations between fatigue and conflict have rarely been pointed out, though some individuals have attributed fatigue to conflict at least in special cases.[1]

Up until about 1937, conflict was used almost exclusively in connection with social, cultural, and antropological studies.[2] Following 1937, "mental," emotional, industrial, and physiological (motor) studies of conflict took precedence. The prevalent use of conflict as pertaining to something that happens within the individual organism is a relatively recent development. But even in studies expected to deal with conflicts within the individual, the reference point is often found to shift back and forth from the organism to circumstances external to it and of which it is only a part. At present the terms "frustration" and "anxiety" seem to be becoming more common labels for the situations formerly identified by the term conflict.

Although *experimental* studies on individual conflict are rather rare, it is obvious that some concept of conflict is becoming more often used to account for various behavioral difficulties. While it could be maintained that this trend springs almost entirely from the direct influence of Freud and analysts, viewed more broadly, it is the natural outcome of a larger tendency to think in organizational terms in studying human behavior.

What is meant by conflict? How is it used? Conflict has frequently

[1] Guthrie, E. R.: "The Psychology of Human Conflict," Harper & Brothers, New York, 1938. Pp. 408.

Horney, K.: "Self-analysis," W. W. Norton & Company, Inc., New York, 1942. Pp. 309.

Miller, N. E.: Experimental Studies of Conflict, in Personality and the Behavior Disorders," J. McV. Hunt, ed., Vol. I, The Ronald Press Company, New York, 1944.

[2] According to the titles found in the *Psychological Abstracts*.

been used to refer to the total picture of the individual when a clash is present, as well as to the condition that initiated the picture. As will be seen more clearly later, the same disagreement has existed in regard to frustration. In addition, the concepts of conflict and frustration are very much confused with each other.

A standard definition of conflict is "the presence of opposing desires or tendencies." In psychoanalytic usage, conflict is a "painful emotional state which results from a tension between opposed and contradictory wishes, and is due to the fact that an unconscious (repressed) wish is forcibly prevented from entering the conscious system."[3] Freud explained conflict as resulting from the forced choice of the ego made among opposing tendencies coexisting in the id.

A recognition of the fact that the dynamics of the individual could be aptly described in terms of conflicts was one of Freud's most valuable contributions to the study of personality. His general assumption was that emotional forces constitute the motivations for behavior and attitudes and that to understand any personality structure the recognition of conflicting emotional drives is essential. Conflict (between desires) is also a common subjective experience, according to Murray,[4] who uses the term freely in a number of other ways. A conflict is also defined as "the pattern of mental activity characterized by unpleasant emotional attitudes involving a discrepancy between one's desires and the acceptance of social or other restrictions to their attainment, or between two contradictory or incompatible desires."[5]

These few examples are characteristic of the general usage. Here we see conflict referring to a pattern of mental activity, a subjective experience, an emotional state, and the mere presence of opposition. Conflict also designates a kind of behavior.

Studies of conflict are diversely conceived. As would be expected from the preceding discussion, they vary from highly "subjective" psychoanalytic analyses, to behavioristic studies where all else is sacrificed to observations of overt behavior. In the present chapter, no attempt is made to cover this field, or even to give samples of each type of work done on conflict. Little will be said, for instance, about the numerous animal studies. The reader should refer to the section on frustration, since often the work done under that label could as well have been done as conflict. We have retained

[3] Warren, H. C.: "Dictionary of Psychology," Houghton Mifflin Company, Boston, 1934. Pp. 371.

[4] Murray, H. A.: "Explorations in Personality," Oxford University Press, New York, 1938. Pp. 761.

[5] Sherman, M.: "Mental Conflicts and Personality," Longmans, Green and Company, New York, 1938. Pp. 319.

the author's terminology, rather than regrouping the studies discussed better to fit the theoretical position of the present volume. For the purposes of the present subsection, two studies will suffice as examples of some of the types of work that have been done on conflict.

1. Measurements of galvanic skin responses in combination with word-association tests have played a role in a large number of studies bearing the term conflict in their title. It is generally assumed in these that the higher the galvanic response, the greater, or more intense, the conflict. One of the most recent studies of this type was performed by Lanier,[6] in which he interpreted "affective conflict" operationally as a certain type of verbal response elicited from subjects instructed to make "objective judgments."

Fifty words were chosen from the standard word-association tests to be spoken to each of the subjects. The subjects, 38 women, were instructed to respond to each stimulus word by judging it "pleasant," "unpleasant," "indifferent," or "mixed." The judgments of "mixed" were supposed to represent "affective conflict" and to indicate the coexistence of pleasant and unpleasant states in consciousness. The responses, reaction times, and galvanic skin responses were recorded. Recognition memory for the stimulus words was tested immediately following the experiment and 1 week later.

Lanier found "mixed" judgments were the fewest and required the largest reaction times. The response, "mixed," was accompanied by the highest galvanic skin response. It also had a superior memory value as shown by the immediate memory test. On the basis of these results. Lanier concluded that the term "affective conflict" is scientifically significant and may denote a dimension of affective behavior.

2. Barker's experimental study of conflict resolution[7] is so commonly referred to in recent treatises on the subject that it will be described here.

The subjects of Barker's study were 19 boys between the ages of 9 and 11 years. Preliminary to the experiment, a preference series for seven liquids was made for each subject by the method of paired comparisons. Three experimental conditions were set up, the concern in each case being with the time elapsing in the making of a choice and the amount of so-called choicelike behavior occurring. Under the first condition the alternatives varied from similar desirability (orange juice and pineapple juice) to very different desirability (orange juice and vinegar). The alternatives

[6] Lanier, L. H.: An Experimental Study of "Affective Conflict," *J. Psychol., 11:* 199–217, 1941.

[7] Barker, R. G.: An Experimental Study of the Resolution of Conflict by Children: Time Elapsing and Amount of Vicarious Trial-and-error Behavior Occurring, in "Studies in Personality," Q. McNemar and M. A. Merrill, editors, McGraw-Hill Book Company, Inc., New York, 1942. Pp. 333.

under the second condition varied from desirable (orange juice and pine-apple juice) to undesirable (vinegar and salt water). The third condition supposedly contrasted "real" and "hypothetical" conflicts. A real conflict was said to occur when the subject experienced the consequences of his choice, *i.e.*, when he was made to drink the liquid chosen. When the subject had only to state his preference, there was said to be a hypothetical conflict.

Preferences were found to vary from individual to individual and from the real to the hypothetical series in one individual. There was a general tendency for time and these choicelike behavior scores to increase when the selection involved alternatives that were both undesirable. Neutral alternatives tended to involve the least time and lowest behavior scores, but this tendency was not borne out statistically. There was an inverse relation between both the time and the amount of choicelike behavior and the "distance" between alternatives in a preference series. The real series involved more time and more choicelike behavior than the hypothetical series.

In drawing his conclusions from this experiment, Barker cites six topo-logical assumptions that he says account for his findings. These specific assumptions regarding the field are used both to account for the observed behavior, and to interpret the results obtained.

Barker attempts to distinguish between "discriminative difficulties" and conflict and to "create conflict situations undisturbed by discriminative difficulties." He points out that in certain situations there is no "conflict of desire"; nevertheless such difficulties hold up intended action. Choicelike behavior, he notes, occurs in these situations as it does in cases in which there are "simultaneously existing but mutually exclusive desires."

While it is possible only in the broadest sense to determine the presence or absence of discriminative difficulties, when present they must form the basis of conflict in the individual. Hesitating and vacillating behavior is Barker's only criterion of the presence of conflict, and this applies as much in the one case as it does in the other.

It is certainly true that the relationship between conflict, as we use the term, and overt behavior is not simple. When measured as roughly as it is in the present experiment, it is also very questionable, especially when no introspective reports were obtained from the subjects.

Since Barker states his conclusions on the basis of field concepts devel-oped by Lewin, the dynamics are all in the external situation. In such topological interpretations, the organism seems deprived of its ability to initiate and direct its behavior and becomes merely the pawn of outside forces that act upon it. Topology, as an attempt to consider the larger situation in which the organism is only a part, is highly justified, but inferences about events within the organism itself derived from this approach are open to objection.

Classification of conflict. Conflict has been classified in various ways. One of these is the frequently noted division: mental, moral, and social conflict. Mental conflict is usually used to refer to the blocking of a "drive." Social conflicts refer to those involving difficulties in social adjustment. The point of reference here is sometimes taken to be the individual and sometimes the social environment. In a sense, nearly all conflicts occurring in adults are at least in part social.[8] So-called moral conflicts are those in which a sense of guilt is involved in one of the conflicting factors. Moral conflicts are also social in that the sense of guilt is said to arise because of real or imagined disapproval of the immediate social group of which the individual is a member. A classification of conflicts in this manner seems not only arbitrary but also not particularly useful. While not all conflicts could be termed "moral," perhaps all, or nearly all, of them are mental and social.

Although it is a fairly common assumption that all conflicts are detrimental to organismic activity, such is certainly far from the case. In fact it is questionable whether without conflicts organismic activity would exist. At least all goal-directed activity would be impossible, as would, of course, all creative thought and integration. Sherman[9] states that conflicts may be divided into the detrimental and the useful. Detrimental conflicts, he says, are those which detract from the progress of the individual, whereas useful conflicts motivate greater activity and productivity.

While it is generally agreed among psychiatrists that the psychoneuroses are essentially the result of conflicts,[10] conflicts and their resolution are also at the base of "normal" and "superior" personality integration and development. In fact, it is not unusual to speak of the detrimental effects of security (supposed lack of crucial conflicts) to the progress of the individual.[11] Conflicts may be looked upon as necessary in the progressive socialization of the individual.[12] They may be considered as undesirable only when no adequate adjustment is made over a long period of time. What constitutes adequate adjustment is an individual matter to a large

[8] Bentley, M.: "The Field of Psychology," D. Appleton-Century Company, Inc., New York, 1925. Pp. 545.

[9] Sherman, M.: How Mental Conflicts Help to Develop Children, in Toward Understanding Children, *Univ. Iowa Extension Bull. 261,* pp. 69-77, 1931.

[10] Horney, K.: "New Ways in Psychoanalysis," W. W. Norton & Company, Inc., New York, 1939. Pp. 313.

[11] Sherman, M.: "Mental Conflicts and Personality," Longmans, Green and Company, New York, 1938. Pp. 319.

[12] Bentley, *op. cit.*

extent, and dependent, of course, upon the culture that prevails. The importance of the particular conflict in the subject's total personality organization also cannot be neglected in estimating its favorable or unfavorable role.

"Needs may come into conflict with each other within the personality, giving rise when prolonged to harassing spiritual dilemmas. Much of the misery and most of the neurotic illness in the world may be attributed to such inner conflicts."[13] Or again, "Usually the basis for many maladjustments is the formation of a pattern of conflicts, the pressure of which causes the individual to assume either symbolic emotional maladjustment or overt maladjustments." [14] Sometimes behavior must be judged as disharmonious from any criterion applicable to the individual as a system. This behavior may be explained only in terms of disorganization and conflict.

Conflicts are also seen to be descriptive of one aspect of the learning process. Mowrer and Kluckhohn,[15] in applying the idea of conflict to learning theory, state that although punishment "weakens" a given habit the explanation should be made in terms of reward. They say that actually a stronger motive, and one calling for an adjustment incompatible with the previous one, is introduced. A state of conflict exists until a new habit is set up which is more powerful than the old one. The earlier habit is then said to become inhibited. These authors, like many others, appear to use conflict only in the sense of conflicts of motives, drives, and the like. This use is not limited to the personal, however, but also includes the social, since they refer to the role of conflict in culture patterns, conflicts between legal principles, etc.

Guthrie[16] points out that the ability to learn has disadvantages as well as advantages and that states of conflict direct learning habits as well as interests. (For Guthrie, conflict is a failure of inhibition in the central nervous system. Conflict occurs when the opposition of two action tendencies is transferred to the muscles.) Conflict resolutions, whether more or less adaptive, tend to be habituated and thus become adjustive or maladjustive personality habits. Guthrie believes that the more adaptive resolutions are ideational and can be externalized, while the less adaptive are said to activate only the nonspeech systems with resulting "random" attempts at solution.

[13] Murray, H. A.: "Explorations in Personality," Oxford University Press, New York, 1938. Pp. 761.

[14] Sherman, *op. cit.*

[15] Mowrer, O. H., and C. Kluckhohn: Dynamic Theory of Personality, in "Personality and the Behavior Disorders," J. McV. Hunt, ed., Vol. I, pp. 69–135. The Ronald Press Company, New York, 1944.

[16] Guthrie, *op. cit.*

Anderson,[17] using "conflict" in a more sociological sense, speaks of "real" and "apparent" types. Apparent conflicts are said to occur when the purposes and desires are not clearly defined. Since this author is dealing primarily with so-called conflicts between different individuals, this distinction is of little value for our purposes.

Another classification is that of the psychoanalysts, notably Alexander.[18] He distinguishes between "structural" and "instinctual" conflicts. Structural conflict is said to arise when instinctual strivings are rejected by the super-ego. Instinctual conflict arises because such processes are said to be manifested in pairs of opposites such as active and passive. Conflict of this sort is inevitable when one of two ego-acceptable strivings must be rejected. Alexander also mentions a third type of conflict—"external" conflict, which is said to be based on external inhibitions. He believes that a differentiation of the conflict type is important to psychoanalytic treatment. Since one type of conflict may serve to intensify another, the structural differentiation is held to have a double effect. It creates tension both by restricting the striving and by disturbing the balance between the conflicting tendencies.

Another classification of conflict types of a quite different nature is that proposed by Lewin in 1931. Lewin analyzed three primary conflict situations in terms of spatial diagrams of "field forces." The three types are (1) approach-approach, (2) approach-avoidance, and (3) avoidance-avoidance. The first situation is supposedly resolved by responding to one or both stimuli, the second and third by "withdrawal from the field." Much of the experimental work on conflict is based on this kind of analysis of conflict situations. It has been put into terms of goal gradients by Hull and enlarged upon by Miller.

Miller,[19] in describing these types of conflict, speaks in terms of approach and avoidance gradients, both of which are said to increase the nearer the individual is to the goal or to the object to be avoided, respectively. The avoidance gradient is said to be steeper than the approach gradient. Miller states that since pure approach-approach choices are easily resolved, conflict does not appear. He explains that whenever unaccounted for indecision occurs there are probably concealed sources of avoidance.

In the following use of the idea of conflict, the distinction between the experience and the situation is made and retained and the classification, therefore, seems unusually insightful.

[17] Anderson, H. H.: Conflicts in Personality Development, *Ment. Hyg., 20:* 605-613, 1936.

[18] Alexander, F.: The Relation of Structural and Instinctual Conflicts, *Psychoanal. Quart., 2:* 181-207, 1933.

[19] Miller, *op. cit.*

Maslow[20] notes the necessity of dealing in terms of the individual facing his own particular problem, in studying conflict and similar concepts. He believes that the important question is whether or not the individual perceives something as a threat. The essential pathogenic characteristics of conflict are seen as a threat of thwarting of basic needs and a threat to the integration of the individual and his basic mastery of the world. In general there are two types of conflict, those which are threatening to the individual and those which are not. Since only the threatening conflicts become pathological, Maslow holds that the concept of threat is more fundamental than the concept of conflict. It hardly seems more fundamental, but if one's aim is to deal with pathogenic mechanisms it is undoubtedly more important. For our purposes, the concept of conflict is certainly the more basic, yet a distinction of the kind made by Maslow is not without value.

Maslow actually points out four types of conflict. The first he calls sheer choice, which occurs between two paths to the same unimportant goal. The second type arises from a choice between two paths to the same important goal. Third are the threatening conflicts occurring between two different and vital goals. If conflicts of this type are of long duration, they lead to pathogenic symptoms of various kinds. The fourth type is called catastrophic conflict which involves no choice.

Conflict and disease.   Conflict is expressed in a change in the experience and behavior of the organism. It is seen to have numerous effects. Fatigue, which results from, and is therefore an expression of, conflict, is only one of these. Although the experience of fatigue is our main interest, it is necessary to say a few things regarding some of the other changes that are expressions of conflict.

At the present time, a great many organic diseases are considered to be "psychosomatic" in origin and progress. These diseases are found to be best cured by psychotherapy, or by an inclusion of psychotherapy with the regular medical treatment. Among the so-called psychosomatic diseases are gastric ulcer, tuberculosis, cardiospasm, asthma, and colitis, to name only a few. The various psychosomatic diseases have this in common: they, like fatigue, are all said to arise from conflict.

The psychoanalytic study of a number of cases of hay fever led Wilson[21] to conclude that hay fever is the "result of unsuccessful olfactory repression." He traces this back to thwarted sexual curiosity, combined with encouraged "indulgence of olfactory perception." Following unsuccessful

20 Maslow, A. H.: Conflict, Frustration, and the Theory of Threat, *J. Abnorm. & Social Psychol., 38:* 81-86, 1943.

21 Wilson, G. W.: A Study of Structural and Instinctual Conflicts in Cases of Hay Fever, *Psychosomatic Med., 3:* 51-66, 1941.

attempts at visual and intellectual sublimation for olfactory stimulation, patients develop a conversion symptom (hay fever) with corresponding diminution in both olfactory and visual perception.

Wilson does not claim to understand the interplay between specific allergies, the inner conflicts, and the attempts at solution. Although pollen alone was not found to be effective in the analyzed cases, Wilson thinks it may occasionally be the only irritant. He notes that psychological factors alone are often sufficient to produce hay-fever symptoms.

Jerome Hartz[22] spent 2 years in a tuberculosis sanatorium, the first year as a patient exclusively, the second as a patient and a physician. He thus had opportunity to observe cases from two perspectives. Among his interesting observations he notes that the patients themselves recognize that emotional factors are intimately involved in their own cases. They refer to "x-ray fever," for example, and a fellow patient is "kidded" when he manifests a slight rise of body temperature for several days before x-rays are to be taken. Hartz believes that the life the patient was living just previous to the onset of his disease is of great significance. He cites cases which seem to indicate that the onset of the disease was partly due to conflict situations in the lives of the individuals.

One patient resented the presence of his ailing mother-in-law in his home, took to drinking and staying away as much as possible, and finally developed tuberculosis. In the sanatorium he improved little until he received the report of the death of his mother-in-law. Following this, his recovery was rapid and complete. Another patient, a 19-year-old girl, strongly resented the excessive demands made by a self-centered mother. This patient had anxiety attacks beginning about a year after she entered the sanatorium. At this time her mother was reported to be recovering sufficiently from a second severe psychotic depression to visit the patient. (The mother's first depression had occurred when the patient was 10 years old. On this occasion the patient identified herself with her father. She stayed away from home, ignoring her mother as much as possible.) When the visit occurred, the patient abruptly voiced her resentment of her mother's behavior in the presence of both parents. She was subsequently free of anxiety symptoms during the remainder of her stay at the sanatorium. As might be expected, however, when eventually she was well enough to return to her home environment, she was again filled with conflict and had a recurrence of the disease.

These two individuals neglected the first signs of their illness to avoid being more closely confined in their unhappy positions. Both of these cases, as well as a third which Hartz cites, show that the development of tuberculosis served the purpose of escaping from situations that gave rise

[22] Hartz, J.: Tuberculosis and Personality Conflicts, *Psychosomatic Med.,* 6: 17–22, 1944.

to intolerable conflicts. The third patient also had a recurrence of the disease when he returned to his insufficiently altered environment.

Hartz believes that these cases suggest that "personality conflicts" play a role in tuberculosis. He says that tuberculosis is often used to guarantee care and affection. It is generally recognized today that the personality of the patient is a determining factor in tuberculosis. Hartz' analysis goes somewhat further than this, but he does not, as some psychiatrists do, produce a rigid list of supposed characteristics of the tuberculosis patient. He merely indicates the importance of the role of conflict in the disease and notes the *individual* character of the behavior. He states that the personal issues are not apparent in ordinary case histories, etc., but only come to light through personal observation and study.

Strangely enough, the patients who developed tuberculosis did not often feel extremely fatigued until after the onset of the illness. On the contrary, they were unusually active and energetic, although in a manner that suggested attempted escape from worry and anxiety. It is possible that such a pattern is characteristic of certain less common alignments, for it is well known that the usual disease process is preceded by the development of a considerable amount of fatigue. Fatigue, without obvious disease, is of course the most frequent outcome of conflict in most people. Ordinarily it is not until the conflicts become prolonged and severe that the fatigue is accompanied by other marked symptoms. The reasons why some persons develop, or emphasize, chronic fatigue, some anxiety, and others so-called physical diseases in the face of unresolved conflicts are yet to be discovered.

An interesting and enlightening set of findings on the subject of conflict in disease is given by Dunbar.[23] Seven classes of patients studied by psychosomatic methods were found to differ in their focal personality difficulties. These Dunbar called the "areas of focal conflict."

The characteristic response of *fracture patients* in their relations to parents and spouse, to school, to work, and to other situations in which authority is involved is avoidance. Such individuals struggle for independence and autonomy. They attempt to minimize and avoid conflicts with authority whenever they can. It is significant to note that most of these individuals have a past history of stern parents, guardians, or strict schooling. Many of them report having had severe punishment for more or less minor misdeeds.

The typical area of focal conflict in the case of patients with *hypertensive cardiovascular disease* also lies in the individual's relation to authority. The trouble with these individuals seems to lie in their fear of

[23] Dunbar, H. F.: "Psychosomatic Diagnosis," Paul B. Hoeber, Inc., Medical Book Department of Harper & Brothers, New York, 1943. Pp. 741.

criticism. They are always apprehensive about not meeting requirements. They tend to feel that the criticisms of their superiors are entirely unjustified, although they do not express resentment against the criticism. Their behavior is a mixture of the attempt to please and persistent noncooperation. In cases of *coronary occlusion,* the conflict is again with authority, and the reaction can be described as the attempt to surpass or subdue authority. Such individuals are easily hurt by superiors, but continue to curry their favor and try to dominate them. In *angina* cases, there is a great similarity to the coronary, but the attempt here is only to equal and not to surpass authority.

Rhematic fever and *rheumatoid arthritis* patients resemble the fracture patients more nearly than those of any other class. These patients tend to identify themselves with the opposite sex and to avoid authority. In patients with *rheumatic heart disease* the major area of conflict is again that involving authority. The characteristic reaction is said to be that of emulating superiors, at least in fantasy, and currying favor with the opposite sex. This group derives its compensation through its abnormalities and ability to suffer.

The *cardiac arrhythmia* patients find their area of focal conflict in meeting the outside world. They tend to be narcissistic, this being opposed by the desire to be influential and admired by others. Except for the fracture group these patients have the highest accident record.

In *diabetes,* the major difficulties are said to lie in areas of adjustment where assumption of responsibility is involved. The difficulty begins long before the disease as such is evident. Such individuals tend to retain their early dependence, and independence develops mainly in words and not in action. Such individuals suffer from strong anxiety until the disease reaches a stage where it gives them an excuse for inactivity, though apparently an unsatisfactory one.

Dunbar sees human personality as an organizational whole. The disorganization involved is characterized by various types of conflict. Disorganization involving vacillation, opposition, and friction among personality components is seen to occur in relation to environment. It would be expected that these conflicts would have a significant bearing on the development of fatigue in the individuals involved.

FRUSTRATION

In recent years, "frustration theory" has come to assume importance in psychological thinking. Notable among its proponents, Rosenzweig[24] con-

---

[24] Rosenzweig, S.: An Outline of Frustration Theory, in "Personality and the Behavior Disorders," J. McV. Hunt, ed., pp. 379–388, Vol. I. The Ronald Press Company, New York, 1944.

siders it a concrete expression of the organismic point of view and offers a theoretical formulation. Frustration, he says, "occurs whenever the organism meets a more or less insurmountable obstacle or obstruction in its route to the satisfaction of any vital need."[25] It may be defined broadly as a failure of biological adjustment.[26] This definition is in no way in disagreement with our conception of frustration, although it is perhaps too broad to be of much value. It is not clear from the statement whether frustration is being taken as a descriptive term for the over-all picture of the organism in a conflict situation, or whether it is taken to be the conflict itself. A further discussion of Rosenzweig's formulation of frustration theory will clarify his views on this score.

Rosenzweig, who favors an operational definition, looks upon frustration as a phenomenon that involves states ranging from mild craving, to thwarting, to traumatic experiences.[27] This phenomenon is said to be created through internal or external privation, deprivation, or conflict. Privations, deprivations, and conflicts are said to be in turn classes of frustration.[28] When Rosenzweig later goes on to speak of "reactions to frustration," we gather he is using the term to refer to the clash itself. This is consistent with considering internal and external conflicts (when one need is frustrated by another) as varieties of frustration, but not so consistent with the original definition, or with the notion that frustration is created through conflict.

Some authors[29] hold that the notion of frustration either as cause or as effect is tenable. Since they point out, however, that frustration must then be related to its proper context, they offer no sanction for frustration viewed both ways in any one system. Yet these same authors state that sins of omission represent the only lacks in current definitions of frustration, each of which, they say, seizes upon some essential or essentials of the frustration process.

Rosenzweig, in discussing "reactions to frustration," points out that his classification refers to mechanisms or types of reaction rather than to the reacting individuals.[30] Reactions to frustration are said to vary in direct-

[25] *Ibid.*

[26] Rosenzweig, S.: VI. A General Outline of Frustration, Character & Personality, 7: 151–160, 1938.

[27] Rosenzweig, S.: I. The Significance of Frustration as a Problem of Research, *Character & Personality,* 7: 126–128, 1938.

[28] Rosenzweig, S.: VI. A General Outline of Frustration, *Character & Personality,* 7: 151–160, 1938.

[29] Britt, S. H., and S. Q. Janus: Criteria of Frustration, *Psychol. Rev.,* 47: 451–470, 1940.

[30] Rosenzweig, S.: Types of Reaction to Frustration, *J. Abnorm. & Social Psychol.,* 29: 298–300, 1934.

ness, and one individual may use as many as all of the types at one time.[31] The two main reaction types are the "need-persistive" and the "ego-defensive." The former refers to the continued tendency to fulfill the need and restore equilibrium. It is said to occur invariably following frustration. The latter occurs when the ego is threatened and includes three "subjective types of reaction." The first is called extropunitive, where the individual attributes his frustration to externals; the second, intropunitive, where the individual blames himself for his condition; the third, impunitive, where there is an attempt to avoid blame altogether, with aggression apparently lacking. All these reactions are said to be adequate when they are warranted by the existing conditions and as long as they represent progressive (as opposed to retrogressive) personality trends.

A number of authors have made use of concept of *frustration tolerance*. Just what such a concept implies will bear some consideration. Although it has some of the same elements, the situation is even more problematical than it is in the case of drug tolerance.

The reason for the special difficulty lies in the reference point or points that are chosen. For example, the individual is faced with a novel situation in which he is thwarted and manifests a certain picture of frustration. At a later date, faced with a similar situation, the individual may show a different and perhaps milder picture of frustration. The question here is whether we are dealing with changed reactions to thwarting, or with a decreased or complete lack of thwart. If it is the latter, which seems most reasonable, the so-called frustration tolerance that has developed is a tolerance to the situation, rather than to frustration.

If the individual has "improved" his reaction to a large number of possible situations that are sufficiently similar to the originally frustrating one, what will happen when an entirely different situation is encountered? A concept of frustration tolerance implies generalization. Here, too, his reactions should be "improved." However, everyday observation does not bear this out. The individual, having gotten a certain adjustment for a specific kind of situation, can generalize this to other situations only to the extent that they are similar to the first one: He shows no "tolerance" for the new situation, but again manifests a marked picture of frustration.

In dealing with the concept of frustration tolerance, no personal reference is possible. If the individual experiences no thwart, there is not need for tolerance. Whenever the individual is thwarted, he is in conflict and shows a picture of frustration, by definition. There is no way of pinning down the situation, when the reference point of the individual is taken.

It is of course true that some individuals are characteristically thwarted more often than others. Only a detailed genetic study of the individual

[31] Rosenzweig, S.: An Outline of Frustration Theory.

would throw some light on the dynamic factors in his adjustments. Such a study might well reveal that the individual, so prone to frustration in adulthood, had experienced an unusually large amount of thwarting as a child. This would belie the assumption, so often underlying the concept of frustration tolerance, that the individual builds up a resistance to thwarting through being frequently thwarted. While this may tend to occur in certain cases, it is by no means an apt generalization. It would be more true, although far from accurate, to hold that thwarting breeds increased susceptibility to further thwarting.

Unlike those who believe that a tolerance for frustration is built up through thwarting, Rosenzweig[32] notes that the determinants of frustration tolerance are largely unknown. He believes that the tolerance may be conditioned either constitutionally or by experience, its degree depending upon the integration of the organism. Rosenzweig defines the concept as "an individual's capacity to withstand frustration without failure of psychobiological adjustment, *i.e.*, without resorting to inadequate modes of response."

Again we are faced with the question of what actually occurs when an individual "withstands" frustration. It seems clear that the individual is simply not frustrated, or else that he is less frustrated than he was on some previous occasion. From a personal or organismic point of view, what then is the criterion for deciding when the individual should be frustrated? The basis often taken in experimental work is a social one. Individuals are compared with one another. If individual *A* shows a more serious picture of frustration than individual *B,* when both have failed a certain test, individual *A* is said to have less frustration tolerance. The use of such arbitrary standards is obviously in error. Rosenzweig, himself, points out that frustration tolerance differs in various aspects of the same personality as well as in different individuals, but he seems to neglect the fact that frustration tolerance, so-called, is bound to vary greatly from time to time in the same person. If for no other reason, this would be true because of the vast complication of the organism as a system and because of the great diversification of the heterogeneous factors impinging on it from the outside.

Approaching the problem in terms of *reactions to frustration* is common in psychoanalytic, as well as in psychological, analyses. Freud defined frustration as the prevention of satisfaction to the instinct. Following this view, reactions to frustration would refer to all that occurs either overtly or within the organism when instinctual strivings are blocked. Freud[33] also

[32] Rosenzweig, S.: An Outline of Frustration Theory, *op. cit.*

[33] Freud, S.: "Civilization and Its Discontents," trans. by J. Riviere, J. Cape and H. Smith, New York, 1930. Pp. 144.

speaks of "cultural privations" as referring to the social restrictions that decrease the possibilities of instinctual gratification for each member of the group.

French[34] holds that it is misleading to speak of goal-directed strivings as simple forces or tendencies, but that such seeking is a highly organized process. He believes that severe frustration (conflict) tends to break up the organization to the original elementary strivings. This disintegration is said to occur when the concept of the goal loses its dominance and emotion inhibits appropriate motor energies. Symbolic acts and wish-fulfilling fantasies are seen as results of such a break-up of goal-directed strivings.

The activity of the organism in attempting to fulfill a wish, or, in other words, aligning behavior for a specific purpose, involves a complex process of integration. French suggests that two things are required of the organism: (1) knowing how to achieve a goal, and (2) subordinating motor energies to the kind of activity required.

French says that all reactions to frustration are "dictated by a conflict between the urge toward the original goal and the urge to avoid the frustrating obstacle." Reactions to frustration are said to be successful when there is (1) concentration on overcoming obstacles, and the original goal is temporarily forgotten, and (2) deflection to avoid the obstacles, either by getting around them or changing the goal. Reactions are unsuccessful (1) when the struggle against the obstacle becomes a substitute goal, and (2) when there is neurotic substitution of an inadequate goal. When the reactions to frustration are unsuccessful, varying degrees and kinds of disintegration may occur, depending upon the intensity and suddenness of the frustration, and upon the momentary state of integration of the organism.

Among the changes frequently attributed to the frustrated organism is an increase in *tension*. Tension is used to refer to (1) the experience of being tense, (2) a nervous system phenomenon, not directly equated with muscular tonicity, or (3) a neuromuscular phenomenon. One might also make a fourth category to include the many cases in which the meaning is either a supposed mixture of the varied uses mentioned above, or so vague as to be intangible. This last group would actually cover the large majority of the uses of tension in dealing with frustration.

Tension used for the *experience* of being tense seems legitimate enough. It is only when a direct parallel with the actual muscle pull is assumed that difficulties are bound to ensue. Although muscle tension has never been adequately measured in the intact organism, it is safe to conclude

[34] French, T. M.: An Analysis of the Goal Concept Based upon Study of Reactions to Frustration, *Psychoanal. Rev., 28:* 61–71, 1941.

that no direct correlation exists between it and the common experience of feeling tense.

If frustration is taken as a general term merely descriptive of an organism that has been blocked[35] in some way, the possible constituents of the total picture are infinitely varied. It is far from justified to claim that a feeling of increased tension, or any other single factor, is always present, or is in any way generally characteristic of the frustrated organism. It is possible only to note what happens in specific cases. The question might also be raised as to the stage of frustration at which the organism is being considered. The term covers the whole process, which may last for years, and at no point is the organism static and inactive. An individual, for example, may react to the blocking first with aggression and a feeling of increased tension. After a period of time he may give up his struggles and react with a feeling of fatigue, the usual counterpart of which is a feeling of limpness, the very reverse of a feeling of tension. At both stages, however, he may be spoken of as "the frustrated organism." We must conclude, then, that the picture of frustration lacks uniform features, although such a view is contrary to that generally taken.

Tension regarded as a central phenomenon that cannot be equated either with a feeling of tenseness or with actual muscular tone seems rather fantastic in the light of our knowledge of the nervous system. Such a concept seems highly impractical since, even if such a phenomenon were to exist, we have no way of being aware of its presence or absence. Possibly those who adopt this view of tension most often wrongly assume it to have a close parallel with tension as an experience and are thus able to claim some value for their approach. If no such parallel is attempted, the concept does indeed seem meaningless.

The use of tension in its original sense, *i.e.*, muscle tension, is of course valid. Again it should be mentioned, however, there is no strict correlation between this muscle tension and a feeling of tension.

We have already given Maslow's classification of conflict in the section of that title and stated that he maintains a distinction between the experience and the external factors involved in the total situation. Maslow and Mittleman[36] are among the few to make a clear distinction between conflict and frustration. These authors view conflict as a clash between the impulses and needs of the organism. Frustration they take to be a threatening or serious nongratification of needs. They point out that some authors

---

[35] In speaking of an organism that is blocked, our reference is the personal one. The block, therefore, is the one that occurs *within the organism*, which may or may not have any direct bearing on an external impediment.

[36] Maslow, A. H., and B. Mittleman: "Principles of Abnormal Psychology," Harper & Brothers, New York, 1941. Pp. 638.

restrict frustration to cases in which psychological threat results from deprivation.[37] Maslow and Mittleman, however, recognize that "intra-psychic" as well as external factors may serve as obstacles to gratification.

Maslow[38] recognizes that only the person as a whole may be frustrated. He deplores the current tendency to speak of a part of an individual, for example, a need, being frustrated. He also deplores the fact that the usual definitions of frustration are made •in terms of a lack of some sort of gratification, without regard to its importance to the organism. Maslow contends that the effects commonly attributed to frustration in general arise only from a threatening (to the personality) deprivation. He feels that two concepts (1) deprivation and (2) threat to the personality would be more useful than the single concept of frustration. This division is not unlike Rosenzweig's "need-persistive" and "ego-defensive" classification. For Rosenzweig, however, both of these are to be included under frustration.

Maslow notes that goal objects may have two meanings for the individual. (1) They have an intrinsic meaning, and (2) they may have a symbolic value. A goal object may symbolize respect, love, prestige, or achievement for the individual. It is only in such cases that being deprived of it will result in much difficulty for the individual, or cause him to manifest a marked picture of frustration.

ASPECTS OF DISORGANIZATION

Analytical study of active systems, such as the human organism, necessarily involves a recognition of organization. Through analysis of organization, one would expect to account for all kinds of human behavior.

Perfect integration is a mere abstraction. Only on conceptually ideal organism is totally integrated. Organic behavior always involves *disorganization*. Although no adjustment can occur without some disorganization, the organism is always striving to maintain unity and integration. When disorganization occurs, it, in some way, impedes the easy directional behavior. Disorganization is thus seen as the basis for many particular kinds of behavior.

Conflicts are viewed as specific disruptions in the organization of the individual—the points of clash between two subsystems. For our purposes, the term conflict is reserved to refer to events *within* the organism. Conflicts may occur at all levels of organic activity.

The fact that conflict occurs is bound to influence the nature of activity.

[37] Deprivation is defined as "the inability to satisfy a need or desire because of external obstacles." This, for some authors, is synonymous with frustration itself.

[38] Maslow, A. H.: VII. Deprivation, Threat, and Frustration, *Psychol. Rev., 48:* 364–366, 1941.

As a result of conflict the organism may be said to present a picture of *frustration,* which may have an infinite variety of patterns. *Fatigue,* one of the most frequent outcomes of conflict, is often primary in the frustration picture.

It is impossible at present to make a really clear-cut distinction between conflict and frustration. As has been stated in the previous section, the two terms are often used synonymously, and the use of each involves much confusion among the various frames of reference that can be adopted, especially among the physical, the behaviorial, and the personal. The main point to consider here is that fatigue always arises from some sort of disorganization.

As the problem is approached rather naïvely, frustrations seems to imply a sort of deadlock, whereas conflict represents a dynamic interaction. If frustration is thought of as an effect of conflict, it is more accurate to say that fatigue arises from conflict than that it arises from frustration. Fatigue is a part of the total picture of frustration, which arises from conflict. Frustration, then, includes all the reactions to conflict within the organism, whereas conflict represents merely the clash or system interference itself.

Conflict and frustration are seen to be inseparable, the former emphasizing the dynamics involved, the latter the descriptive side of the picture.

Whether or not frustration is best viewed merely as a nongratification of some sort, or as a term for the whole picture resulting from conflict, is not at all clear at present. If conflict is taken as the focal point, as it is in this presentation, no particular difficulty arises from using frustration in both of these senses. It cannot be used in any but a descriptive manner, whether the description is specific or general. In other systems, in which frustration is taken as the cornerstone, a more rigid definition is required as well as a clear statement of the reference point used.

If frustration may be taken as the name for the situation of the organism in conflict, it does not refer to all cases of external blocking or deprivation. If an individual is blocked in reaching a goal, he may simply change the goal to one that is more attainable. If this occurs easily, the amount of conflict and frustration present must have been very slight—though the external block may have been sudden and effective. From an organismic standpoint, unless conflict arises there can be no frustration for the organism.

Although it is possible and necessary to separate out different aspects of any given picture of frustration, such a separation is always artificial. Only the whole organism can be frustrated. We may speak of conflict between parts, but the resulting picture must be considered in terms of the whole. Any stance that forms a part of the picture of frustration, *e.g.,* fatigue, is also necessarily of the total organism.

Chapter XIX

CHRONIC FATIGUE AND RELATED SYNDROMES

INTEREST in fatigue includes not only the tiredness that appears from time to time in connection with vigorous or prolonged exertion, or with inherently unpleasant tasks, but also the persistent tiredness that becomes so characteristic of the individual as to be a part of his personality.

Fatigue of this sort has become an increasingly important problem in medicine and psychiatry. Chronic fatigue has long been recognized as the common accompaniment of the large majority of human ills, but, until quite recently, has been somewhat neglected as a clinical picture in its own right. No diagnosis appears to be warranted except that of "chronic fatigue" in an increasing number of cases. This may be due either to actual changes in complaints or to altered opinions of physicians resulting from new medical knowledge, or both.

In attempting to understand and alleviate chronic fatigue, it must be remembered that we are confronted with the *whole person* in trouble and not just some localized part. At this stage of scientific development, it is not an easy matter to analyze human states without leaving the impression that the individual is made up of the psychological *and* the physiological. Immediately upon confrontment with the more obvious symptoms of chronic fatigue, it is natural to inquire into the present and previous health of the individual. If there are no positive symptoms at present, a previous illness may have left some aftermath to which the symptoms of constant tiredness and weakness may be attributed. It is also true that, without any previous or concurrent medical symptoms, individuals may develop attitudes toward life which, under the particular environmental circumstances of the case, induce chronic fatigue.

A number of interrelations exist between fatigue and *anxiety* and, therefore, between chronic fatigue and the so-called anxiety state. Although it is not our purpose to clarify the term "anxiety" here, it should be pointed out that anxiety has a variety of meanings.[1] For our purposes, anxiety may

---

[1] Anxiety is very nearly the exclusive property of psychoanalysis, forming the cornerstone for much of its theory. The nonpsychoanalytic formulations of anxiety are rather piecemeal and incomplete.

be regarded very generally as the pattern arising in a conflict situation in which the general alignment of the individual may be regarded as fear. For us anxiety, like fatigue, refers to a conscious experience. The individual always knows whether or not he is anxious, although he may not know what he is anxious about.[2]

Both anxious individuals and those suffering from fatigue are involved in conflict. By now it has become clear that conflicts either become resolved, dwindle and disappear, or else, in continuing, produce untoward results. Just what the untoward results are is a somewhat variable affair, depending certainly upon the individual involved, and perhaps on other factors as well. We have already described how fatigue arises from conflict. A victim of anxiety is obviously not at peace within himself, and any description of his condition would reveal conflicting elements. Like fatigue, anxiety evolves from personal disorganization. Anxiety is personal, and it tends to be cumulative.

It is possible that the conflicts involved in the case of anxiety are different from those at the roots of fatigue. The difference may be seen as one of pattern rather than of kind. In other words, identical conflicts may be involved, but, other things being equal, different reactions will be produced in organisms that weigh them differently. For example, anxiety, rather than fatigue, would be expected to arise from conflict in which both of the clashing items have great value to the individual. A situation of this sort represents a threat to the basic integration of the individual. Such threats are always present in the case of anxiety.

In the study of chronic fatigue and related syndromes, a mere isolating of "emotional factors" is of course not sufficient and does not embody an over-all approach any more than does a study limited to physiological changes. Both must be considered, and *in relation to each other*. Even this is far from ideal as "both" implies a separation. What we should like to do is study the organism as one process. Although such study will require the development of further methods, a general viewpoint of this sort is far from impossible, and will lead us in the direction of greater knowledge of human behavior.

Medical views on chronic fatigue. As a psychiatrist, Muncie[3] collaborated with internists on cases presenting the vague general complaints characteristic of chronic fatigue. He notes that severe chronic fatigue is likely to occur in relation to certain postinfectious states or gross endocrine-metabolic disturbances. It is also likely to occur as the expression of per-

---

[2] "Free-floating anxiety" occurs theoretically as a warning that repressions are about to break through into consciousness. There is said to be anticipation of the impending danger to the personality integration.

[3] Muncie, W.: Chronic Fatigue, *Psychosomatic Med., 3:* 277-285, 1941.

sonality maladjustment. The examination of a case of chronic fatigue must, he says, take into account at least these three factors. Mixed states are perhaps the most common, the broad relative importance of the factors involved varying from patient to patient and being often not easily detectable.

Muncie has pointed out that, although considerable fatigue is to be found among the complaints of nearly all the important diseases, it looms largest among three classes: (1) endocrine-metabolic disorders, particularly hypothyroidism and hypoadrenalism; (2) postinfectious states, especially influenza, undulant fever, and the dysenteries; and (3) emotional and attitudinal states often grouped under the name of neurasthenia.

According to Muncie, patients whose main complaint is that of being "tired," "weak," or "exhausted" may be divided into two categories. Patients in the first category do not feel like beginning to do anything, while those in the second want to, but seem to be unable to continue activity for any length of time. When patients in the first group force themselves, or are forced, to do things, a variable amount of fatigue results. Muncie makes this distinction to show that feeling tired and feeling weak are not necessarily one and the same. It is not clear whether further implications may be drawn from this distinction, *e.g.*, whether only one of these categories represents what Muncie calls neurotic fatigue.

Prolonged anxiety is frequently seen to result in fatigue. Muncie states that the perpetual feeling of strain, which arises out of the necessity of always being on guard against threats to personal security, results first in chronic anxiety and fear and later in chronic fatigue. Chronic fatigue, then, is sometimes the secondary development of anxiety.

Kepler[4] believes that our modern way of life is ill-adapted to our bodies. Chronic fatigue is seen as an outcome. Many of our difficulties, he says, are intangible, their causes often being unapparent to us. He considers that the symptom complex of chronic fatigue can be best considered at present as "psychologic" rather than metabolic or anatomic. Three features of the chronic-fatigue picture are given to support this view: (1) chronic fatigue is definitely unpleasant; (2) it appears to bear no relationship to the expenditure of measurable energy; and (3) it often seems to follow prolonged periods of unpleasant emotion, such as worry and uncertainty.

In elaborating on the second point, Kepler notes that physical exertion frequently obliterates the fatigue, although the individual may feel disinclined to participate in any form of activity. The patient characteristically awakes tired and may tend to feel somewhat better toward the end of the day. If individuals suffering from chronic fatigue are faced with crisis situations demanding action, they are usually able to meet them,

[4] Kepler, E. J.: Chronic Fatigue, *Proc. Staff Meet., Mayo Clin., 17:* 340–344, 1942.

often displaying an astonishing expenditure of energy, only to relapse later to their previous state.

Chronic fatigue has been attributed to numerous "causes." Kepler gives a partial list of the therapeutic measures which, as a result, have been advocated. It is not surprising, he says, that the results of these treatments have been largely disappointing when the real causes are seen as "psychologic." He seems unnecessarily pessimistic about what can be done to help these patients and suggests that they should learn to live within their limitations. Only occasionally specific situations responsible for the patient's chronic discontent may be altered, thus alleviating his chronic fatigue.

An interesting point made by Kepler is that chronic fatigue tends to be a disease of the intelligentsia. Individuals suffering from it are intelligent, although they may not be educated. It rarely afflicts individuals who work primarily with their muscles. Possibly ambition is at the root of the difficulty, although Kepler does not make this point. The greatest incidence of chronic fatigue is said to be in early adult and middle life rather than in childhood and old age. Some individuals who were always fatigued in their earlier years feel increasingly better as they grow older.

Alvarez,[5] who also writes on chronic fatigue, has a slightly different viewpoint, although he corroborates some of the assertions made by Kepler. Alvarez says that many of his chronic-fatigue patients feel most exhausted at the end of the day. It will be remembered that Muncie says there are two types of chronic fatigue patients, those who are most tired in the morning, and those who experience their greatest fatigue in the evening. Muncie's classification seems to be supported when the findings of Kepler and Alvarez are considered together.

Like most doctors who deal with patients suffering from chronic fatigue, Alvarez recommends that a thorough medical check-up be made. This he says is worth while for purposes of discovering the occasional physical disease that may be supposed to account for the fatigue. However, the diseases he considers most commonly responsible cannot be discovered in the course of an ordinary physical examination. These are "overwork neurosis," "postinfective neurosis," "neurosis" associated with arthritis or fibrositis, "nervous breakdown," "constitutional inadequacy," cerebral thrombosis, "equivalents of insanity," and "actual insanity."

In the case of postinfective neurosis, following a respiratory infection, for example, Alvarez postulates the presense of some encephalitic injury from the virus. Such injury, he says, would account for the prolonged

5 Alvarez, W. C.: What Is the Matter with the Patient Who Is Chronically Tired? *J. Missouri M. A., 38:* 365–368, 1941.

fatigue effect. Following this reasoning, it is not at all clear why this syndrome should be labeled "neurosis." The same holds true for the so-called "neurosis and arthritis or fibrositis."

Alvarez makes a great deal of "poor nervous heredity," thus tending to underemphasize the social factors involved. When "hereditary taint" or "constitutional inadequacy" is found to be present, he feels that the very most that can be done for the patient is to teach him to live within his means. In this way he may be able to decrease his symptoms. Even when hereditary taint is not found, Alvarez, like Kepler, is not optimistic about the prognosis. He seems to feel that there is little the physician can do, although the patient may recover spontaneously in some cases. Alvarez in failing to take adequate account of the social history of the individual or of the social situation in which the individual finds himself, could ill afford to be optimistic as to treatment.

The best way to regard the individual-environment complex still remains a problem. It is all too easy on the one hand to assign behavior symptoms to specific organic disturbances and, on the other, to neglect the possible existence of such disturbances. Although we proceed with the hypothesis that every bit of behavior has its underlying physiology in the organism, the correlation is obviously not a simple one. At times the individual can best be helped by applying influence via social channels, and at others he is best helped through drugs or even more drastic physiochemic means. Whatever the attempted remedy, it must not be applied with the view that the person is out of balance solely psychologically or solely physiologically.

Allan[6] reports an analysis of the findings in 300 cases in which the chief complaint was weakness or fatigue. Nervous conditions were considered responsible in 80 per cent of these cases. In the other 20 per cent, physical disorders were found to account for the complaint. Twenty-four types of physical disorders were encountered. These included diabetes, heart disease, chronic infection, nephritis, anemia, and various neurologic disorders. Interestingly enough, no case of fatigue could be attributed to low blood pressure, liver trouble, or "poor elimination," and both endocrine disorders and vitamin deficiencies were found to be rare.

Relatively few of the patients whose fatigue was attributed to a "nervous condition" were considered neurotic. Most of these patients were said to be suffering from a "benign nervousness." When mild, this benign nervousness was termed "nervous fatigue"; when severe and prolonged, it was classified as "chronic nervous exhaustion."

6 Allan, F. N.: The Differential Diagnosis of Weakness and Fatigue, *N. England J. Med.*, 231: 414–418, 1944.

Allan[7] ably distinguishes between what he calls a benign nervous condition and a neurosis. Benign nervousness is largely due to extrinsic rather than intrinsic factors. The patient is able to date the onset of the condition, and his previous life history is straightforward and consistent. The complaint results from some unusual stress and strain and is of limited duration. Patients of this sort are pleased if the findings of the medical examination are negative, whereas the neurotic patients tend rather to be disappointed.

The fact that chronic fatigue states represent no clear-cut clinical entity is again emphasized by Reeves.[8] He notes that, although no definite physiological basis has been found for fatigue, there is always a definite psychological factor to be taken into account. People usually consult physicians because they are troubled either by pain or by fatigue. In the case of pain, organic illness is usually discovered, but in the case of fatigue this is far less often the case. Although fatigue is one of the first signs of many diseases, it is also the normal sequel to prolonged activity.

Reeves points out that many doctors are too prone to classify fatigued patients as "neurasthenic" or "neurotics" simply because a prompt diagnosis cannot be made. A careful physical and laboratory examination is therefore of great importance. Reeves notes that each patient is a law unto himself and should never be looked upon as "just another case." While fatigue may be symptomatic of a neurosis, it should also be kept in mind that fatigue may produce neurotic symptoms in an otherwise normal person. These statements would seem to support the need for taking a detailed personal history. In regard to treatment, Reeves believes it should be based on a sympathetic understanding of the patient as a whole, combined with a definite effort to lessen his daily load.

Studies of chronic fatigue in children have been made by a number of individuals.[9] Although chronic fatigue is a frequent diagnosis of children's difficulties, just what is meant by the term is even less clear than it is in the case of adults. In dealing with the child, subjective complaints are taken as even more incidental than they are in the adult, and fatigue is therefore even more of a deduction. We have said that fatigue can never be assumed to exist from the mere observation of behavior. Because of the fickleness of the child's motivation, such deduction of fatigue is particu-

[7] Allan, F. N.: The Clinical Management of Weakness and Fatigue, *J.A.M.A.*, *127:* 957–960, 1945.

[8] Reeves, L. H.: What Is Wrong with the Chronically Tired Patient? *Texas State J. Med.*, *39:* 235–237, 1943.

[9] Netzley, R. E.: The Exercise Tolerance Test as a Measure of Chronic Fatigue in Children, *J. Pediat.*, *22:* 194–201, 1943.

Seham, M.: Chronic Fatigue in the School Child. A Psychophysiological Study, *Boston M. & S. J.*, *194:* 770–776, 1926.

larly unjustified. Actually, it is the child's incapacity for activity, called chronic subefficiency by one writer,[10] which is usually being considered. Such study, while well justified, does not belong under the fatigue heading. It is a question whether research on fatigue could be profitably carried on with young children as subjects. A child is unable to describe his own feelings at all adequately, and, in addition, he may not as yet have formed more than a hazy concept of tiredness.

Chronic fatigue in industry is becoming more generally recongized as an important hazard to production. In this field alone, there is great need for further knowledge of the syndrome in order to discover what conditions and treatment are most likely to lessen and alleviate it. Such studies as have been performed have failed to contribute much of value in this respect. One reason for this perhaps lies in the theoretical positions ön which they are based.

Collier,[11] who writes about diagnosing chronic fatigue in industry, sees fatigue as having multiple aspects. He notes that we already have both a physiology and a psychology of fatigue, as well as a "science" of human efficiency. What we still lack, he claims, is a clear view of fatigue as a clinical entity.

From a clinical standpoint, according to Collier, fatigue is separated from disease by only a narrow margin. A strongly motivated person may drive himself to "unphysiological" productivity. This results in fatigue, and later perhaps, illness. Fatigue is thus viewed as a precursor of disease.

Collier believes that fatigue should be classified in terms of the most important factor in the causation. Industrial fatigue, then, is seen as the fatigue resulting from industrial factors. In diagnosing "industrial morbid fatigue" the physician must eliminate not only gross physical disease, but also "normal tiredness" and "learning fatigue." Morbid fatigue is clearly industrial, he says, if the same signs are discovered in other individuals doing the same type of work. For this reason a study of group manifestations appears to be required. What makes this classification particularly intangible is the fact that the "industrial causes of morbid fatigue" cited by Collier include both physical and personal factors.

More recently, Ward[12] made a study of the chronic-fatigue symptoms of industrial workers based on experience with 600 men and 1,200 women workers. About a year after the establishment of a benefit system, a series

10 Seham, *op. cit.*

11 Collier, H. E.: The Recognition of Fatigue with Special Reference to the Clinical Diagnosis of Morbid Fatigue in Industry, *Brit. M. J., 2:* 1322–1325, 1936.

12 Ward, R. V.: Chronic Fatigue Symptoms among Industrial Workers, *Canad. Pub. Health J., 32:* 464–467, 1941.

of similar cases was noted. The number of these cases increased with increased production up to 4 per cent of the personnel.

The main complaint of these patients was that of feeling tired. They awoke in the morning feeling just as fatigued as they did on going to bed at night. Most of them also complained of pain in the back, loss of appetite, and insomnia. They were prone to be irritable and to cry over nothing. The only physical findings were increased pulse rate, low blood pressure, pallor, tremor, and loss of weight. Rest and change were found to be the most effective treatment, although tonics, etc., helped somewhat. The chronic-fatigue syndrome showed a tendency toward recurrence.

From these collected findings, Ward concludes that individuals have different capacities for work. Anyone who works beyond 100 per cent of his capacity is bound to get symptoms. Ward, then, views overwork as the primary cause of chronic fatigue. The fact that this is a typical misconception does not justify the lack of insight into the personal factors involved.

A number of physicians have been willing to attribute some cases of chronic fatigue to *a specific disease picture—glandular imbalance,* for example. However, the glandular imbalance is itself merely a concrete symptom of a larger pattern of difficulty and should be viewed as such. It is conceivable, for instance, that the social situation had sufficient untoward influence on the individual to promote the development of the imbalance. That the general difficulty took the form it did is then largely incidental to the picture as a whole.

Medicine has developed ways of altering the functioning of various glands. Few physicians, however, would anticipate more than a partial "cure" for hypothyroidism, for example, by the oral administration of thyroid extract. The patient may be improved, but he is not likely to become a well-adjusted, energetic, "normal" individual as a result of this therapy. Such an outcome could not be expected since it is scarcely conceivable that a single glandular deficiency could be an individual's only ailment. To compensate for a single deficiency and expect total satisfaction in the majority of cases necessitates an assumption that correction of one factor that is out of balance will automatically readjust everything else. Such an assumption is obviously false.

Most of the authors cited have also noted that prolonged fatigue may be a *sequel to various types of infection.* In convalescence, the individual is often subjected to sensory stimulation in excess of his ability to do anything useful with it. He feels that he lacks the necessary energy to fulfil even what he considers ordinary aspirations. It would seem that a reorganization of the whole person is inadvertently forced upon a convalescent.

It is customary to assign some factors in the individual's case to physiology and others to psychology. Although admittedly the wrong procedure, it is difficult at the present stage of knowledge to do otherwise. We are attempting to get away from such a separation in the case of the convalescent by postulating an organism whose total pattern of component activities has become altered. Such an individual has not readjusted so as to become adequate for the circumstances in which he finds himself. Certain adjustments acquired through the shock of infectious invasions sometimes appear to be perpetuated by their own momentum for long periods. What is needed is something to divert the "momentum" of a reduced state of efficiency toward a new equilibration. Viewing convalescence in this way, rather than accepting the conventional hypothesis that the organism must be rid of lingering toxins, might prove fruitful in gaining further knowledge.

Combat fatigue, chronic-exhaustion states, convoy fatigue, traumatic neurosis, and a number of additional clinical labels have been frequently encountered since the advent of the Second World War. There exists a great deal of confusion and disagreement concerning what terms of this sort are expected to encompass. Since the syndrome, or syndromes, involved would appear to possess some degree or kind of relationship to the typical chronic-fatigue picture, a brief discussion of them seems to the point here.

One might assume, and indeed many persons do, that the term "combat fatigue" refers to a state of chronic fatigue that follows prolonged duty in a combat area. If this were the case, the "fatigue" in the label would apply to the most important symptoms in a more general breakdown. However, a hasty survey of case histories shows that quite often fatigue, as a symptom, is not even mentioned. More typically these patients show an exaggerated startle reaction. They are touchy and irritable, and their chief complaint, rather than being fatigued, is nightmare. At least one writer[13] states that combat plays a more significant role in the development of an anxiety state than it does in the development of other syndromes.

Raines and Kolb,[14] who prefer the term combat fatigue to its variants ("war neurosis," "traumatic neurosis," etc.), throw some light on this problem. They emphasize the importance of the general setting in which the traumatic event occurs. One of the factors frequently encountered is that the patient experienced the traumatic combat situation when he was "suffering from marked physical fatigue." Raines and Kolb state that the term combat fatigue was suggested for the syndrome since fatigue is found to play such a prominent part in its etiological background. Since these writers go on to say that hunger, exposure, prolonged physical exertion,

[13] McElroy, R. B.: Psychoneuroses, Combat-anxiety Type, *Am. J. Psychiat., 101:* 517–520, 1945.

[14] Raines, G. N., and L. C. Kolb: Combat Fatigue and War Neurosis, *U. S. Nav. M. Bull., 41:* 923–936, 1943.

irregular habits, and lack of sleep make the individual prone to this type of emotional disturbance, it would appear that fatigue here refers primarily to impairment. However, elements of both fatigue and impairment seem to be involved, and the concept is not at all clear-cut.

The reason that Raines and Kolb prefer the use of the term combat fatigue to describe this syndrome is that it bears no reference to neurosis. They believe that to classify the uncomplicated syndrome as a neurosis is unjustified. These cases do not conform fully to the criteria of the psychoneuroses. No common "personality structure" has been found among them, and the symptoms are seen to occur in previously stable individuals. Raines and Kolb believe that the precipitating force of combat fatigue lies in the individual's environment. This distinction and the subsequent description of the syndrome seem clearer than most.

It should be pointed out that many other authors have classified the same, or approximately the same, picture as a neurosis. Two of them,[15] while they apparently believe the difficulty to be a neurosis, prefer the use of another term in order to do away with the connotation that the individual is a "weakling." Such a procedure seems highly dubious, but one gains the impression from this paper that the authors would be quite willing to term any type of primarily "psychogenic" disorder a neurosis. These same writers, however, include such factors as anoxemia in their discussion in such a way that it is not apparent whether the difficulty was primarily "psychogenic" in all cases. Confusion of this sort is characteristic of many of these studies.

The same problem of classification was seen to arise earlier in the case of chronic fatigue. The same lack of agreement on the neurotic or nonneurotic character of the syndrome was apparent there also. Such confusion seems unnecessary. In the case of chronic fatigue, the point seems to be that it may occur in both neurotic and "normal" individuals. In the case of combat fatigue, if we follow Raines and Kolb, the syndrome is specifically defined as nonneurotic. However, similar breakdowns may obviously occur in neurotic individuals following combat.

The only objection raised by Raines and Kolb concerning the use of combat fatigue is that "the fatigue of combat is only one of the several factors involved in the production of symptoms."

The other factors considered important because of the frequency with which they are encountered in the etiology of combat fatigue are as follows: (1) The patient lacked confidence in his leader during the combat, or he lost such confidence at a subsequent date. (2) The patient did not know his job sufficiently well. His training was inadequate. (3) The patient

---

[15] Tillisch, J. H., and M. N. Walsh: Chronic Exhaustion State in Test Pilots, *War Med.*, 2: 917–922, 1942.

did not know the men he was with well enough to estimate their conduct under fire. (4) Other factors being equal, patients tended to be either below 18 or over 38 years of age. This is true because two extreme types of individuals are most susceptible to combat fatigue. These are the emotionally and intellectually immature and very dependent, and the fully matured and independent.

Some of the signs and symptoms characteristic of combat fatigue have already been mentioned. These were "repetitive catastrophic nightmares," greatly exaggerated startle reactions, and general irritability. In addition to these, there is said to be a fairly subtle personality change. Besides being irritable, the patient becomes withdrawn, intolerant, and sometimes morose. His facial expression is vacant, and he is frequently observed staring into space. These patients are likely to become disciplinary problems. They often use alcohol to excess. Many of them have mild guilt feelings and are somewhat depressed.

Three further criteria for the diagnosis of combat fatigue deserve particular mention. It was found that (1) the patient had a stable personality prior to his present difficulty; (2) the patient underwent a traumatic combat experience; and (3) the patient showed signs of anxiety in regard to discussing his traumatic experience.

Combat-fatigue patients are said to recover in a comparatively short time (e.g., 2 months) even with superficial therapy. They should, however, be under supervision for a somewhat longer period, as it has been found that their symptoms are liable to aggravation in the presence of family and friends. It is also of interest that patients who have been evacuated to an area near the scene of combat are more likely to be returned to combat duty at an earlier date than those who have been evacuated to more distant points. The difficulty in returning these patients to combat appears to increase with the distance.

From the description above, it can be readily seen that the syndrome called combat fatigue bears little actual resemblance to the picture of chronic fatigue given previously. It is only because of the very common confusion between the two pictures that we have discussed combat fatigue in the present chapter. It is now obvious that much of the confusion between these two states is primarily due to the incorporation of the term "fatigue" in referring to both of them. It hardly seems that the syndrome commonly called combat fatigue merits such a title.

The effort syndrome, etc. Certain individuals present a syndrome characterized by anomalies of cardiac function, evidences of anxiety, etc. No single diagnostic label for this symptom picture has gained universal acceptance, and descriptions of the disease picture itself have varied. It has been called the effort syndrome, Da Costa's syndrome, irritable heart, disordered action of the heart, soldier's heart, neurocirculatory asthenia, and anxiety neurosis. As might be expected, these designations either seize upon a single outstanding manifestation of the difficulty, or reflect what the authority believes to be a primary factor in the etiology.

Manifestations of "irritable heart" were noticed in the Crimean War. Later, in the American Civil War, Da Costa[16] studied 300 cases of cardiac difficulty. He found that the trouble characteristically arose after the soldier was in the service for some time. Most of Da Costa's patients were young. Two-thirds of them were 16 to 25 years old, the majority being 20 to 25 years old. The first symptom was often diarrhea. Examination showed rapid pulse, which usually outlasted the original gastrointestinal disturbance. In other cases the first complaint was cardiac discomfort without the gastrointestinal accompaniment. Other signs and symptoms of irritable heart listed by Da Costa were (1) palpitation, most readily excited by exertion; (2) cardiac pain; (3) rapid pulse, sometimes with palpitation; (4) shortness of breath and oppression on exertion; (5) headaches, giddiness, disturbed sleep, itching skin, and excessive perspiration; and (6) indigestion, abdominal distention, and diarrhea. If the individual was returned to duty after a period of hospitalization, he could not seem to keep pace with his comrades.

Da Costa attributed the syndrome to fevers, diarrhea, hard field service, wounds, rheumatism, scurvy, etc. Tobacco and venereal disease were dismissed as probable causative factors. To Da Costa the illness was essentially a somatic affair. He saw it as one arising from a heart that had become irritable from overaction and had been sustained in this state by disordered innervation. Da Costa noted that improvement in general health was not accompanied by proportionate cardiac improvement. In addition to various drugs, his treatment included rest.

During the period of the First World War, cases involving cardiac and respiratory disorders again became prominent. A distinction was made between cases arising from true organic inadequacy, and those in which the somatic symptoms were merely a part of a larger picture of disorder. Sir Thomas Lewis[17] enumerated the characteristics of cases of the latter type, which were classified as suffering from "effort syndrome." These characteristics were (1) breathlessness, cyanosis slight or absent; (2) pain; (3) palpitation; (4) fainting; (5) giddiness; (6) headaches, especially after exertion; and (7) complaints of fatigue.

In some civilan cases, but rarely in army cases, rapid breathing per-

16 Da Costa, J. M.: On Irritable Heart; a Clinical Study of a Form of Functional Cardiac Disorder and Its Consequences, *Am. J. M. Sc., 61:* 17–52, 1871.

17 Lewis, T.: "The Soldier's Heart and the Effort Syndrome," Paul B. Hober, Inc., Medical Book Department of Harper & Brothers, New York, 1920. Pp. 144.

sisted during sleep. A type found in military hospitals was given to dyspnea only during waking hours. Breathing was shallow and rapid. A rate of 50 to 60 per minute was common, though Lewis reported even higher rates. The commonest type of breathlessness was the kind found only upon exertion.

Lewis stressed the significance of fatigue as a complaint. He found it virtually without exception and used its supposed degree to indicate the severity of the cases. The expression of the face and the droop of the body were taken as objective indications. Accompanying fatigue were tremor of hands and unsteadiness of legs. Lassitude was common in the early morning and late afternoon.

Lewis inquired into the clinical histories of these patients and came to the conclusion that infection was the dominant factor in the etiology. Out of 558 cases, 32 per cent dated their first symptoms from the time of infectious disease. Syphilis, and the use of alcohol and tobacco, etc., were ruled out as etiological factors.

Whereas the British Government had previously classified the kind of cases we are dealing with as those of "disordered action of the heart," a group of military medical officers in 1918,[18] reporting on the treatment of such cases, suggested the term "neurocirculatory asthenia." Their report contained 13 case histories, representative of 13 so-called types.

In 1920, Culpin stressed the psychogenic origin of the cases diagnosed officially as "disordered action of the heart." He stated that recognition of the origin in the treatment of the cases would greatly aid in restoring to social usefulness some of the men who had come to regard themselves as permanent invalids.[19]

Robey and Boas[20] stress "fundamental nervous instability" as a basic factor in neurocirculatory asthenia. Their patients have both a childhood and a family history of nervousness.

Cohn[21] asserts that symptoms described by Lewis and others may clearly be attributed to the heart and the circulation. His patients are described as having "irritable heart." Cases of irritable heart are said to occur in (1) chronic diseases of the heart, (2) acute infectious diseases, (3) hyper-

[18] Oppenheimer, B. S., S. A. Levine, R. A. Morison, M. A. Rothschild, W. St. Lawrence, and F. N. Wilson: Report on Neurocirculatory Asthenia and Its Management, *Mil. Surgeon, 42:* 409–426; 711–719, 1918.

[19] Of 70,000 cases classified as cardiovascular in the First World War, it has been estimated that only one of six suffered from heart disease. The rest were effort syndrome cases. Nevertheless, out of the 70,000, 44,000 became pension cases.

[20] Robey, W. H., and E. P. Boas: Neurocirculatory Asthenia, *J.A.M.A., 71:* 525–529, 1918.

[21] Cohn, A. E.: The Cardiac Phase of the War Neuroses, *Am. J. M. Sc., 158:* 453–470, 1919.

thyroidism, and (4) the neuroses. Cohn points out that whereas Lewis thought of the disorder as resulting from effort in general he, himself, sees it as developing from a specific kind of effort, the unique effort demanded by the war conditions.

While effort-syndrome cases are noted especially during the stress of war, particularly among the military personnel, in peacetime, heart specialists come in contact with many individuals whose symptoms belong in the effort-syndrome category. White and Jones,[22] basing their conclusions on 3,000 heart cases in New England, say that neurocirculatory asthenia is the most common functional heart disorder. Neurocirculatory asthenia was sometimes present in organic heart disease.

Crile[23] denervated the adrenal glands of patients whom he diagnosed as having neurocirculatory asthenia. The operation is theoretically based on the idea that neurocirculatory asthenia is an abnormal state characterized by excessive stimulation of the adrenal-sympathetic system.[24] Crile believed that, since other treatments had failed, direct surgical steps to reduce this stimulation should be undertaken. Crile's view was that denervation of the adrenal glands is indicated in those persons whose "mental and psychic mechanism" lies within the normal limits but whose sympathetic nervous system is under excessive stimulation.

It seems unjustified to postulate that such individuals are undisturbed in a psychic and personal sense. No individual with an autonomic-endocrine imbalance can be presumed to be well adjusted. Theoretically there are, of course, two ways to improve these persons. One is to sever the chain of consequences, as in a denervation operation, so that regardless of the pertubations of the individual undue adrenal activity will not result. The other is to adjust the individual's personal organization so as to do away with the basis for undue adrenal innervation. Since it is easier to perform a surgical operation than to carry on extended psychiatric treatment, the former tends to take precedence.

Master, Muzie, Brown, and Parker[25] came to the conclusion that the type of electrocardiogram found in the effort-syndrome patient is evidence of a small or hypoplastic heart. Such persons tire because they develop anoxemia. The cardiac output is insufficient, and the oxygen saturation

[22] White, P. D., and T. D. Jones: Heart Disease and Disorders in New England, *Am. Heart J., 3:* 302–318, 1928.

[23] Crile, G.: Indications and Contraindications for Denervation of the Adrenal Glands, *Ann. Surg., 100:* 667–669, 1934.

[24] Crile, G.: Denervation of the Adrenal Glands and Neurocirculatory Asthenia, *Surg., Gynec. & Obst., 54:* 294–298, 1932.

[25] Master, A. M., H. C. Muzie, R. C. Brown, and R. C. Parker: The Electrocardiogram and the "Two-step" Exercise, *Am. J. M. Sc., 207:* 435–450, 1944.

of the blood is low. Starr and Jonas[26] also stress subnormal cardiac output. Hick, Christian, and Smith[27] found that patients with "neurocirculatory asthenia" had an inadequate oxygenation of the blood leaving the lungs. These authors say that anoxemia is probably responsible for some of the fatigue and other symptoms of such patients.

In contrast to this, hyperventilation has been considered responsible for some of the symptoms of the effort syndrome. Hyperventilation leads to a set of consequences that has been termed by some the "hyperventilation syndrome."[28] Earlier, Sir Thomas Lewis had suggested a diminution of buffer substances in the blood as a possible factor in effort syndrome. Soley and Shock[29] have concluded that respiratory alkalosis induced by hyperventilation results in the effort syndrome. They suggest diagnosing these conditions as anxiety state complicated by the hyperventilation syndrome.

Immerman[30] proposes that effort syndrome cases are of two types: the neurorespiratory and the asthenic.

Wittkower and colleagues[31] divided their cases of effort syndrome into five types on the basis of personality as judged from careful case histories. They were (1) patients with keen sense of duty, characterized by conflicts over fear of showing fear; (2) resigned grousers, characterized by strained interpersonal relations and insubordination; (3) open rebels, overaggressive; (4) those with inferior physiques and obsessional drives to compensate; and (5) hysterical quitters, characterized by escape into dependence when confronted by heavy odds. Miller and McLean[32] say that Wittkower and colleagues' findings are in harmony with their own psychoanalytic findings.

A review of the effort-syndrome literature was made by Ivy and Roth.[33]

[26] Starr, I., and L. Jonas: Syndrome of Subnormal Circulation in Ambulatory Patients, *Arch. Int. Med., 66:* 1095–1111, 1940.

[27] Hick, F. R., A. W. Christian, and P. W. Smith: Criteria of Oxygen Want with Especial Reference to Neurocirculatory Asthenia, *Am. J. M. Sc., 194:* 800–804, 1937.

[28] Maytum, C. K., and F. A. Willius: Abnormal Respiration of Functional Origin, *Proc. Staff Meet., Mayo Clin., 9:* 308–311, 1934.

Sargant, W.: The Hyperventilation Syndrome, Lancet, *1:* 314–316, 1940.

[29] Soley, M. H., and N. W. Shock: The Etiology of Effort Syndrome, *Am. J. M. Sc., 196:* 840–851, 1938.

[30] Immerman, S. L.: What Constitutes Neurocirculatory Asthenia? *J. Aviat. Med., 12:* 236–239, 1941.

[31] Wittkower, E., T. F. Rodger, and A. T. M. Wilson: Effort Syndrome, *Lancet, 1:* 531–535, 1941.

[32] Miller, M., and H. V. McLean: The Status of the Emotions in Palpitation and Extrasystoles with a Note on the "Effort Syndrome," *Psychoanal. Quart., 10:* 545–560, 1941.

[33] Ivy, A. C., and J. A. Roth: A Review of Neurocirculatory Asthenia, Cardiovascular Neurosis, Effort Syndrome, or Da Costa's Syndrome, *Quart. Bull. Northwestern Univ., 18:* 112–124, 1944.

They concluded that the syndrome is a psychosomatic pattern occurring in the psychoneuroses and that it arises from anxiety, anger, fear, or guilt. The emotional reaction of the patent arises from a misinterpretation of the symptoms evolving from effort. Reflex conditioning was thought to stereotype some of the reactions and to account for the peculiar connections between them. Involved in the over-all picture are (1) the patient's family background; (2) "constitutional timidity and character inferiority"; (3) "bodily symptoms" such as breathlessness, fatigue, palpitation, etc.; and (4) "physical signs" such as marked hyperpnea, palmar sweating, and nervous manner.

Like chronic fatigue, the effort-syndrome picture is one of an individual out of harmony with his surroundings. This disharmony is evidenced in various ways. Frail physique, social insufficiencies, complaints of weakness and fatigue, and obvious illness of certain kinds are among them. The specific form taken by the disorganization depends more upon the organism involved than it does on the circumstances of its development. All these related symptom complexes are seen to arise from conflict. They occur in connection with the individual's activity and particularly his *felt* obligations. The symptoms tend to become most marked when the individual is under pressure, *i.e.*, when the conflicts are intense.

Chapter XX

CONCLUSIONS

THE FOREGOING chapters have given a clear sampling of the kind of work that has been done on fatigue. We have indicated throughout the course of these that very little of the work done on fatigue refers to the experience of feeling tired. The studies reported have included (1) work on localized tissue function, both in vitro and in vivo; (2) studies of work output and its decrement; (3) studies of physiological function under limiting conditions such as extreme heat and cold and water, oxygen, and sugar lacks; (4) work on deterioration in quality of performance, as in perceptual anomalies, motor anomalies, anomalies of speech, etc.; (5) studies of changes in specific physiological functions considered as indices of more general changes; and (6) clinical work on syndromes such as chronic fatigue.

Many of these studies in dealing with impairment, work output, and overt behavior of various kinds have thrown some light on fatigue merely in revealing what it is not. For example, when fatigue was imputed in an anoxemia study, although overt performance deteriorated, many of the subjects reported that they felt unusually well. This study demonstrates the lack of correlation between fatigue and overt behavior. Considerations of bodily sensations, attitudes, and matters of motivation have been almost totally neglected. These "subjective" phenomena generally have been given little consideration because they cannot be treated in a simple quantitative fashion, and because of their frequent lack of correspondence with so-called objective manifestations. In the majority of the studies that have been made, it is not possible to draw any conclusions at all regarding the presence or absence of fatigue, and therefore, naturally, nothing may be learned directly about its character. While a fair amount of knowledge about impairment and a great deal of information about human activity under a variety of circumstances have been collected, knowledge of fatigue from laboratory is very slight.

No clear-cut distinction between fatigue and impairment has ever been made and consistently maintained. Fatigue has been viewed as essentially somatic, and evidence of it has been sought through physiological and

397

biochemical procedures. Energistic rather than organizational concepts have characteristically been utilized to account for it.

At the same time, fatigue is a well-known experience. Every adult knows what it is to feel tired. Since common-sense observations are responsible for our basic knowledge of fatigue at the present time, formal problems, and the formulation of systematic definitions in this field, should have their origin in these.

Any fairly naïve individual has probably made most of the following observations regarding his own experience with fatigue.

1. When he is tired, he feels he should not exert himself for fear of some sort of injury.

2. When he is tired, he makes many mistakes in what he is doing, and this in turn makes him even more tired.

3. He sometimes feels extremely tired without having exerted himself.

4. Following a day of active sport, he sometimes would rather go dancing than rest.

5. His fatigue sometimes disappears abruptly if something interesting suddenly comes up.

6. His fatigue comes on very quickly in certain types of unpleasant social situations.

7. He sometimes becomes extremely tired at the mere thought of doing certain kinds of work.

8. If once he felt tired in a given situation, he is likely to feel tired again when a similar situation occurs.

9. When he is tired, he is unlikely to feel enthusiastic about anything, and when he is enthusiastic he hardly ever feels tired.

10. He has been able in emergency situations to undergo unusual emotional strain, at the same time expending unbelievable amounts of energy without feeling correspondingly tired.

11. He has been able to go for long periods without rest when he was having a "wonderful time."

12. Sometimes he is more tired when he wakes up after a full night's sleep than he was when he went to bed.

Accepting these common observations as valid, we are able to make further deductions about fatigue. Some of the more or less obvious deductions from each observation follow.

1. *When he is tired, he feels he should not exert himeslf for fear of some sort of injury.* Fatigue always involves the individual's evaluation of himself and his abilities. Unless he is called upon to perform certain tasks, his evaluation may be merely tacit. At times, however, it may become highly explicit. The character of the evaluation depends largely upon what the individual has been taught to believe.

2. *When he is tired, he makes many mistakes in what he is doing, and this in turn makes him even more tired.* Fatigue is cumulative. A fatigued individual is more susceptible to thwarting than a rested one. Fatigue is intensified as the individual meets additional thwarts and observes his own lack of accomplishment.

3. *He sometimes feels extremely tired without having exerted himself.* Fatigue is not an energy affair. It bears no consistent relation to expenditure of physical energy. Expenditure of energy should not be confused with feelings of effort, and neither of these should be confused with fatigue.

4. *Following a day of active sport, he sometimes would rather go dancing than rest.* An individual who has been relatively free from conflict during a prolonged period of physical activity is much less fatigued than an individual who faced numerous conflicts in the course of similar activity.

5. *His fatigue sometimes disappears abruptly if something interesting suddenly comes up.* Fatigue cannot be accounted for on the basis of tissue impairment, which always has a gradual recovery period. Fatigue is an organizational affair; as such it is an expression of central nervous function. Recovery from fatigue requires reorganization or realignment. Repatterning may occur fairly suddenly when there is sufficient incentive.

6. *His fatigue comes on very quickly in certain types of unpleasant social situations.* Unpleasant social situations involve the individual in particularly extreme conflicts. Fatigue arises very quickly when the underlying conflicts are intense.

7. *He sometimes becomes extremely tired at the mere thought of doing certain kinds of work.* Fatigue occurs with reference to contemplated activity. The mere anticipation of doing certain tasks may induce extreme fatigue when the individual is involved in conflicts including feelings of obligation.

8. *If once he felt tired in a given situation, he is likely to feel tired again when a similar situation occurs.* Fatigue, like all experiences, is a function of personal continuity. Any one instance of fatigue cannot be understood as an isolated occurrence, but must be viewed as a product of learning. Stances taken by an individual tend to become conditioned.

9. *When he is tired he is unlikely to feel enthusiastic about anything, and when he is enthusiastic he hardly ever feels tired.* Enthusiasm, like fatigue, occurs in relation to activity. General enthusiasm and fatigue tend to be reciprocally related.

10. *He has been able in emergency situations to undergo unusual emotional strain, at the same time expending unbelievable amounts of energy without feeling correspondingly tired.* In an emergency situation the organization of the individual may be understood in terms of a unitary purpose. His alignment with reference to specific activity or to a specific goal

is so strong as to override interfering factors. He transcends changes in external circumstances. In such a pattern, conflicts that occur do not have the force they would ordinarily have. Marked fatigue would not be expected.

11. *He has also been able to go for long periods without rest when he was having a "wonderful time."* An individual consistently enjoying himself is relatively free from disintegrating conflicts. His functional alignment, rather than being rigidly unified as it is in a crisis situation, is highly flexible. The individual is "carefree" and is therefore not in pursuit of any single compelling goal. His adjustments are passively in line with changes in external circumstances.

12. *Sometimes he is more tired when he wakes up after a full night's sleep than he was when he went to bed.* There is no direct relation between fatigue and amount of sleep. If the restoration that occurs during sleep is seen in terms of a reorganization, the effects of sleep would be expected to be highly variable. Fatigue of the preceding evening would be alleviated only when conflicts are mitigated.

It has been asserted that most of what we know about fatigue arises from everyday observations and from deductions made from these. Formal investigations should utilize common experience as a starting point for obtaining knowledge about fatigue. Despite this, it has been customary for experimentation to have little or no basis in significant reality. Success in analyzing fatigue will arise only from asking the right questions. The matter of whether a quick and simple answer may be found from a given research should be considered only secondarily, if at all.

What do we actually need to know about fatigue? In discussing this, the first thing that comes to mind is the necessity of a scientific test for the accuracy of deductions made from common experience. Those found to be tenable would then be subject to refinement.

In furthering fatigue research, the necessity of asking the right questions, those arising from daily life, cannot be overestimated. The techniques that will be necessary in answering the questions asked will have to grow out of the questions themselves. The question determines the method needed to answer it. It is undoubtedly true that not only present methods will bear modification, but also that new methods will need to be developed.

In order to know more about fatigue, we must know more about *the person as a whole*. A number of questions regarding personality, now unanswered, immediately come to mind. Some of these are as follows: (1) What kind of individuals are most prone to fatigue? (2) In what terms can personal organization be delineated? (3) What relations do the individual, his environment, and the physical world bear to each other? (4) How do the alignments in the mature and immature individual differ?

(5) How do conflicts evolve? (6) What is the distinction between work and play?

Questions more specifically about fatigue seem to fall into four categories: those regarding its character, those having to do with its induction and progress, those concerning its relations to various other factors, and those dealing with its alleviation.

We shall give several appropriate questions as examples under each of these headings:

Character of fatigue: (1) What are the experential elements of fatigue? (2) May component phenomena arrived at in the analysis of fatigue occur when the individual is not fatigued? (3) Are there any discernible patterns of systemic function, bodily tensions, or other somatic features characteristic of a given individual during fatigue?

Induction and progress of fatigue: (1) How tangibly can the connections between a specific conflict and fatigue be treated? (2) What kinds of conflicts and what conflict patterns most readily induce fatigue? (3) Is conditioning involved in patterning the bodily stance in fatigue? If so, in what way? (4) Do weather changes play a part in inducing fatigue?

Fatigue and other factors: (1) What are the relations between fatigue and impairment when they occur together in a given individual? (2) Under what conditions may fairly severe impairment occur without accompanying fatigue? (3) What are the interrelations of motivation and fatigue?

Alleviation of fatigue: (1) What changes in alignment are effective in alleviating fatigue? (2) Under what conditions is sleep effective in alleviating fatigue?

As was stated in the previous section, the questions asked of experimentation determine the procedure required to answer them. Since the preceding section has been devoted to listing some of the things that need to be discovered about fatigue, the task of the present section is to suggest what procedures are necessary for this purpose. We have pointed out not only that current views fail fully to recognize the personalistic nature of fatigue, but also that recognition of this would require considerable alteration in the methods of study. Adequate study of fatigue supposes a science of the person, and this as a fully formed instrument does not as yet actually exist. Were the system worked out by Angyal[1] (which appears to embody the essentials of such a formulation) better known, it might well be used as a background for our discussion of means of studying fatigue. The present status of knowledge, however, seems to require the expression of an outlook that pushes from the "known," "accepted," and "understood" toward postulates, devices, and procedures consistent with the personalistic out-

[1] Angyal, A.: "Foundations for a Science of Personality," Commonwealth Fund, Division of Publication, New York, 1941. Pp. 398.

look. What should be done first involves the selection of features of methods already in existence which are appropriate for the study of fatigue.

The major operation in experimentation is often considered to be that of measurement. Questions regarding how fatigue is to be measured are forced upon us by the inevitable inquiry as to how a "subjective" affair such as fatigue, as we define it, can be measured. Since we have defined fatigue so as to exclude it from the "tangible" category of tissue impairment, the question of what to measure and how to measure it becomes a problem.

Measurement, not only in fatigue studies but in all situations, is the ascertainment of relations between two or more items. The simplest form of measurement involves the use of single standards called "units." The property in question is expressed quantitatively in multiples or submultiples of the unit. This sort of measurement implies that properties are aspects of phenomena that vary only in one direction. It is believed that some variables can be held constant while others are intentionally manipulated. The usual technique is to vary one property and determine the related variation in another. That there are such relations is not strictly true. In addition to the resulting quantitative variation of the dependent variable, new properties emerge. Varying the independent variable unavoidably alters more than one other property. In other words, there are many dependent variables. Sometimes the new properties are unrecognized. At times an unrecognized property is the crucial feature in the situation under observation.

Emergence of new properties under changing conditions is the most outstanding feature of biological situations. The techniques required for handling emergent phenomena are not confined exclusively to simple quantification.

Fatigue is not an entity that can be specified in quantitative units. A descriptive statement of fatigue put in quantitative terms would be meaningless. Complex functions like fatigue need not necessarily be related to single unit standards (as for instance in multiples and submultiples), but may be related to other complex functions in equally expressible ways. The virtue of this procedure does not rest on the usual assumption of need for irreducibility (simplicity) in the factors related. The discovery of a set of relationships between the phenomenon in question and others provides for the use of several points of reference. The several phenomena to which fatigue is related serve as standards in place of the single quantitative unit usually sought. This method of measurement seems to be the only one available at present for dealing with complex phenomena.

The situation may be summed up by saying that the functions we must handle evolve from sets of emergent relationships for which we have no "linear" yardsticks. Fatigue grows by changing qualitatively. New qualities emerge quite suddenly either full blown, or to develop gradually. Changes, ordinarily looked upon as quantitative affairs, are inescapably qualitative.

Treatment of emergent phenomena is not entirely without precedent. The ideas of the *threshold*, and the *just noticeable difference* (JND) in psychophysics are quite old. The treatment of the multidirectional JND's in fatigue, for example, in differing from the treatment of linear JND's, involves the simultaneous consideration of a number of emergent items.

It would seem that all the questions asked about fatigue call for analysis of the individual. Procedures for studying groups are contraindicated. Study of groups aims at predictions about them as population units, or as populations in general. In such studies, individuals are treated as unanalyzable units. Study of the individual aims at analyzing the organization which *is* the individual. A number of subjects may be used, if the techniques are actually means toward analysis of the separate individuals. An explanation of the behavior of a single individual cannot be pieced together from the analyses of diverse individuals. The purpose of using more than one subject in an experiment is to make one's investigation cover more kinds of individuals.

There are two broad possibilities in the study of fatigue: (1) the use of situations in which fatigue is indubitably present and (2) the production of a set of circumstances out of which conflict and frustration develop, with the expectation that fatigue may result. In the first kind of study, the aim is to analyze fatigue itself with the expectation that it will be ultimately differentiated from other experiences and its relations to other phenomena become known. In the second kind of study, the beginning is made from the opposite direction. It lies outside of fatigue, and regardless of whether fatigue develops, the understanding of the relation of other phenomena to fatigue will be furthered. Frustration will ensue, for example, from (1) inducing conflicts in social situations, (2) inducing conflicts by disorienting the individual in his relations to the physical world, (3) inducing sensory discomfort, or (4) inducing systemic inadequacy.

1. *Definitions are required as a basis for fruitful experimentation.* This caution is particularly pertinent in the field of fatigue, owing partly to the experiential nature of fatigue, and partly to the customary tendency of investigators to make conceptual formulations, if they make them at all, only after prolonged random experimentation. It has not been the tendency in dealing with fatigue to examine it as an experience, or as something presumably distinguishable from something else, or to inquire into its origins. The taboo on "armchairizing" has been responsible for considerable general paralysis in thinking, and for much irrelevant experimentation.

A large part of the problem of fatigue consists in the attainment of a sufficiently comprehensive formulation of it. It seems reasonable that some skeleton formulation of the concept should be made before the study of fatigue is attempted.[2]

2. *Concepts must form a unitary system with regard to the phenomena studied.* The phenomena dealt with in the field of fatigue must be seen as aspects of a single functioning unity. Specific items in a situation gain their value from the situation as a whole. Definitions must not be formulated without regard to the other terms in the field. All the definitions must fit together describing a consistent, unitary, functional interrelationship within the individual.

3. *Phenomena change with the passage of time, and this fact must be taken into account in fatigue experimentation.* The direction, rate, and extent of these spontaneous changes is one of the objects of fatigue study. The mere process of studying phenomena tends to change them in particular ways, and changes of this sort must be minimized as much as possible.

4. *In studies of human activity the individual must be taken as a reference.* In dealing with fatigue, it is the organization of the individual that is under study. Fatigue, frustration, monotony, boredom, and other concepts in this field are meaningless except when the individual is taken as the point of reference.

5. *The full set of dynamic factors operating in the individual must be taken into account in the experimental plan.* In the study of fatigue the essential variables cannot be readily confined to the immediate circumstances of the experimental setup. As one instance of this, fatigue on any given occasion has antecedents that must be taken into account. For this reason when fatigue arises in an experimental situation it should not be viewed as solely the outcome of the immediate circumstances involved. Conditioning would seem to play a significant role in accounting for the particular organization of the individual at any given moment, and thus in the experimental situation. *It should be recognized that prolonged experiments are learning experiments regardless of whether or not they are planned as such.*

6. *The experiment should be as much a part of "real life" to the subject as possible.* "Real-life" conditions are best approximated when the subject is unaware of the nature of the experiment.

To summarize, the main considerations involved in the fatigue problem have been briefly reviewed. The discussion may be seen to fall roughly into four sections: (1) a review of the kinds of formal studies that have already been performed under the name of fatigue; (2) a survey of the things we

[2] A preliminary formulation was made for our purposes in Chap. III.

now know about fatigue; (3) an indication of the things we need to know about fatigue; and (4) a discussion of the general methods and procedures, both logical and experimental, for finding out the things we need to know. In short, this concluding chapter has dealt with fatigue in terms of (1) what has been done, (2) what is known, (3) what we need to know, and (4) suggestions for finding out.

LIST OF VISUAL AIDS

The following list of visual aids can be used to supplement some of the material in this book. The films listed are only samples of available material and should be previewed before using to make sure that the subjects will fit the interest of the audience.

These films can be obtained from the distributor or producer listed with each title. (The addresses of these distributors and producers are given at the end of this listing.) In many cases these films can be obtained from your local film library or local film distributor; also, many universities have large film libraries from which films can be borrowed.

The running time (min) and whether it is silent (si) or sound (sd) are listed with each title. All the motion pictures are 16mm.

Each film has been listed only once in connection with the chapter to which it is most applicable. However, many of the films can be used advantageously in connection with other chapters.

CHAPTER IV—ELECTROPHYSIOLOGICAL STUDIES OF FATIGUE

The Nervous System (EBF 10min sd). Describes the nature and function of the nervous system; shows the anatomy of the spinal cord, axones, dendrites, nerve trunks, receptor and effector organs, nerve impulses, and the reflex arc.

The Nervous System Series (Brandon)
The Nervous System (30min si)
The Brain (75min si)
Conditioned Reflexes and Behavior (60min si)
The Spinal Cord (30min si)
Reflex Action (15min si)
Muscles (EBF 15min si). Shows the structure of muscle tissues and functions of muscle groups.

CHAPTER V—ANOXIA AND RELATED LIMITING CONDITIONS

Mechanisms of Breathing (EBF 10min sd). Pictures the breathing process including gaseous exchange both in the lungs and other tissues; the nervous control of breathing, including factors influencing rate and depth of breathing; demonstrates certain pathological conditions.

CHAPTER VII–TEMPERATURE EXTREMES, AND WATER AND SALT LACKS

Control of Body Temperature (EBF 11min sd). Shows the role played by nerve, gland, and muscle in the control of body temperature; pictures the blood as the distributor of heat and the hypothalamus as the thermostat in the system.

CHAPTER VIII–METABOLISM AND NUTRITION

Foods and Nutrition (EBF 11min sd). Shows normal dietary requirements; growth of culture tissue; discusses metabolism.

CHAPTER IX–CONVENTIONAL VISUAL FATIGUE STUDIES

Eyes and Their Care (EBF 10min sd). Depicts the anatomy and physiology of the eye; shows eye movements, receptor cells, the visual field, night blindness, double vision, visual difficulties such as near- and far-sightedness, etc.

CHAPTER X–HOURS AND CONDITIONS OF WORK

Motion Study Principles (Iowa 22min sd). Illustrates motion study principles by several assembly jobs.

CHAPTER XI–DRUG ACTION IN RELATION TO FATIGUE AND IMPAIRMENT

The Dissociative Effects of Curare (PCR 10min si). Shows how conditioned activity of isolated muscle is established in dogs under curare; the learning is demonstrated only during the curare period; poses that the neurological mechanism for the conditioning under curare is subcortical, whereas normal learning involves the cerebral cortex.

The Effects of Morphine on Learned Adaptive Behavior and Experimental Neuroses in Cats (PCR 15min si). Shows the effect of morphine on animals; how it abolishes more complex and more recently acquired behavior; suggests certain parallels between the effects illustrated and human drug addiction.

Neurosis and Alcohol: An Experimental Study (PCR 24min si). Shows that the administration of alcohol to cats abolishes certain recently learned habits, decreasing the complexity of behavior until only primitive feeding responses remain; pictures animals made neurotic by subjection to conflictual motivations.

The Effects of Various Drugs on the Emotional Mimetic Reactions of the Hypothalamus and Cerebral Cortex of the Cat (PCR 16min si). Demonstrates the effects of alcohol, metrazol, morphine and sodium amytal.

CHAPTER XII—ORGANIZATION AND NEUROMUSCULAR ACTIVITY

The Electrical Recording of Eye Movements (PCR 28min si). Shows the apparatus and methods for electrically recording eye movements; demonstrates relation of eye movements to the alpha activity in the electro-encephalogram.

Posture (EBF 15min si). Shows the influence of posture upon the size of the chest, position of the abdominal organs, and over-all personal appearance.

Posture and Exercise (EBF 10min sd). Explains the physiology of exercise, presenting concepts of the relation of the nervous system to the skeletal muscles; muscle tonus in relation to posture; the relation of circulation to general physical efficiency.

CHAPTER XIII—SLEEP AND OTHER PERIODICITIES

Behavior in Hypnotic Regression (PCR 16min si). Gives various demonstrations to illustrate the characteristics of the hypnotic state.

Modern Weather Theory: Primary Circulation (Castle 19min sd). Pictures weather under normal conditions; shows the creation of winds; deals with the "mechanics" involved in the production of principal air currents in both northern and southern hemispheres.

The Weather (EBF 10min sd). Shows circulation of air on earth's surface; traces progress of a cyclone; describes warm and cold fronts; shows instruments used in weather observations.

CHAPTER XIV—THE LONG-TERM EFFECTS ON THE INDIVIDUAL

Conditioned Reflexes in Sheep (PCR 6min si) . Demonstrates the typical Pavlovian technique for conditioning a response.

Mechanics of the Brain (Brandon 90min si) . Illustrates conditioned reflexes and methods used by Professor Pavlov.

Animal Studies in the Social Modification of Organically Motivated Behavior (PCR 12min si). Demonstrates a competitive food getting situation in which the animals develop a marked form of "sharing" behavior; shows a competitive situation in which the opposite happens; exemplifies the influence of social situations upon behavior.

CHAPTER XVI—PERSONAL FACTORS IN THE WORK SITUATION

The Boss Didn't Say Good Morning (Association 11min sd). Shows the psychological effect of a superior's failure to greet an employee upon arriving at work in the morning.

CHAPTER XVII—VISUAL PERFORMANCE AND FATIGUE

The Mirage (TFC 15min si). Presents actual photographs of mirages.

CHAPTER XVIII—CONFLICT AND FRUSTRATION

The Dynamics of an Experimental Neurosis: Its Development and Techniques for Its Alleviation (PCR 4 parts si):

Part 1—*Conditioned Feeding Behavior and Induction of Experimental Neuroses in Cats* (19min). Deals with simple conditioned response learning and production of neuroses in animals.

Part II—*Effects of Environmental Frustration and Intensification of Conflict in Neurotic Cats* (14min). Deals with the factors which intensify neurotic behavior in cats.

Part III—*Experimental Diminution of Neurotic Behavior in Cats* (16min). Deals with treatment of neuroses in animals.

Part IV—*Active Participation in Establishing More Satisfactory Adjustment* (15min). Deals with treatment of neuroses in animals.

SOURCES OF FILMS LISTED ABOVE

Association Films, YMCA Motion Picture Bureau, 347 Madison Ave., New York 17.

Brandon Films, Inc., 1600 Broadway, New York 19.

Castle Films, 30 Rockefeller Plaza, New York 20.

EBF—Encyclopaedia Britannica Films, Inc., 20 N. Wacker Dr., Chicago 6.

Iowa—University of Iowa, Dept. of Visual Education, Iowa City, Iowa.

PRC—Psychological Cinema Register, Pennsylvania State College, State College, Pa.

TFC—Teaching Film Custodians, Inc., 25 W. 43rd St., New York 18.

AUTHOR INDEX

A

Adams, S., 170
Adler, F. H., 42, 83
Adolph, E. F., 105, 106, 110, 111, 114, 127–129, 132
Aitken, R. S., 132
Alexander, F., 41, 239
Allan, F. N., 385, 386
Allen, E., 254, 257
Allen, E. V., 199, 239
Alles, G. A., 195
Allphin, W., 170
Altmann, M., 255
Alvarez, W. C., 78, 384
Ames, A. Jr., 42–46
Anderson, F., 369
Anderson, H. H., 369
Anderson, I. H., 360, 361
Anderson, K., 317
Andrews, T. G., 198
Angyal, A., 50, 51, 401
Arai, T., 219
Armstrong, H. G., 72–74, 76
Asch, S. E., 219, 220
Ash, I. E., 27, 28, 233, 234
Ashe, B. I., 131
Asmussen, E., 235
Atkins, E. W., 171
Aubert, H., 192

B

Baker, K. H., 317
Balázs, J. v., 261
Barborka, C. J., 157, 192, 201
Barbour, H. B., 288
Barcroft, J., 22, 89, 90, 289
Bard, P., 20, 104
Barker, N. W., 239
Barker, R. G., 365, 366
Barmack, J. E., 197, 198, 309

Bartley, S. H., 33, 34, 59, 172, 173, 218, 314, 345
Bass, M. G., 278
Batterman, R. C., 207
Baumberger, J. P., 209
Bazett, H. C., 101, 103
Beacher, L. L., 359
Bean, J. W., 76, 77
Bedford, T., 180
Behnke, A. J., Jr., 72
Belding, H. S., 114
Benedek, T., 260
Benedict, C. G., 306
Benedict, F. G., 306
Bentinck, H. C., 179
Bentley, M., 32, 33, 367
Berens, C., 163
Bergel, A., 256
Berger, H., 206
Bergeret, P. M., 76
Bert, P., 76
Best, C. H., 20, 282
Beutell, A. W., 169
Bielschowsky, G. A., 42
Billings, E. G., 155
Bills, A. G., 8, 302, 303, 305, 308, 309, 312, 315
Binger, C. A., 289
Black, D. A. K., 130
Blair, E. A., 59, 63
Blake, H., 275, 278
Blankenstein, S. S., 161
Blatt, N., 66, 162
Bloech, J., 256
Blount, W. P., 168
Boas, E. P., 393
Bock, A. V., 66, 176, 283, 289
Bohn, D. F., 76, 77
Booth, W., 283
Bortz, E. L., 297

411

SUBJECT INDEX

A

Abulia, 96
Acapnia, 209
Accidents, frequency of, 339
Accident proneness, 26, 338*ff.*
Acclimatization, 280, 286*ff.*
Accommodation, 3, 43, 59, 162*ff.*, 344
  amplitude of, 165, 167
  convergence, 168
Accomplishments, 7, 27, 28, 299
Acetylcholine, 68, 70, 139*ff.*, 189, 272
  (*See also* Drugs)
Acetylphosphate, 140
Achievement, human, 297
  visual, 33
Acid, acetylsalicylic, 141
  amino, 91
  ascorbic, 153
  barbituric, 189
  benzoic, 141
  lactic (*see* Lactic acid)
  nicotinic, 153
  pantothenic, 153
  pyruvic, 91
  salicylic, 141
  uric, 152
Acid phosphates, 17
Acidosis, 251
Action current, 65
Activity, biological, 240
  chemical, 101
  clonic, 95
  human, 240, 241
  muscular, 99, 113, 217, 223
  nerve complex, 65, 67
  sweat gland, 115
  sympathetic, 79
  tonic, 95
Adaptation, 3, 32, 236, 286
  dark, 85, 159*ff.*

light, 346
  sensory, 20
  temperature, 113
  visual, 155*ff.*
Adenosinetriphosphate, 136*ff.*
Adiadochinesia, 205
Adjustments, autonomic, 233, 292, 320
  bodily, 99, 100, 321
  to climate, 289
  industrial, 6, 329
  oculomotor, 360
  physical, 122, 123, 197
  sensory, 304
  to work, 259
Adrenalin, 79, 92*ff.*
Adrenalin action, 70
Adrenergic substances, 190
Adrenergic system, 189
Aeroembolism, 72
Aftercontraction, 206
Afterimage, 82, 84
Afterpotential, 60*ff.*
Aging, 281, 296*ff.*
Alcohol, 89, 211, 212, 291
  (*See also* Drugs)
Alertness, 265–267, 301, 333, 334
Alignment, changes in, 222, 279, 401
  expressions of, 261
  of individuals, 295, 352–353
Alkali reserve, 284
Alkalosis, 251, 290
Altitude, 72*ff.*, 287*ff.*
Alveolar tension, 74, 75
Anaerobic processes, 77, 134, 136, 137
Analgesia, 206, 207
Angioscotoma, 85
Angle of muscle contraction, 65
Anhydremia, 126
Anoxemia, 76*ff.*, 83, 182, 251, 290
Anoxia, 71*ff.*, 94, 182, 183

419